# PARKER HANNIFIN'S
# 100-YEAR
# JOURNEY

## POWERING THE MACHINES
## THAT CHANGED THE WORLD

BY THOMAS A. PIRAINO JR.

SMART BUSINESS® BOOKS
*An Imprint of Smart Business® Network Inc.*

Parker Hannifin's 100-Year Journey
COPYRIGHT © 2017 Thomas A. Piraino Jr. and Parker Hannifin Corp.

Published by:
Smart Business Network
835 Sharon Drive, Suite 200
Westlake, OH 44145

Printed in the United States of America
Cover and interior design: Stacy Vickroy
Cover layout: April Grasso and Stacy Vickroy
Interior layout: April Grasso and RJ Pooch
Editor: Dustin Klein

ISBN: 978-1-945389-95-5 (hardcover)
ISBN: 978-1-945389-96-2 (e-book)
Library of Congress Control Number: 2017941262

*"It is doubtful if aeroplanes will ever cross the ocean...The public has...[imagined] that in another generation they will be able to fly over to London in a day. This is manifestly impossible."*

—William Pickering, a Harvard astronomer, 1908[i]


*"Why shouldn't I fly from New York to Paris?"[ii]*

—Charles A. Lindbergh on the St. Louis-Chicago
Airmail run, September 1926


*"To claim that...[a rocket could travel to the Moon] is to deny a fundamental law of dynamics."*

—An editorial in The New York Times, January 13, 1920


*"Houston, Tranquility Base here, the Eagle has landed."*

—Neil Armstrong from the Moon, July 20, 1969

# CONTENTS

NASA/Scan by J.L. Pickering

Jim Lovell at the Apollo 13 launch pad April 6, 1970.

Parker's evolution from the supplier of the fuel system on the Spirit of St. Louis to the maker of the valves to control the propulsion system that brought the Apollo 13 astronauts safely back to Earth is a great American success story.

I should know.

I owe my life, and the lives of my fellow crew members, to the commitment, steadiness under pressure, and just plain courage of the Parker engineers who never gave up on us, and never left their posts until they knew we had safely splashed down in the Pacific Ocean.

Capt. James A. Lovell Jr.
Lake Forest, Illinois
January 2017

I t was a daunting sight: A long gray train that lay hissing steam at the Cleveland Union Station, early on a July evening in 1918. The train, formerly known as the "20th Century Limited," had been converted to a troop transport when America entered the Great War a year earlier. It was waiting to take a 32-year-old Army recruit named Arthur LaRue ("Art") Parker and hundreds of his companions on a trip that would end in France at the Western Front.

Ahead of Art in France lay a stalemated war that had already consumed 7 million lives. Behind him in Cleveland lay everyone and everything he cared about—his parents, his two brothers, his sister, and his life-long dream, the company he had founded in March 1917 in a machine shop in a second-story loft on a bluff above the western bank of the Cuyahoga River. For 10 years, Art had scrimped and saved until he accumulated $6,000, enough to afford a few machines, the lease for the loft, and the salary for his partner, a wooden pattern maker named Carl Klamm. Now Art would have to defer his dream for the duration of the war and entrust his company to Klamm.

Art named his company the Parker Appliance Co. In putting his name on the door, he was following the same impulse that drives artists to compose, write, draw, or sculpt a masterpiece—to make a lasting mark upon the world, even to achieve a type of immortality. Art used the term "appliance" in his company's name because it was a synonym for products with a variety of applications. His ambition was to build a company that would use a new technology called fluid power, which would use air, water, oil and hydraulic fluids under pressure to control moving parts in trucks, buses, trains, industrial machinery, construction equipment, and a recent invention people were calling the "aeroplane."

The odds were stacked against Art, even before he left for the war. He had only one product, and not a single customer. Most of Art's friends did not expect his company to survive the war. During the next 100 years, Art's company defied the odds, growing to an enterprise with more than 50,000 employees, 9,000 independent distributors, more than 300 facilities in more than 50 countries, annual sales of more than $11 billion, more than 400,000 customers and hundreds of thousands of different products in every region of the world, powering nearly every type of machine that moves.

I worked in Parker's legal department for 33 years, starting in 1981. I was the company's General Counsel, responsible for supervising all its legal work, from 1998 until I retired in 2014. One question kept recurring to me during my years at Parker: Why, I wondered, had the company prospered during one of the most tumultuous 100 years in history, while most of the companies that existed in 1917 failed? I found the answer in Parker's offices, around the coffee machine, at employee parties, and in the company cafeteria, as I heard Parker's men and women tell stories of the obstacles their predecessors overcame to build the company.

The stories Parker's people chose to tell each other were meant to explain what it took to be a Parker person—to serve customers, to trust and empower each other, to work together as a team, and never to give in to hard times, no matter how long the odds. In the retelling, the shared stories of the best accomplishments of Parker's men and women provided the foundation of the company's culture. This book is a compilation of that 100 years of oral history.

Jack Breen, a long-time Parker director and former CEO of Sherwin-Williams, has explained the effects of Parker's culture: "Parker people possess a rare feeling of family. Like family members, they never want to let anyone in the family down. This family attitude enables Parker leadership to always find the right way and right thing to do. This wonderful tradition of doing the right thing is somehow passed on to successive management generations. It's just part of the Parker culture."[iii]

Parker's men and women saw a higher purpose in their work—helping their customers power the machines that changed the world. Those customers included several of the most daring innovators of the last 100 years—Charles Lindbergh, Bill Boeing, Donald Douglas, Neil Armstrong, Jim Lovell, and Steve Jobs, as well as forward-looking companies such as General Electric, General Motors, Cincinnati Milacron, John Deere, Rolls-Royce, Lockheed Martin, United Technologies, Siemens, and Caterpillar. Helping customers make the world a better place gave Parker's men and women meaning for their work. Their passion for their company's mission gave them the will to persevere through a series of challenges, including an accident that destroyed most of the company's assets, a bankruptcy, the Depression, two world wars, the Cold War, the Space Race, numerous recessions, unprecedented technological change, and the globalization of industrial markets.

Hard times forged a bond among Parker's employees. They learned they could survive in a fast-changing world by helping and caring for each other. They had a sense they were facing each crisis together. Secure in the knowledge their colleagues would support them, no matter what, Parker's men and women were not afraid to take risks. Because they dared greatly, sometimes they failed greatly. When they failed, their fellow employees were there to pick them up and help them do better the next time. Every time they survived a crisis, they became more convinced they could meet the next challenge that came their way.

The values espoused by Art Parker still guide the company. The seven chief executives who succeeded him shared his values—a desire to serve others, resilience in the face of crises, trust in their colleagues, and a fierce desire to win. The persistence of Art's values over 100 years demonstrated the truth of Ralph Waldo Emerson's belief that certain institutions can become "the lengthened shadow of one man."[iv]

Parker's technologies helped its customers master space, distance, time, and motion, making life richer, safer and more comfortable for billions of people. Most people in the world have been touched in some positive way by a Parker product.

When Art Parker started his company in 1917, factory work was backbreaking and dangerous. Parker's products enabled machines to perform the lifting, positioning, and movement of objects previously done by hand, making the workday easier for millions on assembly lines, and enhancing productivity at a rate National Public Radio reporter Adam Davidson says has been "unseen at any time in human history."[v] Other Parker products powered construction equipment used to build dams, airports, bridges, highways, waterways, high-speed rail, mass transit systems, chemical plants, oil refineries, steel mills, skyscrapers, and other infrastructure that made possible the modern middle-class lifestyle.

Parker recently began applying its technologies to the control of human motion itself. The company's newest customers are men and women paralyzed by spinal cord injuries. Until recently, they could only dream of freeing themselves from their disabilities. Today, with an exoskeleton controlled by Parker sensors, they are standing up and walking away from their beds and wheelchairs.

By helping accelerate the speed of travel, Parker's products altered long-held perceptions of space, distance and time. Distance is a function not only of miles or meters, but of speed—the time it takes to travel from one place to another. John Kasarda and Greg Lindsay, authors of "Aerotropolis; The Way We'll Live Next", have written that "space is fungible; it can be overcome with speed," and Karl Marx referred to the "annihilation of space by time."[vi]

In May 1927, Lindbergh pointed his Spirit of St. Louis away from Nova Scotia, toward the North Atlantic, with his knees leaning up against Art Parker's fuel system, and marveled that he might fly to Paris in 36 hours. He thought, "Flying has torn apart the relationship of space and time; it uses our old clock but with new yardsticks."[vii] Seventeen years later, after Parker's aircraft products helped make international passenger flights possible, Wendell Wilkie was able to say, "A navigable ocean of air blankets the whole surface of the globe. There are no distant places any longer; the world is small and the world is one."[viii]

When Art started his company in 1917, it took three days to drive a truck from Cleveland to New York; today drivers complete the trip in eight hours, on interstates built with construction equipment activated by Parker products.

In 1917, the fastest ocean liners crossed the Atlantic in five days; today passenger jets equipped with Parker flight controls make the same trip in seven hours.

In 1917, a New Yorker could send her son in London a telegram, or a letter that, with luck, might arrive two weeks later; today, using a cellular phone equipped with Parker shielding devices, a mother can have a face-to-face conversation with her son anywhere in the world within seconds.

In 1917, the world marveled that three men had driven a Hupmobile across the world in 14 months; in 1963, John Glenn circled the world in 90 minutes in a spacecraft protected by Parker's seals.

In 1917, the moon was an unattainable object in the night sky, the subject of myth and superstition; in 1969, when Neil Armstrong and Buzz Aldrin landed at Tranquility Base, brought by a propulsion system controlled by Parker valves, the moon became earth's close neighbor.

How all that became possible is the story of this book. It is a story that will matter to anyone who dreams of creating a business that will withstand the test of time.

Thomas A. Piraino Jr.
Cleveland Heights, Ohio
June 1, 2017

Art Parker at his desk.

PART 1

# BUILDING THE FOUNDATION

## 1885 TO 1927

*"When you get into a tight spot and everything goes against you, until it seems that you cannot hold on for a minute longer, never give up then, for that is just the place and time that the tide will turn."*

Harriett Beecher Stowe, *Old Town Folks* (1869)

# CHAPTER 1

# Dreams

A rt Parker was born in Cleveland on November 13, 1884, the youngest son of William and Margaret Streeter Parker, who had recently moved from upstate New York. Art came from a family with a proud tradition of making things. His grandfather, John Parker, emigrated from Scotland to upstate New York in the early 1800s. He owned a farm near Oswego, and taught his son William at an early age how to mend fences and perform carpentry. When he was just 16 years old, William joined the Union Army to fight in the Civil War. One of seven children, he had little prospect of taking over his father's farm when he returned from the war. In the mid-1870s, William married Margaret ("Maggie") Streeter, and moved to Cleveland, a city with plentiful job prospects for a hardworking man. The Parkers had four children, Maud, born in 1876, William, born in 1878, Robert, born in 1880, and Art, born in 1884. William initially worked as a carpenter in Cleveland, outfitting the captains' quarters of ships plying the Great Lakes. Through the years, he worked his way up in the world, becoming the superintendent of a shipyard, and later, of a factory.

William and Maggie arrived in Cleveland in the mid-1870s, just as it was about to experience a radical transformation into one of America's greatest industrial centers. It was a time when Americans marveled at how their world was shrinking. The New York Central Railroad had reduced the travel time from Cleveland to New York to a mere 22 hours, and steamships crossed the Atlantic in an astounding eight days. Bustling cities like Cleveland were filled with the sounds of clamping horses' hooves, clattering wagons, hissing steam engines, and boys hawking newspapers. No one in the city, however, had yet opened a refrigerator, watched a motion picture, spoken into a phone, or heard the sound of a vacuum cleaner, radio, phonograph, television, automobile, truck, bus, or plane.

Art, his sister Maud, and brothers William and Robert grew up in the Tremont section of Cleveland, at 1613 Brainard Avenue, on a bluff above the west side of the Cuyahoga River. The streets in Tremont were shaded by tall hardwood trees, like all other Cleveland neighborhoods, earning the city the nickname "the Forest City." The neighborhood was filled with bungalows occupied by hard-working immigrants from Ireland, Germany, Italy, Poland, Lithuania, the Ukraine, Russia, Slovenia, Syria, and Greece, all eager to make their fortunes in America.

Every night, Art, his sister, and brothers went to bed by the flickering light of a kerosene lamp. From their front porch, they could see smoke billowing from the nearby "Flats", an industrial area along the Cuyahoga River, where John D. Rockefeller was operating the Standard Oil refineries on the river's east bank. The refineries provided the kerosene that lit lamps in cities all over the world. Art and his siblings often rode their bicycles down the steep, winding roads to the river, where they watched heavily laden ore boats, surrounded by tugs, nav-

Western Reserve Historical Society

An ore boat on the Cuyahoga River, early 20th century.

igating the twisting Cuyahoga as they headed upriver to Cleveland's three steel works—U.S. Steel, Otis Iron & Steel Co., and the Corrigan-McKinney Steel Co.

Five miles east of Art's family's home, at the Cleveland city limits, sat the westernmost escarpment of the Appalachians, marking the beginning of the Great Plains, which extend from Cleveland to Denver and the foothills of the Rocky Mountains. Except for the slopes leading down to the Cuyahoga, the Cleveland area is as flat as the prairies of Kansas and Nebraska. In 1796, Moses Cleaveland led a group of surveyors from the Connecticut Land Co. to the banks of the Cuyahoga. Relieved to find flat land after weeks of riding through the hills of Pennsylvania, the surveyors were able to lay the city out in a grid, with Public Square, a New England style commons, in the center. Over the years, the Square evolved to become a favorite meeting place, with large trees, a fountain, benches and a bandstand.

The Cuyahoga is a remnant of a vast inland sea that covered most of the Upper Midwest after the Great Glacier melted at the end of the Ice Age. Thirty miles east of Cleveland, in an upland meadow filled with wild flowers, the river begins its 84-mile journey to Lake Erie from a collection of springs and ponds, swiftly flowing through forests where kingfishers, herons and beavers sit along its banks. The river flows faster through Kent and Akron to Cuyahoga Falls, where it falls over the last foothills of the Appalachians, falling two hundred feet into a long wooded valley. As the river reaches the northern end of the valley, it follows a winding course, earning the name the Iroquois gave it: Cuyahoga, which means "crooked river."

Five miles south of Lake Erie, the Cuyahoga's current slows and its channel deepens, creating a perfect waterway for boats heading upriver from Lake Erie through the Flats to supply Cleveland's industries.

At the mouth of the Cuyahoga lay the Great Lakes, a vast inland sea comprised of five lakes, with a circumference of 10,500 navigable miles, nearly half the distance around the world. Captivated by the sight of freshwater extending all the way to the horizon, the early French explorers called the Great Lakes "the sweet seas," and believed they stretched to the Pacific.[1]

By the turn of the 20th century, Cleveland entrepreneurs could count on the blessings of geography, financial capital, and human resources to help sustain their businesses. Half of America's population—and more than half of its manufacturing facilities—lay within 500 miles of the city. Cleveland's business owners sat at the center of a transportation network that allowed them to send their products to all points of the compass.

The Cuyahoga River, with Lake Erie in the background.

Western Reserve Historical Society

Cleveland businesses could transport their goods by water throughout the Great Lakes; to New York City via Lake Erie, the Erie Canal, and the Hudson River; and to New Orleans through the Ohio Canal, the Ohio River and the Mississippi. The city was served by six major railroads and was the terminus of parallel rail lines from the south, east and west, giving its businessmen leverage in freight negotiations.[2] Thirty-two banks opened their doors in Cleveland between 1900 and 1903 alone, and hundreds of wealthy Clevelanders were investing in start-up companies. The city was home to a pool of talented immigrant craftsmen, who had come to Cleveland to work in Rockefeller's refineries and the steel mills in the Flats. At the turn of the century, one-third of Cleveland's population was foreign-born, and another 40 percent had foreign-born parents.[3]

Economists credit business clusters—concentrations of related businesses—with helping new companies succeed. They believe that locations where like-minded entrepreneurs and inventors reside promote a virtuous cycle—sharing innovative ideas, nurturing a supply of skilled workers, and making available the capital necessary to finance the growth of new firms. Examples of business clusters today include Hollywood for movies, Silicon Valley for semi-conductors, and New York City and London for finance.[4]

In the early 20th century, Cleveland was a business cluster for Second Industrial Revolution industries such as iron and steel, oil refining, machine tools, chemicals, electrical apparatus, automobiles, and aviation. The breakthrough that made the Second Industrial Revolution possible was a new way of thinking about business problems. This new discipline applied rigorous analysis to promote manufacturing efficiencies, and it facilitated new methods of mass production.[5]

Cleveland was the early 20th century version of Silicon Valley, generating the innovations for heavy industry that would drive the American economy for most of the century. Since Cleveland was home to so many emerging manufacturers, it was an ideal laboratory for the exchange of ideas about how to make high-quality products in the most efficient way.

In the first decade of the 20th century, Cleveland led the nation in the number of patents filed per capita.[6] As Doug Clifton, a former editor of The Plain Dealer, explained: "Cleveland inventors racked up patents the way short order cooks fry eggs."[7] Many of the inventive men and women in the Cleveland area chose to start new firms to exploit their inventions, such as Frank and Charles Seiberling's Goodyear Tire & Rubber Co., Harvey Firestone's Firestone Tire & Rubber Co., W.H. Hoover's The Hoover Co., Charles Thompson's Thompson Products (later TRW), and Alexander Winton's Winton Motor Carriage Co. Those entrepreneurs "sparked a technology boom in Cleveland that helped to propel it from a medium-sized city...to one of the largest and most prosperous industrial cities in the nation."[8]

Cleveland had one of the highest per capita incomes in America. A string of mansions along twenty blocks of Euclid Avenue, on spacious landscaped grounds, high on a ridge overlooking Lake Erie a few blocks east of downtown, was known the world over as "Millionaires' Row". It was a visible reminder of Cleveland's importance as the manufacturing center of the American Midwest. The historian John Fiske wrote that Euclid Avenue's "double row of arching trees and handsome stone houses...yielded vistas reminding one of the nave and aisles of a huge cathedral."[9] Baedeker's Travel Guide designated the avenue a "must see" for European visitors, comparing it to the Champs Elysees in Paris and Unter den Linden in Berlin. Mark Twain called Euclid Avenue "one of the finest streets in America."[10] In 1892, the New York Tribune concluded that 53 of the 68 wealthiest persons in America lived on the street. The tax valuation of the mansions on Millionaires' Row exceeded those of the houses on New York's Fifth Avenue.[11]

Beneath the arching elms of Millionaires Row lay the mansions, gardens and fountains of a Cleveland aristocracy born of oil, iron, timber, railroads, politics, and engineering expertise. John D. Rockefeller lived at 424 Euclid Avenue from 1868 to 1884, when he was building the Standard Oil Trust.[12] Charles Brush, the inventor of the electric street light, owned a 30,000-square-foot mansion, constructed on a seven-acre plot, filled with oak from England, rosewood from Japan, and stained glass windows, skylights and lighting fixtures designed by Louis Comfort Tiffany. Behind other wrought-iron gates and vast lawns had lived the families of Jeptha Wade (one of the founders of Western Union Telegraph), Samuel Mather (the owner of an iron ore company), John Hay (personal secretary to Abraham Lincoln and Secretary of State under President William McKinley), Ambrose Swasey (co-founder of Warner & Swasey, a machine tool manufacturer), and Mark Hanna (President McKinley's closest adviser and a powerful U.S. Senator).

IN 1903, ART PARKER entered the Case School of Applied Science with the goal of obtaining a degree in electrical engineering. Standing 5 foot 11 inches, at a spare 140 pounds, with penetrating blue eyes and light brown hair, Art had the look of a curious scientist. Beneath his quiet exterior lay a personality well-suited to the business world. He had a never-ending curiosity, a willingness to take risks, and a strong desire to make a mark upon the world. He rarely lost his temper or raised his voice. He was a perennial optimist, not easily discouraged, and looked at hard times as challenges to overcome, rather than as circumstances to fear.

For a young man like Art with a curious mind and a scientific bent, the first decade of the 20th century was an exciting time to begin studying engineering in Cleveland. All around him, he saw how the products streaming from Cleveland factories were changing people's lives. Public Square, which in Art's youth had been a bucolic escape from urban life, a place where people hitched their horses to posts along the curbs, was filling with "horseless carriages" made in Cleveland.[13]

The American automobile industry began in Cleveland on the morning of March 24, 1898, when Robert Allison, a mining engineer from Pennsylvania, arrived at Alexander Winton's motor carriage factory on East 45th Street. Winton had operated a bicycle manufacturing company before turning to the manufacture of horseless carriages. Allison paid Winton $1,000 for one of his inventions. It was the first purchase of an American-made self-propelled road vehicle. By the end of 1898, Winton had sold 23 automobiles.[14]

On May 22, 1899, Winton had driven one of his automobiles to New York City on a publicity trip sponsored by the Cleveland Plain Dealer. The interest it engendered would establish the automobile in the mind of the American public. Winton and a Plain Dealer reporter and publicist named Charles B. Shanks reached Buffalo on the first night, where Shanks sent a dispatch to 30 newspapers. When Winton and Shanks arrived in New York, they were met by a million cheering people.[15] Before Winton's trip, automobile makers had been looking for a name to replace the awkward term "horseless carriage," which had been ridiculed in many national publications. Shanks used the French word "automobile" in his dispatches to describe Winton's motorcar. After the trip, the word entered the American lexicon.[16]

When Art was in engineering school, Cleveland was the number one maker of automobiles in the country, ahead of the up and coming city of Detroit. Cleveland was producing nearly six thousand cars a year, and more than five thousand workers were employed making automobiles.[17] Nine automobiles with a national reputation were being made in Cleveland, and automakers such as Winton, White, Peerless, Jordan, Baker Electric, Stearns, and Hupmobile were known worldwide. The Chandler Motor Car Co. was turning out a five-passenger touring car called the "Cleveland."[18] Demand for the Cleveland was so great that Chandler purchased a 283,000-square-foot plant at 17325 Euclid Avenue to add to its production capacity.

The Cleveland automobile industry was based on technologies first developed for bicycles. Bicycle makers like Winton developed pneumatic tires, which were later used on automobiles. Bicycle chain drives transferred energy from pedals to wheels. Automotive pioneers such as Winton and Henry Ford (whom Winton had once declined to hire) used the same concept to move the wheels of their horseless carriages. The energy source for an automobile—the internal combustion engine—was connected to wheels by a drive chain, just as the pedals on a bicycle were connected to the back wheel by such a chain.

Art's engineering professors at Case explained that the emerging aviation business was also being built upon engineering concepts derived from the bicycle. The American aircraft industry had begun a few hours' drive southwest of Cleveland, in a Dayton, Ohio, bicycle shop operated by Orville and Wilbur Wright.[19] The Wrights understood the common dynamics of bicycles

and airplanes. Wilbur realized that, in order to maintain stability, a flying machine had to be able to bank right or left, little by little, much as a person on bicycle leans gently into a turn.

In late 1903, Wilbur and Orville built the "Wright Flyer," a double-decked plane made from wood, wire and fabric. On December 17, 1903, the brothers, wearing their customary white shirts and dark ties, carried their airplane to the head of a launch rail on Kill Devil Hill, on the beach at Kitty Hawk.[20] Orville climbed into the pilot's position, lying prone between the wings, where he could work the warping controls for the wings. Wilbur held up the right wing for balance. Orville released the line holding the airplane in place, and closed his eyes against the wind and blowing sand. The plane clattered down the rail, with Wilbur running alongside. Suddenly the plane rose 10 feet above the sand and flew 120 feet forward. The plane remained aloft for only 12 seconds, but it flew. Orville had become the first person to pilot a controlled mechanical flight.[21] The brothers' aircraft made three more flights that day, the last of which traveled 852 feet in 59 seconds.[22]

IN 1907, ART GRADUATED from the Case School of Applied Science with a degree in electrical engineering. All around him, Art saw Cleveland entrepreneurs who were starting businesses. He began to dream of building his own manufacturing business that could serve the already thriving automobile business, and perhaps someday, the nascent aviation industry. Art looked to the men on Millionaires' Row for inspiration on how to achieve his dream. He found Rockefeller to be the most fascinating of all. As a boy, Art had seen the brightly painted Standard oil wagons, always pulled by handsome horses that brought kerosene to his home for lamps and cookstoves. The Standard Oil brand symbolized quality, as Rockefeller demanded excellence in every phase of his operations—from the refining process to the final delivery of products to customers.

Art noted that Rockefeller began his business career at a menial level, working as an assistant bookkeeper in a commission merchant's shop, along the east bank of the Cuyahoga River. Like Art, he was not born into wealth or power. In 1870, Rockefeller took a risk and left his bookkeeping position to open a refinery in Cleveland's Flats. He developed a means of cleansing oil with sulfuric acid to produce a higher quality brand of kerosene for illumination. The kerosene provided by earlier refiners had been of uneven quality; filled with volatile contaminants, it was prone to igniting. Before Standard

Oil, nearly 6,000 Americans died each year from accidents caused by faulty kerosene in household lamps.[23] Rockefeller's new refining process standardized the quality of his kerosene (hence the name "Standard" Oil), and eliminated the risk of fire.[24]

The early years of the Standard Oil Co. were perilous. Rockefeller's first refinery sat on the banks of a stream called Kingsbury Run that emptied into the Cuyahoga three miles upstream from Lake Erie. Tall trees shaded the refinery—nothing more than a few sheds scattered across a hillside—and cows grazed next to its walls.[25] Hundreds of gallons of gasoline (an unwanted by-product of the refining process) spilled every day into the Cuyahoga. Whenever a steamboat captain shoveled hot coals over the side, the river burst into flames. Rockefeller lived in constant fear that vapors from his refining process would catch fire, destroying his entire business. Several other refineries in the Flats had been leveled by fires. Rockefeller later recalled, "I was always ready, day and night, for a fire alarm from the direction of our works."[26]

Rockefeller realized sales volume would be critical to his success. He later described the foundation principle of Standard Oil: "The theory...was that the larger the [sales] volume the better opportunities for the economies, and consequently the better opportunities for giving the public a cheaper product...."[27] He sought to achieve economies of scale by buying up hundreds of refineries and consolidating their operations at his refinery in the Flats. By running his refinery at full capacity day and night, seven days a week, he could deliver kerosene at a lower price to millions of customers. Previous grades of kerosene sold for 88 cents a gallon. Rockefeller was able to provide his new, improved brand of kerosene for only five cents a gallon.[28] Customers beat a path to his door, attracted by his high-quality, low-price products.

By 1907, when Art graduated from Case, Standard Oil was producing 87 percent of all kerosene in the world. The company had become such a global giant that when the Geodesic Association announced plans to measure the earth, the World newspaper said it would "enable the Standard Oil Trust and other trusts to learn the exact size of their property."[29]

In order to save the funds to start his own business, Art first had to work for someone else, just as Rockefeller had. He had a choice of several research positions at Cleveland automobile companies. In 1907, Art accepted a position with a firm making a critical part for automobiles, the most dynamic and innovative industry in town. Theodore A. Willard was operating his Willard Storage Battery Co. on East Third Street in downtown Cleveland.

The company was at the forefront of electrical innovation. It made storage batteries for radios, phonographs, and automobiles, and had a hand in developing the automobile ignition, electric starter, and headlamps. In 1923, Willard would found and operate the WTAM radio station, Cleveland's first 1,500-watt "clear-channel" radio broadcaster.[30]

Willard assigned Art to a 10-person team that was researching ways of making more powerful batteries for automobiles, an area considered to be at the forefront of electrical engineering. In his spare time, Art kept his dream of starting his own company alive by tinkering with new inventions. In 1908, he filed his first patent, for a mechanism that regulated the speed of a generator, allowing it to produce a constant output of electricity.[31] In 1914, he filed a patent for a pneumatic braking system for large vehicles. He would file 160 more patents during his lifetime.

Willard's expansion tracked the exponential growth of the automobile industry, which was transforming the look of Cleveland, as automobiles began to outnumber horse-drawn vehicles on the streets. In 1912, Willard originated the service station concept, when it built the first automobile battery service station. In 1914, the first two-color (red and green) traffic light was erected in Cleveland at the corner of East 105th Street and Euclid Avenue.[32] By 1915, Willard was selling 85 percent of the automobile batteries made in the U.S., and the company employed 3,000 people. The company built a 350,000-square-foot plant on East 131st Street, devoted to battery production.

Art's responsibilities and compensation increased as Willard grew. By 1917, however, he had grown tired of taking orders from someone else. He decided to take advantage of an emerging technology, called "fluid power", to create his own enduring business in Cleveland. Like Rockefeller, he was confident enough in himself to leave a secure, well-paying job for the chance to make his own mark upon the world.

# CHAPTER 2

# Fluid Power

For more than 2,000 years, inventors, scientists, engineers and dreamers of all kinds struggled to discover how to enable a small force to lift a large weight. With such a force, the Egyptian pyramids, the Parthenon in Greece, and the temples of Rome could have been built by fewer workers in a fraction of the time spent by thousands of slaves.

A Greek mathematician, astronomer, physicist, and inventor named Archimedes wrestled with the problem of lifting large objects in Syracuse, Sicily in the 3rd century BC. Working from a hypothesis of Aristotle, Archimedes developed the first theory of fluid motion, which recognized that liquids in motion could produce pressure, and move any given weight.[33] After years of trial and error, he was able to apply a principle called "the law of the lever." Archimedes designed levers, pulleys and seesaws that could move objects many times their weight or size. He boldly proclaimed, "Give me a place to stand, and I can move the Earth."[34]

It would be more than two millennia before Archimedes' dream to move anything on Earth was realized in the products Art Parker and other inventors were designing in the early 20th century. Scientists coined a new term, "fluid power," to describe recent engineering breakthroughs that had solved the problem of how to use air, water, oil or other fluids under pressure to move heavy objects.

As fluids accumulate within a fluid power system, they build up energy which, when released, provide the muscle to lift, push, and pull weight.

Engineers called this new form of energy the "hydraulic force multiplier," because it allowed fluid systems to move objects many times their size and weight. As Art studied fluid power during his evenings after work at Willard, he became confident that if this force could be controlled properly, humanity would have at its disposal a much more powerful form of energy than could ever be produced with mechanical levers and pulleys.

Fluid power had several advantages over steam, the main source of power in the nineteenth and early twentieth centuries. The air, water or oil in a fluid power system could be controlled more effectively than steam, which tended to leak easily. Steam could only be used in tandem with a nearby power source, such as coal; fluid power systems could operate simply from the internal force of their own liquids. Steam had been the source of power for the First Industrial Revolution; Art intended to help make fluid power the source of energy for the Second.

Just as Rockefeller supplied the world with a new means of illumination, Art hoped to give the world a new form of power—one that would allow machines to perform tasks far beyond the capabilities of any human being. He saw an unmet need for customers in a host of mechanical applications, and he believed he had a way to meet it. Nearly every type of machine could be powered by the elements of a fluid power system. Art dared to dream his products would revolutionize the way any mechanical work was performed.

Art knew the greatest challenge would be to devise a way of sealing fluids stored under pressure. If any air, oil or water escaped, a fluid power system would lose pressure and collapse. No one had yet devised an effective way of sealing the connections within a fluid power system. Art was convinced that if he could develop fittings, seals and connectors that knitted together the components of a pressurized fluid power system without allowing any leakage, and valves that controlled the flow of the fluid, he could leave Willard and set out on his own to master the entire market for fluid power components.

Cleveland was the perfect place to launch a fluid power business. The three steel mills in the Flats were turning out millions of tons of quality steel every year. Their steel had the strength to withstand high pressures, and the flexibility to be machined to the tight tolerances a fluid power system would require. The Warner & Swasey plant on East 55th Street was building machine tools that could take raw steel and shape it into a finished product. The company had built a number of telescopes, viewed by many as one of the crowning achievements of the Second Industrial Revolution. Art believed that, with the expertise to shape a lens to illuminate the heavens, Warner & Swasey would have no problem making machines that could produce fittings and valves that could maintain the high pressures in a fluid power system.

Art planned to concentrate first on the growing market for braking systems in the 3.5 million automobiles and 250,000 trucks and tractors just starting to move along America's roads and fields. They had to compete for space with 21 million horses still moving plows, wagons and carriages.[35] The new motor-driven vehicles were using steel rods and levers to operate clutches, braking and gear-shifting mechanisms. Drivers had to push heavily on a clutch, gearshift or brake pedal to command a movement or change a vehicle's speed. Often drivers could not muster enough force to stop a vehicle quickly enough to prevent an accident.

Art devised a new way of controlling the motion of vehicles, which he described in a patent application he filed in August 1914. The braking device consisted of a complex, interconnected system of compressed air, produced by a pump, stored in a series of tanks under pressure, and connected to brake, clutch and gear-shifting mechanisms by precisely calibrated piping, valves and fittings.

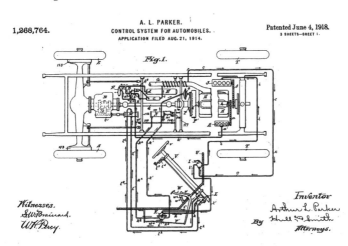

Air, the most insubstantial substance of all, was to be the muscle for Art's braking system. He believed the system would allow the drivers of automobiles, trucks and buses to operate their vehicles more easily and safely. As he wrote in his patent application, the use of fluid under pressure, rather than heavy steel rods and levers, would provide a "particularly flexible" system that would "eliminate the jars of impact" and enable a driver to "feel the operation of the movable parts," intuitively sensing how much pressure to apply to bring a large vehicle safely to a stop.

In the midst of the second decade of the 20th century, manufacturers were designing and building more powerful internal combustion engines that could move heavier loads on trucks, buses and tractors. The increasing sophistication of engines broadened the market for Art's pneumatic braking system. His new patented system was a dramatic example of the hydraulic force multiplier. A truck equipped with Art's pneumatic brakes multiplied the force of a driver's push on the brake pedals many times over, allowing for the safe and easy transportation of heavy loads that previously could only travel by train.

Art wanted to do more than invent new products. Like the best engineers, he wanted to turn his dreams into reality, to take abstract designs and mathematical formulae and make them into usable products. The historian Neil Sheehan captured the essence of Art's vision when he explained that for the most talented engineers, "fulfillment comes from creating the new, bringing into being that which no one else had yet achieved."[36] Art realized his ideas could only endure if he created an organization capable of manufacturing, distributing and servicing the products that currently existed only on paper.

During his last years at Willard, Art used his evening and weekends to tackle a problem that was bedeviling most fluid power systems—the threat of fluid leaking under high pressure. He learned from automobile mechanics in Cleveland that air and oil leakage was compromising the effectiveness of pneumatic brake systems, like the one he was patenting. Art sketched a diagram for a new type of coupling he called a "die form coupler," which could tightly seal the connections in a fluid power system. His breakthrough was in flaring the coupling, bending it out to form a tight seal that could withstand nearly any pressure from oil, water, air or hydraulic fluid passing through the piping in a fluid power system.[37]

With his patent for pneumatic brakes about to issue and his encouraging work on the die form coupler, 32-year-old Art felt ready to take an irrevocable break from working for someone else. He formed a corporation on March 13, 1917, which he called the Parker Appliance Co.[38] (Art lived by the scientific method, but he also had a superstitious bent that was unusual for an engineer. He believed the 13th day of each month was a propitious time to start something new—he was, after all, born on the 13th day of November.)

Western Reserve Historical Society

The Angle neighborhood, early 20th century.

Art took all the savings he had accumulated during his 10 years at Willard—a total of $6,000—and invested it in machinery to build components for pneumatic brake systems. A few weeks later, on April 6, 1917, America entered World War I, which had been raging in Europe since 1914. Art had registered for the draft two years earlier, and he worried that someday he might find himself fighting in Europe.

Art found a second-story loft for rent above a garage in a red brick building on the west side of the Cuyahoga River, in a Cleveland neighborhood called "the Angle," after a wedge-shaped area of land sloping down to the river from West 25th Street. The Angle was home to the immigrant Irish who built Cleveland's railways and worked on its docks.[39] Nearby buildings housed the American Ship Building Co., the Forest City Foundry, and the Sherwin-Williams Co. A few blocks from Art's loft stood St. Malachi's, the Catholic church where the Irish worshiped. At the crown of the steeple burned a gas-fired flame, illuminating a cross, which acted as a beacon to the ships arriving from Lake Erie, as they navigated the bends in the river.

South of Art's loft, on West 25th Street, lay a retail and entertainment district, known for the Majestic, Rialto and Fairyland theaters (where patrons could see a show for a nickel), several breweries, F.W. Woolworth's, and the West Side Market. Just to the west sat St. Ignatius School, a Jesuit institution which included a high school and a college called John Carroll University. Directly across the river lay the small brick building in which, 50 years earlier, a young bookkeeper named John D. Rockefeller had gazed out from his ledgers at the boats and barges plying their way up the Cuyahoga.

Rockefeller's Standard oil refineries were a mile upriver from Art's loft, and the mills that supplied steel for his fittings were half a mile away, three bends up the riverbank. Warner & Swasey's machine tool factory was a mile and a half east, on East 55th Street. Every morning, Art left his parents' home and walked two blocks to an electric streetcar stop on West 25th Street, for a 10-minute ride to his loft. As the streetcar ran north over the red-brick street, it jostled for space with Model Ts, buses and horse-drawn wagons. It was a time and place where the past, present and future of transportation all collided.

Emerging from the street car at his factory's front door at the corner of West 25th Street and Detroit Avenue, Art could smell the sulfurous red smoke belching from the steel mills upriver and hear the screams of sea gulls circling over the Cuyahoga. Soon, he discovered everything was his responsibility—designing products, purchasing raw materials and machinery, setting up the shop, and finding customers. Art learned to do all these things on the run. As historian and Harvard University professor Niall Ferguson explains, "There is something uniquely educational about sitting at the desk where the buck stops, in a dreary office you've just rented, working day and night with a handful of employees just to break even."[40]

Art spent the next several months looking for investors and customers to help him sustain his new enterprise. He planned to benefit from the new aircraft industry being born right at his front door. Cleveland area makers of automobile components, such as Goodyear, Firestone, B.F. Goodrich, Thompson Products, Sherwin Williams, American Steel & Wire, the Aluminum Co. of America, and Standard Oil were turning out steel, aluminum, tires, paint, fuel, and precision metal parts that were just as suitable for planes as for automobiles. Thompson Products traced its history back to 1904, when its founder, Charles E. Thompson, began to make engine valves for Alexander Winton's horseless carriages.[41]

Aircraft engineers, designers, entrepreneurs, pilots and just plain adventurers who were jump-starting the American aviation industry were flocking to the Cleveland area. Art intended to befriend them, and to make them his customers. He believed the growing aircraft industry could provide a market for the types of valves, piping and fittings he was making for his pneumatic brake system. He was confident those components could provide leak-proof fuel systems for the new airplanes just starting to be produced around the country. Art was even more encouraged in September 1917, when Glenn L. Martin, who owned one of the largest aircraft manufacturers in the country, moved from Los Angeles to Cleveland.

Many aviation historians are convinced Martin was the person most responsible for converting the Wright Brothers' aeronautical breakthroughs into a practical way of making airplanes. From 1910 to 1925, he was considered by many to be the best designer of airplanes in the world. No one could have appeared less suited for that accolade. Martin was a shy, formal man, the last person one would mistake for the innovator, adventurer, and showman he turned out to be. The Pulitzer prize-winning reporter Wayne Biddle described him as something of a "dandy," a "businessman who rarely went anywhere without his mother. Tall, slender, narrow-shouldered, with a bulging forehead and heavy black hair, he showed a preference for Continental-style hats and artistic round eyeglass frames."[42]

Martin was born in Iowa in 1886, less than two years after Art Parker was born in Cleveland. He built his first plane in Los Angeles in 1910; it crashed on its first flight. Undaunted, he kept building planes. In 1912, he formed the Glenn L. Martin Co. and opened a small aircraft factory in a Methodist Church in Los Angeles. He tried to create interest in his planes by performing stunts at air shows. He liked to frighten late-arriving patrons by swooping down just over their heads.[43] On May 10, 1912, Martin captured the imagination of the Los Angeles area when he made the longest flight yet attempted over water: a trip in a Martin Model 12 float plane from a dock on Newport Bay to Catalina Island, 33 miles away.

Handing his watch to his chief engineer just before the flight, Martin said, "Take care of this, in case I go for a swim."[44]

After 30 minutes, he descended through breaks in the clouds to find himself over Catalina's Avalon Bay.

The publicity from the flight convinced several customers to buy his biplanes.[45]

On August 7, 1914, a few days after World War I began, Martin published a grim prophesy in the Los Angeles Evening Herald about the destruction planes could wreak in war: "The aeroplane will practically decide the war in Europe. Veritable flying death will smash armies, wreck mammoth battle ships and bring the whole world to a vivid realization of the awful possibilities of a few men and a few swift winging aerial demons.... [An airplane] will drop not only the known explosive shells, but it will introduce a new kind of projectile into modern warfare."[46]

To illustrate the destructive power of the airplane, Martin performed a mock aerial battle, throwing bombs over the side of his plane and demolishing a temporary fort built for the occasion. The Los Angeles Times called the flight an "epoch-making event."[47]

At the beginning of the 20th century, a career in aviation was considered a foolhardy endeavor. Biddle wrote, "Flying was considered craziness in the early days, and anyone who chose to build flying machines for a living dwelt on the outskirts of polite society."[48] Martin's father Clarence told him, "I don't see the sense of throwing away all you've got by messing around with those flying machines."[49] The family doctor sent Martin's mother Minta a letter warning her to try to convince him to stop flying: "For Heaven's sake, if you have any influence with that wiled-eye [sic], Hallucinated, Vissionary [sic] young man, call him off before he is killed. Have him devote his energies to substantial, feasable [sic] and proffitable [sic] pursuits, leaving dreaming to the professional dreamers."[50] Minta tried to discourage her son, but he refused to give up flying.

In the summer of 1917, a Los Angeles businessman introduced Martin to Alva Bradley, the owner of the Cleveland Indians. Bradley told Martin he and seven other Cleveland businessmen were prepared to finance the move of his company to Cleveland for $2.5 million. Martin realized the Cleveland area, where automobile parts companies were diversifying into the manufacture of aircraft parts, would be an excellent source of components for his planes. He also knew that Woodrow Wilson's Secretary of War,

A Martin advertisement for the MB-1 bomber.

Newton D. Baker, had been the mayor of Cleveland. His Assistant Secretary, Benedict Crowell, another prominent Cleveland businessman, was in charge of military procurement. Bradley and his friends had maintained close ties with Baker and Crowell after they moved to Washington. Martin believed the Cleveland businessmen could help him convince Baker and Crowell to order the Army to buy his new "MB-1" bomber, just coming off the drawing boards.

On September 19, 1917, Martin opened his 61,000-square-foot Cleveland plant, eight miles east of downtown, on St. Clair Avenue. He built a 71-acre airport next to the plant, called "Glenn L. Martin Field." Martin chaired a committee that established the first regular airmail service between Cleveland and Chicago, and his airport became the intermediate stop for planes carrying the U.S. Mail between New York and Chicago. Just as Cleveland had been a major rail center on the Chicago-to-New York corridor, it now became a major link on transcontinental airmail routes.

Martin's Cleveland investors insisted, to his mother's delight, that he give up flying. He never flew a plane again, and his mother joined him in Cleveland. Martin became a well-known, and rather eccentric, figure around town as, dressed in a three-piece suit, he drove a Stutz touring car equipped with snakeskin upholstery. He never drank, never smoked, and never attended parties. He also never married and lived with his mother until she died, when he was in his 50s.[51]

Martin hired an extraordinary group of men to run his company in Cleveland; they would go on to start their own successful aircraft companies. Lawrence Bell, the manager of the Martin factory, would found Bell Aircraft, which would build helicopters and the first supersonic plane; James H. ("Dutch") Kindelberger, Martin's chief draftsman, would start North American Aviation, the company that would build the B-25 bomber and P-51 "Mustang" fighter during World War II, the F-86 "Sabre" jet that defeated the Russian MIGs during the Korean War, and the Apollo service and command modules in the 1960s; and Donald Douglas, Martin's Chief Engineer, would found the Douglas Aircraft Co., which for decades would be the world's preeminent commercial aircraft manufacturer.

Together, Martin, Douglas, Bell and Kindelberger designed and produced the massive MB-1 bomber at Martin's Cleveland plant.[52] The bi-plane was a 10,000-pound wood-framed monster, with two engines and a 72-foot wingspan.[53] It was the first U.S.-designed-and-built bomber to enter production, and the first, anywhere in the world, capable of carrying a significant enough

A Goodyear truck equipped with Parker brakes, circa 1918. The first Parker plant—the "second-story loft" just above the garage—can be seen in the background, with James Vetter's business at the far left.

payload of bombs to inflict real damage upon an enemy.[54] Wayne Biddle called the MB-1 "a killing machine. Manned by a crew of three...[and] powered by two...engines, it could reach a maximum speed of 105 miles per hour and climb to over 10,000 feet. It carried five machine guns and 1,000 pounds of bombs. Here for the first time from American drawing boards was a formidable offensive air weapon with a single purpose—mass destruction."[55]

Art soon discovered investors for his new company were easier to find than customers. Despite repeated efforts, he was not able to convince Martin to take a chance on buying Parker products for the fuel system of the MB-1. Art was fortunate, however, that many Clevelanders were flush with cash, and looking for promising new companies to support. Just a few feet from Art's loft, James Vetter was running the Vetter Mantel and Tile Co. Intrigued by his new neighbor, Vetter stopped by the Parker Appliance Co. one day, and Art confided his plans to build his business into a diversified manufacturer of fluid power products. Vetter, a carpenter and builder, began to visit Art regularly, helping him construct dividing walls in his loft and a large desk for his office at the back of the loft. Several weeks after meeting Art, Vetter decided to invest $3,000 in his company.

Soon thereafter, Art met a truck and trailer dealer named Richard T. Carroll, who was selling trucks and trailers on Carnegie Avenue, three miles east of Public Square. Carroll was driving trucks and attached trailers for the Goodyear Tire & Rubber Co. of Akron, on the "Akron-to-Boston Express," along the newly built Lincoln Highway. On the trip east to Boston, Carroll filled his trailer with tires, made in Akron, and delivered them to Goodyear's plant in New England. On the return trip, he filled the trailer with fabric that would be molded into tires at Goodyear's Akron plant.

Art told Carroll of his pneumatic brake system, and Carroll was so impressed that he agreed to invest $1,500 in the company. Carroll convinced Art that they could demonstrate the effectiveness of Art's pneumatic brake system by equipping a trailer with his braking system and driving it to the East Coast on a run for Goodyear. The Goodyear truck route over the Lincoln Highway crossed the Allegheny Mountains in Pennsylvania, over muddy roads, where trucks had to climb dangerously steep grades. If the braking system in the trailer survived the rigors of that trip, Carroll said, it could survive nearly any other long excursion.

Before Art and Carroll could schedule the trip, Art received a notice that he was being drafted into the Army. He realized he would need to hire a partner to watch over the business while he was away in Europe. The perfect candidate was working in the Flats at the most respected wooden pattern making firm in Cleveland, called "Fifth City Pattern Works," in reference to Cleveland's status as the fifth largest city in the country. The company was located just across the Superior Viaduct from Art's loft, on the eastern bank of the Cuyahoga, at 1577 Columbus Road. Art had outsourced the making of patterns for his pneumatic brake system to Fifth City Patterns.

A few minutes after Art walked into the plant, he noticed a group of workers in a semi-circle, listening intently to a man explaining how to design a wooden pattern for an industrial part. The man spoke softly, but it was clear to Art the workers respected him, and deferred to his judgment. After the man ended his discussion with the workers, Art walked over and showed him a design he had in mind for a fitting that would control the flow of air in his pneumatic braking systems.

The man introduced himself as Carl Klamm, and he told Art that he had already been designing patterns for Art's company. He said in a quiet yet authoritative voice, "I think, sir, I can recommend a better design for your part."

He proceeded to explain how he could design a new part that would more effectively prevent air from leaking in Art's brake system.

At 30 years of age, Klamm was two years Art's junior. After completing the fifth grade, he had given up formal schooling to learn the art of wooden pattern making when he was just 12. When he turned 18, he was apprenticed to John Remesch, a German immigrant, who was running the only wooden pattern making shop in Cleveland—on Merwin Road in the Flats. Klamm learned from Remesch how to master the complex art of wooden pattern making, which required the talents of a draftsman, an artist, a sculptor, and an engineer. First, Klamm made a detailed pencil drawing by hand of a finished metal part. Next, he made a final ink drawing. Then he completed the most delicate and complex step of all—using knives, lathes and saws to fashion a piece of wood into a model of the part, accurate to tolerances within small fractions of an inch. Finally, he took the wooden pattern to a foundry that would make a bronze casting from the pattern, into which workers would pour molten metal to make the finished part.

Remesch died in 1912. In 1913, Klamm joined two of Remesch's employees in starting Fifth City Patterns. In 1916, Klamm married Remesch's daughter Alvina, whom he had met while she was working as a bookkeeper at her father's plant. Klamm became well-known among the close-knit fraternity of pattern makers in the Midwest, many of whom were buying up copies of his signed drawings of wooden patterns for industrial parts, and using them as models for their own designs.

Impressed by Klamm after their first meeting, Art began to inquire about him at several Cleveland foundries. He learned that Klamm had a reputation for creativity, innovation, the utmost precision in workmanship, dedication to his customers, and steadiness under stress. Warm-hearted and approachable, with a good sense of humor, he was well liked by everyone who worked with him. Art returned to Fifth City Patterns and told Klamm he was prepared to make him his partner, with responsibility for overseeing the design and production of products. A few days later, Klamm showed up at Art's loft and accepted his offer.

In July 1918, Art boarded the troop train at the Cleveland Union Station, bound for the war in Europe. His last words to Klamm before leaving for the war were to encourage him to continue trying to convince Glenn Martin to buy Parker fuel system valves and fittings for his MB-1 bomber.

# CHAPTER 3

# On the Western Front

I n August 1914, few Europeans could have predicted their peaceful world would be shattered by war. It was a time when they felt more interconnected than ever because of the rise of global trade. The increasing use of the gold standard, combined with the decline in transportation costs, led countries to jump into what was quickly becoming a global economy. In the first decade of the 20th century, intercontinental telephone cables, transcontinental rail lines, faster oil-fired ships, and the airplane were making the world interdependent. After Orville Wright's 1903 flight at Kitty Hawk, he said, "We thought we were introducing into the world an invention which would make further wars practically impossible." The Frenchman Louis Bleriot, after flying across the English Channel in 1909, told The Independent newspaper of London that the airplane would help ensure peace because it "creates propinquity, and propinquity begets love rather than hate."[56]

The volume of world trade reached a peak in 1913 that would not be achieved again until the 1970s. The Model T became the world's first global consumer brand, driven in most countries of the world. A popular cartoon showed a startled Martian looking at Earth through a telescope and seeing it swarming with Model Ts.[57] Europeans were living in a harmony that seemed like it would last forever.[58] One German said in May 1913: "Thank God for Now! These present times are the greatest and the best the world has ever seen."[59]

Beneath the surface of peace and prosperity, however, Europe was descending into two armed camps—the "Central Powers" of Germany and

Austria-Hungary, and the "Triple Alliance" of France, England and Russia. The members of each alliance were bound by treaties that obligated them to come to each other's aid if attacked.[60] The war historian Peter Hart explained that Russia, Germany, France and England each had their own gigantic arms manufacturers churning out "the best, the most reliable, the most deadly weapons possible."[61]

What would later become known as the "Great War" was precipitated in Sarajevo, Bosnia, on June 28, 1914, when Archduke Franz Ferdinand, the heir to the throne of Austria, and his wife Sophie, were assassinated. The assassin was a young Serbian nationalist named Gavrilo Princep.[62] When Serbia refused to take action against his terrorist group, Austria responded by invading Serbia on July 28, 1914. The complex web of European alliances brought France, England and Russia to war against Germany and Austria-Hungary, proving the truth of Otto von Bismarck's 1888 prediction that "some damned foolish thing in the Balkans" would trigger the next great European conflict."[63]

On August 4, German troops wheeled through the Low Countries, descending toward Paris from the north. The Germans advanced to the Marne River, within an hour's drive of the city's center. The French government, and most ambassadors from other nations, fled south to Bordeaux. The American Ambassador, Myron T. Herrick, refused to leave his post in Paris. The 73 year-old Herrick had been born in a small town, 20 miles west of Cleveland. He attended Oberlin College and served as a Cleveland City Councilman and the Governor of Ohio. He turned down an offer to join Rockefeller's Standard Oil Co., spurning the opportunity to make a fortune in the oil business, in order to continue his public service. He earned France's undying gratitude when he declared to the French President, "I shall not leave Paris. Some defender of the law of nations ought to stay.... I can speak in the name of the United States, and have no fear—I will find a way to prevent pillage and massacre!"[64]

The French, helped by English troops, pushed the Germans back to the Loraine region, on the eastern border of France. The battle lines then stalemated into a 468-mile-long line of trenches that extended from the English Channel to the Swiss border. It was soon to be called the "Western Front."

When the war began in the summer of 1914, President Wilson promised the American people he would not involve the country in a European conflict. His biographer, A. Scott Berg, explained, "Like most Americans...[Wilson] thanked God for the isolation the Atlantic Ocean provided."[65] The President, however, eventually concluded America would have to enter the war in order to play a role in a peace he hoped would prevent any future world wars. Wilson asked Newton D. Baker, the mayor of Cleveland, to become his Secretary of War, and to begin to mobilize American industry to produce war material.[66] On April 2, 1917, Wilson went to the Capitol and asked Congress to declare war against Germany and Austria-Hungary.[67]

America was not prepared for Wilson's war. The U.S. Army had only 107,461 men, making it the 17th largest fighting force in the world. The German staff ranked the U.S. militarily "somewhere between Belgium and Portugal."[68] Wilson called upon U.S. manufacturers to become "more prolific and more efficient than ever," believing American industry would become "a great international...army...engaged in the service of the nation and the world, the efficient friends and saviors of free men everywhere."[69]

American manufacturers responded to Wilson's call by retooling their factories for war. Henry Ford and the other automobile makers began to produce a new weapon called the "tank," as well as planes for reconnaissance and bombing enemy targets. Manufacturers began to depend more upon new entrants to the workforce—women and African-Americans—as experienced factory workers were drafted for duty on the Western Front.

In late July 1918, Art Parker boarded a troop ship at the Hoboken, New Jersey docks. His father had been tight-lipped about his experiences in the Civil War, but what little he had told Art about battle had made him even more fearful of what lay ahead of him in France. Out in the Atlantic, German U-Boats were waiting beneath the waves, poised to attack ships like Art's troop transport. The ship pointed down the Hudson, along the west side of a Manhattan skyline not yet punctuated by the Empire State or Chrysler buildings, past excursion ships, the Battery, the 33-year-old Statue of Liberty, and Ellis Island. The ship passed through the Narrows, between Staten Island and Brooklyn, and then out into the open Atlantic. An hour later, the North American continent receded to a small dark line on the horizon.

By the end of July, Art was on a train in Brest, France, headed for the trenches in the Argonne Forest, a few miles northwest of Verdun, France. Dense groves of pine trees covered the hilly landscape. The Meuse River lay 15 miles to the east, and 30 miles beyond the river sat the Hindenburg Line, a series of hilltops fortified by the Germans along their border with France.

The Western Front was a shocking sight to even the most hardened soldiers. For Art, the ultimate rational man, the Front must have seemed like something from a nightmare. Smoke from artillery and poison gas shells hung thickly over the trenches, like a fog. Many French and English soldiers had lived most of their lives underground for more than three years, in a long muddy hole where they endured continual attacks of artillery shells and poison gas. One British private said, "It was impossible to see beyond a few yards outside as the misty fog was so thick and the cascade of screaming shells, explosions and vivid flashes everywhere was something one just endured, and waited for it to go, but it didn't."[70] Another private remembered, "Nobody could stand more than three hours of sustained shelling before they started feeling sleepy and numb. You're hammered after three hours and you're there for the picking... It's a bit like being under an anesthetic."[71]

There is an irony to war, the most destructive endeavor undertaken by humankind; it also has produced some of the most useful inventions in history. As Art delivered supplies to the Front, he was able to observe two inventions that would provide a market for his fluid power products after the war: the truck and the airplane.

Biplanes flew over the Front, piloted by men the press were beginning to call "Aces." They included Germany's Manfred von Richthofen (called the "Red Baron") and Hermann Goring (who would command Hitler's Luftwaffe in World War II), America's Eddie Rickenbacker, and France's Renee Fonck, Charles Nungesser, and Francois Coli.[72] Their planes were primitive machines at best, incapable of carrying a sufficient bomb load to inflict significant damage, and rarely able to hit their targets. Their most important function was to provide reconnaissance for the artillery, as the pilots used wireless transmitters to show artillery captains the location of enemy troops and gun emplacements.[73]

In July 1918, when Art arrived at the Front, the American Expeditionary Force under the command of General John Pershing was preparing an offensive designed to end the war by pushing the Germans back to the Hindenburg Line. The European armies of 1914 had depended upon horsepower, just like the armies of Napoleon. By the time Art arrived at the Western Front, trucks had replaced most of the horses. Art was assigned to drive a truck delivering food, weapons and ammunition to the soldiers on the front lines. He traveled over a road the French called the "Voie Sacree," meaning "Sacred Road." The road wound over steep grades on the hilly terrain. It was revered by the French, because two years earlier, in the winter of 1916, it had helped them deliver the supplies that won the battle of Verdun, the bloodiest battle of the war.

More than 260,000 Americans would engage in what would later be known as the "Meuse-Argonne Offensive." It would be the first time Americans had engaged in the war on a large scale. Art and his fellow soldiers were about to be thrown into a battle for which they had received little training.

The Meuse-Argonne Offensive began on September 26, 1918, as the French Fourth Army and American First Army attacked along a 44-mile front northwest of Verdun, between the city of Reims and the Meuse River, in the dark Argonne Forest. A coordinated barrage of 2,700 artillery pieces announced the beginning of the attack. More than 800 Allied planes circled overhead, seeking out German artillery so they could direct Allied fire to the right location. The Americans and French advanced seven miles before they stalled in the woods, ridges and valleys of the Argonne, in the face of withering machine gun fire from well-entrenched German soldiers.[74] A young man from Kansas named Harry Truman led an artillery battery that helped prevent the Germans from counterattacking. The Americans, however, were running out of food and ammunition, growing desperate as they waited for new supplies to arrive from the rear.

As Art drove his supply truck through the Argonne, he discovered all was not right on the Sacred Road that had saved the French in the first battle of Verdun. The Army's supply trucks, equipped with traditional mechanical brakes, were breaking down repeatedly on the hilly road. The drivers had to apply exactly the right amount of pressure on their pedals to operate their mechanical brake systems. Many of the drivers stomped too hard, causing

Army supply trucks on the Sacred Road, 1918.

their brakes to lock up and creating miles-long traffic jams that delayed the delivery of badly needed supplies to the soldiers on the front lines.

Art's supply truck became a makeshift ambulance as he brought hundreds of wounded American and French boys to the hospital tents behind the front lines. One of those tents was manned by a group of doctors from Cleveland, led by George Washington Crile, who had developed new methods of using gas for anesthesia, eliminating much of the pain of surgery. Ambassador Herrick had helped raise funds from Cleveland businessmen to send Crile's team to the Front.[75] Using the new surgical techniques they had first tried in Cleveland, the doctors were able to save the lives of many of the young men Art and other ambulance drivers were delivering to their door. After the war, Crile and his colleagues would return to Cleveland and found the Cleveland Clinic, where they would use the techniques they learned on the Western Front to save lives in their hometown.[76]

Art was disappointed not to see any of Martin's MB-1 bombers flying over the battlefield. In September, Martin had flown his first MB-1 to the Army's McCook Field in Dayton. He arrived two weeks earlier than the Army had expected. The Army guards, worried about enemy infiltrators, arrested Martin and his crew. An Army Captain soon arrived and sorted out the situation. He took the MB-1 up for a test flight. After an hour challenging the plane to every possible test, the captain returned with nothing but praise for the aircraft. The MB-1 became the first American-made bomber purchased by the Army, but the war would end before it could be deployed in combat.[77]

By mid-October, the Americans had cleared the Argonne Forest, and the Germans were retreating east, toward the Hindenburg Line. During the next few days, French troops occupied Sedan and cut a railroad junction there that was operating as a strategic supply point for the entire German line. On November 11, 1918, the German armistice ended the fighting. More than 26,000 Americans died and nearly 100,000 were wounded in the Meuse-Argonne Offensive, the decisive battle of the war. The German Field Marshall Paul von Hindenburg later admitted that "the American blow in the Argonne decided the war for the Allies and that...without the American troops...the war could have ended in a sort of stalemate."[78]

A corporal was sitting in the German trenches near Messines, Belgium, 200 miles northwest of where Art was driving his supply truck in the Argonne. The corporal had volunteered in 1914 and since then had served as a dispatch officer, shuttling messages between German Army Headquarters and the front lines. Diminutive in stature but outsized in personality, he ingratiated himself with the German generals by painting their portraits. On October 15, 1918, he was temporarily blinded by a mustard gas attack from a British battalion. Later, in the 1920s, after he gained notoriety for blaming the Bolsheviks and Jews for losing the war, his followers would refer to him as the "Little Corporal." His name was Adolph Hitler.

Nearly 10 million soldiers and 6 million civilians died in World War I.[79] Sadly, their deaths did not lead to a better world. The 1919 Treaty of Versailles stripped Germany of large portions of its territory and required the country to pay $33 billion in reparations to France and England.[80] Marshall Ferdinand Foch of France said, "This is not a peace. It is an Armistice for twenty years."[81] He had it right, almost to the day. Resentment by the Germans of the punitive terms of the treaty helped give rise to the Nazi party. Hitler promised to restore Germany to greatness and take revenge against England and France.[82] Twenty years after the treaty was signed, he would start another world war, even more terrible than the first.

In late October 1918, Art boarded a troop ship, bound for America. After his service on the Western Front, he would never again think of Europe as a foreign place, or of Europeans as foreign people. He would also never again view war in romantic terms. He had seen thousands of young men die before they could make a mark upon the world. He was relieved to escape the sounds, smells, and business of death, and return to the working world, where he could once again work on inventing products that would improve peoples' lives.

# CHAPTER 4

# Hard Times

In November 1918, Art was back in his second-story loft in Cleveland, explaining to Klamm that, after seeing the truck and the airplane operate in war, he believed the two inventions would soon transform how Americans traveled and moved their goods. Art and Klamm decided to concentrate first on the market for pneumatic brakes on large vehicles, the one fluid power application for which Art held a patent. Art was convinced his pneumatic braking system could have prevented the truck accidents he had witnessed at the Western Front, and was determined to convince America's truck manufacturers to purchase the system to prevent the same problems from occurring on America's highways.

Art soon came to appreciate how fortunate he was to have Klamm as a business partner. The two men shared the same vision. They both went into business to serve their customers, and both placed their faith in the people who they knew did the real work—those closest to a customer. They were not afraid to take risks in pursuing better products. When they made mistakes, they refused to give up, and vowed to learn to do better the next time.

Art assumed the role of CEO, conceiving of new products and dealing with prospective investors, and Klamm acted like a COO, turning Art's inventions into engineering drawings, supervising production, and calling on customers. Even their personalities complemented each other. Art was the quiet and reserved, serious-minded scientist and inventor, and Klamm, the more easygoing and approachable operations expert, builder, tinkerer and salesman.

Both, however, shared traits that equipped them for success—an unshakable optimism, resilience, the will to persevere through hard times, a desire to make a difference in the world, and a steely determination to overcome any challenges that came their way.

Art and Klamm badly needed to find a customer. During Art's four months on the Western Front, Klamm had concentrated on preparing the shop to make pneumatic brake parts, but he had not been able to convince a truck manufacturer to purchase any of those parts, nor had he any luck in convincing Glenn Martin to take a chance on Parker's fuel system fittings and valves. Martin had recently received bad news from the War Department. With the war ending, the government saw little need for Martin's MB-1 bombers. In November, the Army dropped its orders from 50 to just 16 of the planes. Martin feared the government might eventually cancel delivery of all planes, so to avoid a total loss he made plans to convert the MB-1 to carry mail for the U.S. Postal Service.

Art got back in touch with Richard Carroll, who was still willing to help him test his braking system on a driving trip to the East Coast. Art took what little funds the Parker Appliance Co. had left and bought a Troy trailer and Walter truck from Carroll. Klamm outfitted the truck and trailer with a Parker pneumatic brake system. Then Art contracted with Goodyear to fill the trailer with pneumatic tires made in Akron that Art would deliver to Goodyear's plant in Connecticut.[83]

Driving a truck from Cleveland to the East Coast in 1918 was a hazardous undertaking. A State Department report published at the time explained that road conditions in the U.S. were "far worse than any other major nation except Russia and China."[84] Most roads were little more than muddy, unpaved tracks through the countryside. Henry Ford designed his Model T for those early roads, making sure the chassis was high enough to be eased along "even when the car sunk nearly to its axles in mud."[85] One of the new Model T drivers was 11-year-old Charles Lindbergh, whom according to Douglas Brinkley, drove his mother "at a perilous twenty-five miles per hour along the unpaved, deeply rutted, and often icy roads of northern Minnesota."[86]

In Pennsylvania, Goodyear's "Akron-to-Boston Express" line ran along the Lincoln Highway, dedicated in 1913 as America's first coast-to-coast highway. The idea for the road originated with Carl Graham Fisher, the founder of the Prest-O-Lite Co., which made the first dependable headlights for automobiles. He would become better known for developing the Indianapolis Speedway and turning thousands of acres of Florida swamp land into a city he called "Miami Beach."[87]

The Lincoln Highway began at Times Square in New York City and ran for 3,389 miles to Lincoln Park in San Francisco. Despite its impressive name, the Lincoln Highway was, like most roads of the time, little more than a primitive dirt trail. A guidebook for the highway warned motorists "to expect and put up cheerfully with some unpleasantness." One observer recommended that travelers carry, among other things, "an ax, shovel, and four-foot hardwood planks, fifty feet of rope and sixteen of cable...and a pile of cooking and camping gear and possibly a small pistol of some sort."[88]

In 1919, the author Beatrice Massey joined her husband on a drive across the country on the Lincoln Highway. In her 1920 travelogue *It Might Have Been Worse*, she wrote, "You will get tired, and your bones will cry aloud for a rest cure; but I promise you one thing—you will never be bored! No two days were the same, no two views were similar, no two cups of coffee tasted alike... My advice to timid motorists is, 'Go.'"

From Pittsburgh, the Lincoln Highway followed U.S. Route 30 eastward across Pennsylvania, linking together pre-existing turnpikes, and paralleling what is now the Pennsylvania Turnpike. In the middle of the state, the highway traversed the Allegheny Mountains, in an area Frank B. McClain, the author of the first Lincoln Highway road guide, called "one of the most scenic drives to be found in the state of Pennsylvania or the entire east coast."[89] It was also the most dangerous portion of the highway, where it narrowed around steep grades as it climbed the mountains. As the historian Brian Butko, an authority on the Lincoln Highway, wrote, "The Alleghenies were the mountains to cross, and they were a formidable barrier. Early automobiles usually overheated on the way up, so enterprising businessmen put rest stops at each summit to offer free water. They hoped travelers would stay for a soda or sandwich, and to make sure, almost every mountaintop stop sprouted a lookout tower with telescopes."[90]

One of the most difficult parts of the Lincoln Highway was a section nine miles east of Ligonier, Pennsylvania, and 100 miles east of Pittsburgh. There, the road climbed the western slope of the Allegheny Mountains up to the Laurel Highlands, rising to a height of 2,684 feet at the top of Laurel Mountain. In one section, vehicles had to climb a grade of eight per cent. Frank Seiberling (whose family owned Goodyear) was an early president of the

Lincoln Highway Association, which was created to maintain the road. He arranged for Goodyear employees (called "missionaries") to drive "touring cars" up and down the mountain. It was their responsibility to meet trucks and assist them if they had difficulties negotiating the steep slope.[91]

Art and Carroll were able to bring their truck and 5-ton trailer safely through all the mud, bridges, narrow roadways, and steep grades on the Lincoln Highway between Cleveland and the East Coast. They were bothered, however, by continual leaking at the point where the truck's oil lines connected to a pump. The leakage was caused by the constant vibrations from the truck, as it negotiated the primitive Lincoln Highway. By the time Art and Carroll arrived in New York, the sides of the truck were stained with oil. They met with a group of engineers from the truck's manufacturer, the Walter Truck Co., for lunch at the company's offices on West 64th Street, near Central Park. It was November 11, 1918, the day the Allies signed the Armistice with Germany, and the streets were filled with jubilant New Yorkers waving American flags. Walter's engineers were concerned about the oil leakage. To reassure them, Art took out a napkin and drew a diagram of his "die form coupler," which he said could produce a tight seal that would prevent the oil lines from leaking in future versions of his brake system.[92]

Upon his return to Cleveland, Art told his contacts at Goodyear about his trip to New York. He convinced the company to install his pneumatic brake system on a few of its trucks. Art received $1,500 from Goodyear in December 1918. He would never forget how it felt to receive his first check. At last, he had a customer, someone willing to pay for a product he had designed and made.

On January 12, 1919, the Cleveland Plain Dealer described how well Art's brake system had performed as the truck and trailer traveled over the Allegheny Mountains. The article noted the truck was pulling a trailer "loaded to capacity" with Goodyear tires. The article claimed "no truck similarly equipped had ever ventured over the Alleghenies.... Both truck and trailer were equipped with air brakes, and their successful application on that trip threatens to revolutionize haulage methods. Cleveland is especially interested in the performance because the air brakes are the invention of a Cleveland man, A. L. Parker, and the brake system was manufactured by the Parker Appliance Co.... The system is to be placed on the market, Mr. Parker has announced. The trip over the mountains was made possible only by the fact that the air brakes prevented the trailer from swinging around on grades, although on two occasions the whole outfit coasted down steep hills at the rate of thirty-five miles an hour."[93]

The article described the intricacies of Parker's braking system, powered by air tanks and compressors, connected by Parker valves, piping, and fittings. The Parker valves had to operate precisely to equalize the braking action between the truck and trailer. The article explained how the Parker braking system prevented a serious accident: "The tractor broke away on a steep grade and it would have crashed downward into traffic at the bottom of the hill had not the brakes set automatically and stopped the trailer within its own length."[94]

Art and Carroll's driving trip over the Lincoln Highway had consumed most of the company's cash. Without customers to generate sufficient cash flow, Art was forced to seek out new investors. He needed more capital to develop the die form coupler that would perfect his pneumatic brake system. One day in the spring of 1919, Art was visiting the grocery stalls at the West Side Market. He struck up a conversation with Frank J. Wutrich, who operated several trucks that delivered vegetables to the market from farms just outside Cleveland. Wutrich visited Art's factory and saw a demonstration of the air compressor Art was using for his pneumatic brake system. Wutrich suggested they test the system on one of his trucks on a hill "with a 10 percent grade" near his home in the Old Brooklyn section of Cleveland.

Wutrich filled one his trucks with a load of steel. Art practiced bringing it to stops on a road that led down to a valley where the Cleveland Zoo was located.

The brake system worked perfectly.

Wutrich was so impressed that he agreed to invest $2,500 in the Parker Appliance Co. Later, he convinced his brother to also invest $2,500 in the company.[95]

Encouraged by the Wutriches' investment, the promising tests of his braking system, and his first sales to Goodyear, Art decided in April 1919 to abandon his tiny loft and move to a larger factory a few blocks away, directly behind St. Malachi's Church, where Vermont Avenue connected to the Superior Viaduct, a stone and steel bridge that crossed the Cuyahoga River over the Flats.

Art entered into a 5-year lease for the 10,000-square-foot factory with the Cleveland Trust Co. From the windows of their new factory, Art and Klamm could watch the construction of the "Detroit-Superior High-Level Bridge," with 12 concrete arches and a 591-foot steel arch spanning the Cuyahoga.[96]

The April 27, 1919 edition of the Cleveland Plain Dealer described the company's new quarters: "The Parker Appliance Company announced the acquisition of a two-story building fronting 130 feet on the Superior Viaduct at Vermont Avenue with a 150-foot depth from the Standard Parts Co. for a five year period. The company...is installing complete equipment for the manufacture of their pneumatic brake controls for trucks and trailers.... The property gives ample floor space for a large volume of business in this line, and a separate plant for the manufacture of the pneumatic clutch, brake and gear controls for passenger cars is to be acquired in the fall... Considering the past performance of the truck and trailer brake equipment and the orders now on the books of the company it is reasonable to expect the universal adoption of this equipment by the truck and trailer industry in the very near future."[97]

The second plant of the Parker Appliance Co. on the Superior Viaduct.

Soon after their move, Art and Klamm drafted a booklet on pneumatic controls that they sent to engineers at General Motors and several other bus and truck manufacturers. They also began placing advertisements in the Plain Dealer and various trade publications for their brake system. At first, the two were disappointed their publicity efforts resulted in very few orders for pneumatic brakes. In order to keep money coming in the door, Art and Klamm resorted to using their production capacity to make plumbing fixtures for new homes being built in Cleveland's fast-growing suburbs.

Later in 1919, Art told Klamm they needed to drive their truck and trailer to the upcoming Boston Automobile Show, the largest truck show in America.[98] Art was convinced that at the show they would be able to demonstrate the capabilities of their brake system to several large bus and truck manufacturers. More than 50 brands of trucks were represented at the show, including Pierce-Arrow, Rainier, Republic, White Motor, GMC, Nash, International Harvester, Defiance and Avery.

Klamm tried to convince Art they were not equipped to drive a fully loaded truck and trailer over the mountainous terrain of the Lincoln Highway in Pennsylvania. He argued they should take a train to New York and rent a truck there to demonstrate the brake system. Art admitted the trip would be risky, but he reminded Klamm he had negotiated the most difficult portions of the Lincoln Highway on his previous trip with Carroll. The trip, he said, had been much easier than driving supply trucks on the Western Front. He tried to reassure Klamm by telling him their truck was a version of the same Army vehicles he had driven in France.

At the same time Art and Klamm were planning their trip, a young Lieutenant Colonel in the U.S. Army named Dwight D. Eisenhower was leading a 3-mile long convoy of 81 army vehicles along the Lincoln Highway, from Washington D.C. to San Francisco. A band sponsored by Goodyear (in an attempt to promote highway travel) played at every town where the convoy stopped along the way. The convoy reached San Francisco after 62 days of struggling over muddy roads and broken bridges, traveling at an average speed of 5 miles an hour, just slightly faster than a walk.[99]

The truck and trailer Art Parker and Carl Klamm drove over the Lincoln Highway.

Art realized they were betting everything they had on the success of the trip. He believed, however, the gamble was necessary, if they ever hoped to gain the biggest truck and bus manufacturers as customers. Seeing how determined Art was, Klamm gave in, and they emblazoned their truck, equipped with Parker brakes, with the banner "From Akron to Boston," filled the truck and trailer with Goodyear tires and their entire inventory of brake parts, hitched the trailer to the truck, and set out one morning toward the east.

Carl Klamm at a gas station on the Lincoln Highway.

On the third day of the trip, Art and Klamm drove 100 miles east of Pittsburgh in three hours along the Lincoln Highway, a good pace for driving through the foothills of the Alleghenies. By mid-afternoon, they were winding up a narrow road on Laurel Mountain, the westernmost peak of the Alleghenies. The two-mile drive to the crest would end on the "Allegheny Plateau," the backbone of the Appalachians, and the Eastern Continental Divide, which separated waters flowing to the Mississippi from those heading to the Atlantic. It was the part of the trip Art had found most difficult to negotiate on his previous drive with Carroll. The stretch was more like a cow path than a road, with a surface of dirt and gravel, deeply rutted by cars and trucks that had passed by earlier.

Art Parker and Carl Klamm proceeding up Laurel Mountain.

Art and Klamm proceeded up Laurel Mountain at a slow pace, anxiously glancing down at the steep ravine on their left. Their truck barely had enough power to move the heavily-laden trailer up the 8 percent grade. At times, it seemed the trailer was going to pull the truck back down the mountain.

As Art and Klamm neared the top of the mountain, they heard the hitch between the truck and trailer snap with a sickening pop. The trailer began to roll back down the hill, slowly at first, and then faster and faster, shooting over the left side of the road and down into the ravine, taking nearly all the assets of the Parker Appliance Co. with it.

Art and Klamm jumped from the truck and ran to the edge of the ravine. They were looking down upon a canopy of white pines that rose 100 feet from the bottom of the ravine. The forest had swallowed their trailer and inventory of brake parts. The only good news was that the brakes on the truck had locked, as they were designed to do, and it remained sitting intact at the edge of the road.

Art, momentarily at a loss for words, glanced over at Klamm.

When Art regained his composure, the only thing he could think to say was, "Well, Carl, at least this wasn't the fault of our brakes."

As luck would have it, a pair of Goodyear "missionaries" had been driving their Model T right behind Art and Klamm, keeping an eye out for trucks that might need assistance up the hill. The missionaries took a picture of Art and Klamm, staring disconsolately from the edge of the ravine.

Art and Klamm walked away from the wreckage, but they feared their new company might not survive the accident. Art had used up nearly all his own money, and his investors', in buying the truck and trailer and outfitting them with his brake system. Everything he had worked to accomplish lay in ruins in the Pennsylvania ravine. He feared he might have to abandon his dream and return to a mundane life, working for someone else. Twelve years after receiving his engineering degree, he seemed to be back where he had started.

Art Parker and Carl Klamm just after the accident on the Lincoln Highway.

The next day, the pair returned to Cleveland on the Pennsylvania Railroad. As the train chugged west, Art promised Klamm he would never again bet the future of the company on the outcome of a single event, or the fortunes of a single customer.

Art tried to cheer up the glum Klamm by promising him he was not about to give up on the Parker Appliance Co. He told him they would have to scrimp and save everywhere they could, and redouble their efforts to gain new customers and investors, but Art was convinced they would survive their disaster on the Lincoln Highway.

Over the years, as succeeding generations of Parker's men and women told the story of the accident on the Lincoln Highway, it acquired the status of near-myth for Parker's employees, a metaphor and inspiration for never giving in to hard times.

After Art and Klamm returned to their factory along the Superior Viaduct, they signaled their intention to remain in business by taking out an advertisement in the Business Transport Magazine that touted the Parker Appliance Co.'s new "four-wheel air brake equipment...available for distribution" for "motor buses."

In a December 1921 article in the Iron Trade Review, Art boldly predicted the company would shortly obtain new bank financing, and he boasted the Parker Appliance Co. "has enjoyed a good business during the past eighteen months."

Art, the perennial optimist, was not about to give up on his company, despite its precarious condition. His optimistic public face masked the true condition of the company. He and Klamm were short of capital. They had not been able to develop the die form coupler for their pneumatic brake system. Without a solution for the leakage of oil, sales of their pneumatic brakes were plummeting. They tried to compensate by finding a market for their line of fittings and valves for the fuel systems of airplanes. Klamm began to visit Glenn Martin in Cleveland, hoping to convince him to purchase Parker valves and fittings for the fuel systems of his planes.

Art hired an engineer and draftsman named S.S. Fisher to help Klamm in the factory.[100] He also brought in a stenographer named Mary Hamlin.[101] They were the company's third and fourth employees. Art and Klamm continued their efforts to obtain new investors, who would receive stock in the company and be given a seat of the board of directors. Art convinced his brother Robert, who had become a stockbroker in New York City, to invest $3,000. Art talked Louis Dingleday, the owner of a shoe repair business near Art's plant on the Superior Viaduct, into investing $2,500. One day, Art met Harry Allshouse on a streetcar, and convinced him to invest $2,000.[102]

In October 1922, Art met Richard Carroll at the Hotel Cleveland to show him and a potential investor named Bob Smith a diagram of the die form coupler. Art told Carroll and Smith his new invention would eliminate the problems with oil leakage that had plagued his pneumatic braking system. Carroll noted that the new coupling was formed from "two small pieces of brass, a threaded nut, and another piece of coupling that was also threaded and would fit into the nut."[103] Art told Carroll and Smith that Klamm was beginning to work on production drawings for the die form coupler.[104]

By the fall of 1923, work on perfecting the die from coupler and rent for the company's expanded factory had consumed nearly all the funds invested by Art and his investors—all of whom had become members of his board of directors. Klamm had made several production drawings and samples of the die form coupler, but the company continued to lack the necessary capital to make commercial quantities of the product.[105]

In October 1923, Mary Hamlin left the company. Art and Klamm placed an advertisement in the Cleveland Plain Dealer for an assistant who could help with the books and the administration of the office. On November 6, 1923, a slim, well-dressed, 20-year-old woman walked confidently into the Parker Appliance Co. to apply for the job. Her name was Helen Fitzgerald, and she came from a large Irish family that lived a 15-minute streetcar ride away from the factory, not far from Art's family's home in Tremont.

Helen's grandfather, Edward Fitzgerald, barely survived Ireland's Potato Famine. In 1858, he decided to immigrate to America. Edward moved into a boarding house in Tremont, near a bluff overlooking the Flats. In 1865, Edward married an Irish immigrant named Mary Haggerty. Their oldest son, Patrick Fitzgerald, was born in 1876; he would become Helen's father.

In 1895, Patrick began working as a plater for a stove manufacturing company in the Flats. In June 1901, he married Helen's mother, Mary Matthaeus, who had immigrated to Cleveland with her parents from Baden-Baden, in the northern foothills of the Black Forest of West Prussia. The Fitzgeralds' first child, Charles, died at birth in 1902. Helen was born in 1903, and in quick succession, the Fitzgeralds brought three other girls and two boys into the world.

In 1910, the Fitzgeralds bought a home at 3915 Spokane Avenue, in the Old Brooklyn neighborhood on Cleveland's West Side, just a few blocks from the hill where Art had tested his pneumatic brake system with Wutrich. The 1600-square-foot house had four bedrooms and one bathroom for the Fitzgeralds and their six children.

Helen's mother taught her, her brothers, and sisters to speak German, and it became their first language for several years. As the oldest of six, Helen was expected to help her mother care for her younger siblings. Tragedy struck the family when her 12-year-old brother Wilbert was killed by a speeding automobile while sledding on a road near their home.

Like most other West Side Clevelanders, the Fitzgeralds looked to the nearest Catholic parish for their social as well as their religious needs. Much of Helen's family life revolved around the St. Augustine parish in Tremont. Her grandparents had been members of the church. Helen's parents were married there, and she was baptized, attended school, and had her First Communion there. With a winning smile, a confident demeanor, and a flair for being noticed, Helen had been popular with the boys in her class at St. Augustine. Helen's parents expected that someday she would be married at the church.

Helen's father loved to tell his children stories of how immigrant Irish families were rising from lowly backgrounds to higher stations in life. He used Cleveland's geography as a symbol of the rise of the Irish. When Helen's grandfather arrived in Cleveland in 1858, most Irish immigrants were living in shanties on "Whiskey Island," a swampy area at the mouth of the Cuyahoga, where they worked on the docks and in the Lake Erie salt mines. Their children obtained better jobs, working in factories in the Flats, and they were able to buy homes in the "Angle" neighborhood. The Irish were working their way up the hill, a metaphor for their increasing economic status. Helen's father told her that, just as he had obtained a better job than his father, she should expect to work at a better job than his, in an office rather than one of the dirty and dangerous factories in the Flats.

Helen drew inspiration from women's recent victory in earning the right to vote, when the 19th Amendment was passed in 1920. Like many of her generation, she embraced the idea of the "New Woman," who could live on an equal footing with men. For years, the "Gibson Girl," with long luxurious hair, restrictive corsets, and elegant gowns, had been the model of femininity. By the middle of the 1920s, women like Helen had adopted a new look and attitude, cutting their hair in a "bob," rejecting corsets in favor of loose fitting dresses, and starting to wear make-up.

From her father's stories of Cleveland's Irish immigrants, Helen learned how determined people could start at the bottom and work their way up in the world. After graduating from secretarial school, she had worked for a collection agency, but she was not comfortable chasing down people to pay their debts. Next, she took a job as a stenographer at the Starr Piano Co. on Huron Road in downtown Cleveland. Helen dreamed of doing something more consequential than selling pianos. One day, a neighbor mentioned to her that he had heard the Parker Appliance Co. was looking for an office assistant. That chance encounter brought Helen to Art's front door. Accustomed to dealing with a group of raucous siblings, Helen was not a bit awed as she chatted with Art and Klamm during her job interview. She told them she was sure she could handle the company's books and the other requirements of the job.

Art and Klamm were so taken with Helen's poise, confidence and intelligence that they offered her the job on the spot. There was only one catch. They told Helen their company had been in a financial bind ever since the accident on the Lincoln Highway. They were already deferring most of their own salaries, living as frugally as possible from week to week. They could not ask their board of directors to authorize her salary, since the directors had not yet seen any return on their investments.

Helen was a bit taken aback, but she agreed to come to work on the condition Art and Klamm pay her a bonus to make up for her lost salary if they found her work acceptable.

After Art, Klamm, S.S. Fisher (the additional engineer in the shop), and Mary Hamlin, Helen had become the fifth employee of the Parker Appliance Co. She sat in an open reception area just opposite the front door, so she could greet every visitor. Behind her desk was a gate with a swinging door that led to a large office where Art and Klamm sat side-by-side at a flat "partners' desk." To Helen's left was a drafting room dominated by a single large table, and on the right, through a pair of swinging doors, was the factory, where machines kept up a steady roar, turning out fittings, valves, and air compressors for pneumatic brake systems. Up the stairs, on the second floor, was a larger room where Art and Klamm kept their inventory of raw material and finished products.

Art and Klamm may have dreamed of re-engineering the world with their fluid power inventions, but their reality had become a day-to-day slog just to remain in business. No visitor entering their small, dark, dirty and noisy factory above the Cuyahoga River could ever have imagined that the Parker Appliance Co. would grow to a multi-billion-dollar behemoth over the next 100 years, making products that would carry passengers across oceans, and ultimately into space.

At the end of February 1924, Art and Klamm used some of their last cash to pay Helen a bonus to cover her three months of unpaid service. They had not told Helen how close their company was to insolvency, but as she examined the company's books, she discovered its perilous condition.

On March 25, 1924, Art told Helen he was taking a desperate step to raise money. He mortgaged all the company's assets, including machinery, tools, and inventory, to the W.M. Pattison Co. in exchange for $12,521 in badly needed cash. Five days later, one of the company's biggest creditors, the Co-Operative Machinery Co., which had sold several machines to Art, won a ruling from the Ohio Supreme Court requiring the Parker Appliance Co. to pay $4,000. Knowing the company was unable to raise the money, the Co-Operative Machinery Co. quickly filed a petition to put the Parker Appliance Co. into bankruptcy.

Art tried to appease his directors by promising not to take any salary until the company's financial condition improved.[106] The directors, however, had lost all their faith in Art and Klamm. Frank Wutrich testified at the bankruptcy hearing that Art "stated that he needed money at every directors' meeting."[107]

Art believed the intellectual property rights to the die form coupler (which he had not patented) should belong to him personally, rather than to the Parker Appliance Co. in bankruptcy. He had conceived the invention himself, and he did not believe a creditor should be able to take it away from him. The coupler, he knew, could form the foundation of any fluid power system, providing a means of sealing the components of the system tightly enough to prevent any leakage.

Art told the bankruptcy trustee he and Klamm had signed a contract entitling Art to retain all rights to the die form coupler. The directors, who understood the invention's value just as well as Art, argued the agreement was null and void because Art and Klamm had signed it without board approval. The directors were suspicious of the close relationship between Art and Klamm and believed Art treated Klamm more like a partner than an employee. When asked at the bankruptcy hearing about the scope of Klamm's responsibilities, Art replied, "He is my associate," a term considered at the time to be synonymous with "partner."[108]

Depositions were taken, and the bankruptcy trustee called Helen to testify as to which directors were at the factory on the day Art and Klamm signed the contract for the die form coupler. One of the directors referred to Helen in his deposition as "Miss Fitzgerald, the stenographer and telephone girl." When asked to describe the scope of her duties, Helen replied, "I have been the stenographer at the plant since November 1923. I was given special instructions at the time I went there in regard to keeping up on callers. I was told to keep track of all telephone calls and all people calling at the plant. That record was kept on index cards in a card file.... As to the arrangement of the offices at that time, I was in the front office and Mr. Parker was in the rear, back of my office. People going in to see him and going out would pass me.... I had other duties besides the stenographic, acknowledging orders that came in, any kind of typing that was to be done, and I did the billing and filing."[109]

Helen brought cards to her deposition showing that a majority of the directors had been present when the contract was signed. The directors disputed her testimony, and the bankruptcy judge later ruled the rights to the die form coupler belonged to the company, and not to Art.

The Harry H. Packard Co. had recently purchased title to Parker's plant from Cleveland Trust, becoming Art's new landlord. From December 1923 until July 1924, Art had stopped sending rental checks to Packard. He and Klamm had decided to use their remaining cash to finish developing the die form coupler instead of paying rent. Packard served Art with an eviction notice on June 30, 1924. On August 1, the last day before the eviction was to take place, Art sent Klamm to the offices of Packard's attorney, Joseph C. Breitenstein, with a check for one month's rent. Breitenstein refused to accept the check, and told Klamm Packard planned to proceed with the eviction proceedings.

Art came up with one last idea to save his company. He offered to pay his creditors 20 cents on the dollar, and to deposit the amount with the bankruptcy court by October 8, 1924. The deadline came and went, but Art was unable to raise enough cash to meet the terms of his own offer. Now the bankruptcy court prepared to order a sale of the company's assets. Bowing to the inevitability of bankruptcy, Art prepared to begin his company anew.

Parker Appliance Co. factory on Berea Road, circa mid-1920s.

On October 31, 1924, Art formed a new corporation, also called the Parker Appliance Co.[110] Art had more than enough experience with the difficulties of bringing investors into his business. He was determined to retain total control of the Parker Appliance Co. for himself and his family. He therefore formed his new company as a sole proprietorship. Klamm's mother-in-law offered to loan $5,000 to the new company. Art and Klamm used the money to enter into a lease for a new factory at 10320 Berea Road, on the western boundary of Cleveland. The factory had been part of Alexander Winton's automobile plant, until Winton entered bankruptcy in 1922. Art negotiated a favorable lease from Winton's bankruptcy trustee, and by the end of November he had moved the contents of his plant along the Superior Viaduct to the Berea Road location.

On December 21, 1924, the Cleveland Plain Dealer announced a bankruptcy sale at the Berea Road plant of all the assets of the original Parker Appliance Co. The announcement listed the company's remaining assets, which included the truck that survived the accident on the Lincoln Highway, work benches and tools, brass fittings, patterns, steel tubing, forgings, work in process, an adding machine, a typewriter, a filing cabinet, and the double desk used by Art and Klamm.[111] The assets were sold at an auction on January 5, 1925. There is no evidence of who bought the assets of the Parker Appliance Co. in the bankruptcy sale. The sale netted only $1,489.75 for assets that had been appraised a few weeks earlier at $5,915.[112] Most of the assets were uniquely suited for a fluid power business. It is entirely possible that Art Parker, the man to whom those assets were most valuable, either bought the assets himself, or found someone willing to buy them on his behalf. In such a case, Art would have had everything he needed to restart his business at a bargain price.

The culture of Cleveland in the early 20th century was much like today's Silicon Valley—forgiving to entrepreneurs whose businesses failed. As James B. Stewart wrote in the New York Times: "'Fail fast, fail often' is a Silicon Valley mantra, and the freedom to innovate is inextricably linked to the freedom to fail." Stewart quoted David Bytow, who said, just after shutting down his San Francisco-based social app start-up, "I believe in failing fast in order to go on and make only new and different mistakes."[113]

Henry Ford's first company went bankrupt, and he was ousted from his second company by his directors, who like Art's had lost confidence in his ability to run the company. Undeterred by his two false starts, Ford said, "Failure is the opportunity to begin again, more intelligently."[114] He started the Ford Motor Co. in 1903.[115]

Like Ford, Art planned to begin again, more intelligently. He realized he needed to diversify his customer base beyond the automobile, truck and bus markets. He found the means to do so in the invention he believed would have universal application in all fluid power markets. Art took note that the creditors of his first company had not taken the step of patenting the technology for the die form coupler. On February 27, 1925, he filed a patent for a two-piece flared tube fitting, using the same principles he had conceived for the coupler he had first sketched out on a napkin at the Armistice Day lunch in New York with the Walter truck engineers. Vowing never again to lose the right to one of his inventions, he filed the patent in his own name. He would do the same with every one of his 158 patents yet to come.

Using an interlocking mechanism, Art's new fitting was capable of connecting tubes and other metal devices tightly enough to prevent any leakage of gasoline, oil, water, air, gases or other fluids, even at high pressures. His new fitting would be the foundation upon which he would build his new company. For decades to come, it would be known as "the standard Parker fitting," and it would be used in millions of applications throughout the world.

# CHAPTER 5

# Starting Over

In August 1925, armed with the patent for the flared tube fitting he believed would revolutionize all heavy labor, Art began his business anew and debt free at the new location on Berea Road. He immediately rehired Klamm, Helen, and several of the machinists that had worked at his Superior Viaduct plant. With those employees in place, his knowledge of the science of fluid power, and his patents for the pneumatic brake system and the two-piece flared tube fitting, Art's second Parker Appliance Co. was, in every real sense, a continuation of the enterprise he had started in 1917.

Art's first company had become trapped in what entrepreneurs and venture capitalists today call the "Valley of Death," described by one business writer as "the arduous terrain between proof of concept and the beginning of major production and significant sales."[116] Art had concentrated on inventing new fluid power products. Now he needed to spend more time on sales. The reborn manufacturing company's success depended on finding long-term, loyal customers.

It was the height of the Roaring Twenties, a perfect time for Art to re-start his company. Between 1920 and 1929, America's gross national product would grow by 4.2 percent per year, a rate it never again would approach in peacetime. The market for fluid power products was growing as American manufacturing plants expanded to meet the demand from a middle class that was embracing the consumer culture. A family could purchase a Model T Ford for just $295, and a new financing scheme called the "installment payment plan" put the automobile within reach of millions.[117] General Motors introduced yearly model changes that convinced consumers to buy new cars long before they wore out. The toaster, the vacuum cleaner, the refrigerator and the radio had become mainstays, and housing boomed, led by sunny Florida and California.[118]

In 1920, a quarter of American families had cars; by the end of the decade, more than half the families in the country would fill American roads with their new automobiles. The automobile culture was changing the look of America. New paved roads, lined with motels, retail stores and service stations, extended to housing developments in the first suburbs.[119] The largest tire manufacturers—Goodyear and Firestone—were located in nearby Akron. Like other American manufacturers, the tire makers had developed new machines that used compressed air to move, hold and position heavy objects. Art began to sell Goodyear and Firestone fittings and couplings for those machines. Due to manufacturing efficiencies made possible by innovations such as compressed air systems, the cost of producing a tire declined from ten dollars in 1910 to less than one dollar in 1930.[120]

The assembly of a MB-2 bomber, circa 1924.

Western Reserve Historical Society

A MB-2 bomber at Martin Field, circa 1924.

Art was encouraged in 1924, when air power's greatest champion in the Army, Brigadier General William ("Billy") Mitchell, devised a way to demonstrate the power of Glenn Martin's new and more powerful bomber, the MB-2. He positioned four German ships captured during the war a few miles off the Virginia coast. Among them was the Ostfriedland, considered to be unsinkable. The MB-2s sank the three smaller ships in just a few minutes. Seven MB-2s filled with one-ton bombs sank the Ostfriedland in just over 20 minutes.[121]

Martin, however, found it difficult to borrow the funds he needed to finance the production of the MB-2 bombers for the Army. Most banks were not willing to loan money to aircraft manufacturers because they considered aviation to be an untested, risky business. The financiers knew the government had canceled most aircraft orders within days after the war ended, and they feared it might soon do the same to Martin. Their fears had been confirmed when the Army had reduced its order for MB-1's from 50 to 16. In 1924, Martin, facing a possible bankruptcy, lost nearly $100,000.[122]

As the former owner of a bankrupt company, Art could sympathize with Martin. Art was confident enough in the future of aviation to bet money on it, and he offered to supply the Parker components for Martin's MB-2 bombers on credit. He told Martin to pay him when he was able.

In late 1924, Martin's fortunes took a turn for the better. His company made nearly $300,000 before taxes, as the Army ordered 20 of his MB-2 bombers after the sinking of the Ostfriedland and the three other captured

German ships. Martin also received a large order from the Navy for a seaplane and the first torpedo bombers, each of which would be equipped with Parker fuel system valves and fittings.

Suddenly, Martin had become the largest manufacturer of planes in America. More importantly for Art, he finally started to make regular payments to the Parker Appliance Co., giving Art the funds he needed to continue to develop pneumatic brakes for trucks and buses and fittings for a variety of industrial applications.

A MB 2 bomber takes off from Martin Field, circa 1924.

Martin never forgot how Art helped his company survive hard times. He not only became a loyal long-term customer; he also went out of his way to introduce Art to other aircraft manufacturers and recommend Art's products to them. To Art, this was an early lesson in the value of taking good care of his customers.

Over the next 90 years, Glenn Martin's company would become a $46 billion a year supplier of aircraft and other military products to the Pentagon and one of Parker's largest customers. In 2014 alone, the company (known as Lockheed Martin after its 1995 merger with Lockheed), would purchase $62 million of fluid power products from Parker.

When Parker's engineers and sales people traveled to Lockheed Martin's top secret "Skunk Works" in Burbank, California, where the company was developing the latest technologies for fighter aircraft, they were proud to remind their hosts that Parker was not only one of Glenn Martin's first suppliers of aircraft components, but was also responsible for saving the company from bankruptcy when Art agreed in 1924 to supply fuel system fittings for the MB-2 bomber on credit.

One of Martin's closest friends in the aircraft industry was William E. ("Bill") Boeing. Born in Detroit three years before Art, Boeing was the son of a wealthy lumber baron. After obtaining an engineering degree from Yale, he worked as a timber salesman in his father's wilderness reserves on the Olympic Peninsula, near the small frontier town of Seattle. Boeing took his first flight in 1914, when a barnstormer named Teah Mahoney agreed to take him and a friend up in a Curtiss floatplane over Lake Washington. Boeing's friend told him he could not "find any definite answer as to why the plane held together,"[123] and Boeing replied, "You know, there isn't much to that machine. I think we could build a better one!"[124]

"Building something better" later became a Boeing tagline. In the fall of 1915, Boeing traveled to Los Angeles to take flying lessons from Martin, who was operating a school for pilots at the time. Martin took Boeing up in a Martin Model TA training plane. Boeing asked Martin constant questions about how he built the aircraft. Soon after completing the course, Boeing bought his own Model TA from Martin. After studying the plane, he decided to start a company to make his own aircraft.[125]

Boeing founded his company at nearly the same time Art opened the doors of the Parker Appliance Co. Boeing's first quarters were just as modest as Art's second-story loft. Working in a small red boathouse in a shipyard on the Duwamish River in Seattle, Boeing made parts for a two-passenger seaplane. On June 15, 1916, Boeing took the plane on a 75-mile-per-hour flight over Lake Union. A month later, at the age of 35, Boeing formed Pacific Aero Products Co., and in May 1917, two months after Art founded the Parker Appliance Co., and a month after America entered World War I, he renamed his firm The Boeing Airplane Co. During the war, Boeing made airplanes for the Army in the boathouse, employing 28 carpenters, seamstresses, boat builders and pilots.[126] His planes were built from Washington State timber, and his company's early slogan became "Built Where the Spruce Grows."

On July 1, 1925, in an effort to cement its reputation as the center of the aircraft industry, Cleveland opened the first municipally-owned airport in the country. City leaders believed the new airport would insure that the federal government would make Cleveland an important stop on the new U.S. Air Mail routes crossing the country. Glenn Martin had chaired a civic committee that chose the airport's location on Cleveland's west side, due to its 1,000 acres of "level, well-graded...approaches as nearly perfect and free from hazards as ever greeted a man from the air."[127] Instead of runways, the airport built a large square concrete area, much like a parking lot, called a "landing mat," where planes could take off and land in any direction, depending upon which way the wind was blowing. The landing mat was surrounded by a metal fence, with gates where passengers could pass through to the planes. The "gates" on airport concourses today owe their name to the original gates in the fences at early airports like the one in Cleveland.[128]

The Cleveland airport was the first in America to install landing lights and a radio-equipped air traffic control tower that could signal planes the direction in which to land or take off from the landing mat. During its first year of operation, 4,000 aircraft took off from the airport, most of them U.S. Air Mail planes on coast-to-coast flights. The airmail routes later became routes for passenger air travel. Some of the first passenger flights were between Cleveland, Detroit and Chicago.[129] The Cleveland airport remained the largest in the country for several years and became a favorite stop for executives of aircraft manufacturers looking to exchange ideas on the latest improvements in aircraft design.[130]

In the summer of 1926, Bill Boeing flew into Cleveland to attend a dinner hosted by Martin for several aircraft makers. The gathering was held at the Union Club in downtown Cleveland. There, in oak-paneled rooms dimly lit by ornate chandeliers hanging from high ceilings, the men from Millionaires' Row had gathered to negotiate mergers, pressure politicians to reduce their taxes, and occasionally, fix prices. Art was still a young entrepreneur with a relatively unknown company. He was not yet important enough to join the Union Club, but Martin invited him to the dinner, hoping he would be able to spend some time with Boeing.

Something happened in those oak-paneled rooms that began Parker's 90-year relationship with the Boeing Co. It is likely that Martin made sure Art and Boeing were able to spend some time together. The two of them had much in common. They were nearly the same age, and the owners of new companies working to establish themselves in the aviation market. Martin would have been eager to tell Boeing how Art had helped him survive his early years by extending him free credit until the Army began ordering large numbers of his MB-2 bombers.

What is certain is that not long after that dinner in Cleveland, Boeing began to buy fittings for the fuel systems of his planes from the Parker Appliance Co. His first purchases were for the P-12/F4B fighter, which Boeing made for the U.S. Army and Navy in the late 1920s. It was the beginning of a relationship that would make Boeing one of Parker's most important customers for the next 90 years.

Art's friendship with Donald Douglas would also pay his company dividends for decades to come. After Art returned to Cleveland from the war in 1919, he and Douglas began to meet regularly to discuss new developments in aircraft design. Douglas left the Glenn L. Martin Co. in 1920 and moved to Los Angeles to start his own aircraft manufacturing company. He preferred to live in Southern California, where the weather allowed him to fly year-round. Douglas convinced five of his former engineering colleagues from the Glenn L. Martin Co., as well as Martin's chief test pilot, to join his new firm.

In 1924, Douglas built four versions of the "Douglas World Cruiser," or "DWC," for the Army, which sponsored an around-the-world flight of the DWCs. The 175-day journey of four aircraft started at the Santa Monica airport and traveled west across the Pacific, Southeast Asia, India, the Middle East, Europe and the North Atlantic. Just like Winton's automobile trip from Cleveland to New York, and Martin's flight from Newport Beach to Catalina Island, the around-the-world trip of the Douglas DWCs caught the public's imagination.[131]

After the flight, Douglas adopted a new logo, a picture of planes circling the globe, and the company began an expansion that for the next 40 years would make it the largest manufacturer of commercial and military aircraft in the world. That growth benefited Parker, which supplied Douglas Aircraft with a wide range of components for its planes.

Noted business authors Jim Collins and Morten T. Hansen ( the authors of *Good to Great*) conducted a nine-year study of what makes business leaders successful. They concluded "resilience, not luck, is the signature of greatness." The critical question, they believed, "is not whether you'll have luck, but what you do with the luck that you get."[132] Among their findings, they determined that the most successful business people were "skilled, strong, prepared, and resilient enough to endure the bad times long enough to eventually get good luck."[133]

That definition fit Art well. He had suffered more than enough bad luck, including the disaster on the Lincoln Highway and his first company's bankruptcy. In both cases, Art had refused to give in to adverse circumstances. The American historian and author H. W. Brands wrote that "great success in any number of endeavors...requires the complicity of fate."[134] Fate had dealt Art losing hands for the previous decade. Little did he know that his fortunes were about to change, due to a piece of luck that would start his company on a march toward unexpected growth.

In just its second year of operation, the Cleveland airport already had become one of the busiest in America. An important stop on transcontinental airmail flights, the airport was equipped with a revolving navigational beacon, called a "guide light," which pilots used for nighttime landings. Shortly after sunset, late one evening in the fall of 1926, a young pilot for an airmail carrier was searching for that light as he approached the Cleveland airport on a flight from St. Louis. He was planning to spend the night in the city and meet at the airport the next morning with engineers from Cleveland companies that would supply parts for a new plane he was designing. Park Drop Forge (today, Park-Ohio Holdings Corp.) was supplying his motor mounts, the Aluminum Co. of America (ALCOA) a new aluminum alloy for his propeller, Sherwin-Williams the silver paint for his fuselage,[135] and Thompson Products (a predecessor to TRW) 18 sodium-filled valves that would keep his engine cool throughout his flight.[136]

Wesley Smith, another airmail pilot who was traveling the country at the same time, wrote "If anyone is slightly bored with life and craves a little excitement, let them hop into a plane some dark and stormy night and try to fly to Cleveland."[137] The young pilot approaching Cleveland on that night in 1926 was about to find out exactly what Smith meant.

As the pilot circled the city in the night sky, he was unable to locate the airport beacon. He saw flashing lights near downtown Cleveland, but they were coming from a lighthouse on the lakefront. The young man was nearly out of fuel. He headed south toward an area of farms, where he planned to don his parachute, climb out on the end of a wing, and jump far enough away to avoid being cut to pieces by his propeller. Twenty-seven years later, in a book that would win the Pulitzer Prize, he described what happened next:

> *"Suddenly there was a flash from the ground and about two miles to the west. I straightened out the wings and waited. Another flash. I banked toward it. Yes, it was the...[Cleveland*

*airport]. Floodlights blinked on as I approached."*

*"Say, do you make a practice of flying around unannounced af-
ter dark,' the chief postal clerk had asked after I landed."*

*"'I thought mail beacons were turned on all night,' I'd countered."*

*'No, sir, not ours. When there aren't any planes coming in we
turn it off. What's the use wasting electricity?'*

*"'How did you happen to turn it on?' I asked."*

*"'Some fellow up the line telephoned the post office. He said
there was a plane flying around and he thought the pilot was
lost. Well, guess we might as well turn it off again now.'"*[138]

The next morning, the pilot returned to the hanger where he had parked his plane. He noticed fuel had leaked into his cockpit from one of the lines leading into the fuel tanks in the wings. He began tightening the fittings on the fuel line to stop the leak. He was frustrated with the problem, knowing how catastrophic any fuel leakage could be during the flight he was planning to take within the next few months.

Klamm was in the same hangar that morning, repairing the fuel system on one of Martin's MB-2 bombers. He noticed the young pilot next to him. Klamm could tell he was becoming more and more frustrated as he tried to fix his fuel system.

Klamm explained he worked for a company named Parker Appliance that made a primer pump, plug valves, and a new kind of leakproof fitting for aircraft fuel and oil lines. In fact, Klamm said, Martin had purchased those products for the fuel and oil lines of his bombers, and they had worked perfectly.

The pilot told Klamm he knew Martin well, and that he respected the quality and durability of his planes. Fixing Klamm with his steady gaze, he said a small aircraft maker named the Ryan Aeronautical Co. was building a plane for him in an old fish cannery on the San Diego waterfront. The plane was being designed for a 36-hour flight, most of which would be over water. He was going to need a reliable fuel distribution system in his cockpit, capable of keeping fuel evenly balanced in five separate tanks during the flight. The pilot promised Klamm he would discuss with the engineers at Ryan the possibility of using Parker components for his fuel distribution system.

The pilot's name was Charles A. Lindbergh. He told Klamm he planned to call his new plane the Spirit of St. Louis.

# CHAPTER 6

# The Spirit of St. Louis

B y 1926, new technologies were making long-distance airplane travel possible. Since 1910, the speed of aircraft had increased from 40 to 278 miles per hour, payloads from 200 pounds to more than six tons, and flying altitude from one to 7.7 miles.[139] Improved engines, fuel systems, and navigational aids were allowing men and women to dream of traveling farther, quicker and safer by air than ever before. Some dreamed of regular flights across the U.S., and even perhaps, all the way from America to Europe.

In 1919, Raymond Orteig, a French immigrant who owned two Manhattan hotels, had offered a $25,000 prize to the first pilot to fly non-stop in either direction between New York and Paris. For seven years, no aviator had been willing to attempt the challenge. Even Orville Wright doubted any pilot would ever claim the prize, saying "No flying machine will every fly from New York to Paris."[140]

And then, in 1926, a group of World War I aces, well-financed by various corporations, began to compete for the Orteig Prize.

In preparing for the flights, the aces followed conventional approaches—adding a second, or even third, engine; a copilot; extra fuel; and plenty of provisions. One contestant, Rene Fonck, France's most famous World War I ace, planned to fly eastward to Paris from Roosevelt Field on Long Island with a copilot and two other crew members. Fonck contracted with Igor Sikorsky, a Russian aeronautics engineer, to build a three-engine aircraft.[141] Fonck hired an interior decorator to install carpets, draperies, a refrigerator, a red leather couch, and rich mahogany walls in the cabin. On September 15, 1926, the overweight plane strained to lift off at Roosevelt Field, nosing down a 20-foot embankment into a gully at the end of the runway. The aircraft burst into flames, incinerating the two crewmen. Fonck and his copilot escaped without injury.[142]

Another contender for the Orteig Prize was not taken seriously—either by the press or his competitors. Charles Lindbergh was the 25-year-old chief pilot for a fledgling airline called the Robertson Aircraft Corp.[143] Robertson Aircraft was one of several small airlines that would later merge to form American Airlines. Robertson had assigned Lindbergh to fly five round-trips a week between St. Louis, Chicago and other Midwest cities, delivering the U.S. Mail.

At the time, flying was still too dangerous for airlines like Robertson to even consider transporting paying passengers. The airmail pilots endured fog, thunderstorms, and forced landings, often after running out of fuel. Thirty-one of the forty pilots flying the mail between 1919 and 1926 were killed in crashes. One pilot remarked, "It was pretty much a suicide club."[144] Twice Lindbergh ran out of fuel while becoming lost in foul weather between St. Louis and Chicago, and had to parachute out of his plane. On the evening of September 15, 1926, his plane crashed in heavy fog near Chicago. No one had told him his 120-gallon fuel tank had been replaced by one holding only 80 gallons.[145]

One night while flying the mail, Lindbergh wondered, "How far could a plane go if it carried nothing but gasoline? With the engine throttled down, it could stay aloft for days... Possibly—my mind is startled at its thought—I could fly nonstop between New York and Paris."[146] Lindbergh concluded, "A winter on the air mail holds fully as much dangers as a flight across the ocean."[147]

Lindbergh believed the challenge was worth pursuing—not for the prize money, but to promote the peaceful use of aviation. The Orteig Prize would barely cover the cost of his plane and fuel. Lindbergh hoped his flight would help bring the world closer together, accelerating the time for beginning regular passenger air travel between the continents. He thought: "New York to Paris nonstop! If airplanes can do that, there's no limit to aviation's future."[148]

Lindbergh was the only contestant to come of age after World War I. Free of the assumptions of the past, he had a single-minded focus on efficiency unlike any of the other contestants. Lindbergh decided to make the flight in a single engine plane. After Fonck's crash, he concluded a multi-engine plane would be too heavy to lift off with the full load of fuel required for the flight.

Lindbergh approached the Fokker Aircraft Co. and the Wright Aeronautical Corp. for help, but both were unwilling to build the single-engine plane he envisioned, believing only a multi-engine plane could make the flight. In late 1926, Lindbergh read of an outfit in San Diego called the Ryan Aeronautical Co., which had been building high-wing, single-engine planes for an airline flying mail along the West Coast.[149]

In February 1927, Lindbergh contacted Ryan's owner, B.F. Mahoney, who immediately sensed he could make a name for his company if Lindbergh's flight was successful. Mahoney agreed to build a plane for $10,580. Lindbergh paid for the plane with his life savings of $2,000 and funds he raised from Harry H. Knight, a St. Louis insurance executive, and eight other businessmen in the city. He told his backers a successful crossing of the Atlantic would boost the city's ability to become a hub for commercial aviation. He planned to name his plane the Spirit of St. Louis in their honor.

In early March, Lindbergh showed up at Ryan's small, cluttered office in an old fish cannery on the San Diego waterfront. He could not help but notice the shattered windows, and the unmistakable smell of fish throughout the building.[150] He was, however, impressed with Ryan's owner, Ben Mahoney, and his chief engineer, a handsome, tanned man of Lindbergh's age named Donald Hall, who had recently left Douglas Aircraft in Santa Monica to join Ryan. Mahoney and Hall were shocked when Lindbergh told them he planned to make the flight alone. Hall worried Lindbergh would not be able to stay awake for the entire flight, and said, "I thought you'd need somebody to navigate and to be relief pilot. I thought it would be much too long for one pilot."

Lindbergh replied, "I've thought about it a good deal. I believe the chances for success are better with one pilot than with two. I'd rather have extra gasoline than an extra man."[151]

Lindbergh moved to San Diego so he could help Hall supervise the construction of the plane. Lindbergh knew several other contestants were working feverishly so that their planes could make the trans-Atlantic crossing as soon as the winter weather cleared. He kept pressuring Hall to finish the plane quickly, without sacrificing quality.

Hall took Lindbergh to the San Diego public library, where he measured the distance of his flight by stretching a piece of string across a world globe. Later, on a drafting table at the Ryan factory, Lindbergh charted his course, the same route traversed by trans-Atlantic flyers today, a curve of 36 100-

mile segments, now known as the "Great Circle Route." The route takes into account the roundness of the earth. As the aviation writer Winston Groom explained, "If you tried flying a straight line from New York to Paris, you'd probably end up in Portugal, or even Africa."[152]

At the end of each hundred miles, Lindbergh planned to use his compass to alter his heading just slightly. Lindbergh thought, "The flight to Paris... curves gracefully northward through New England, Nova Scotia, and New-foundland, eastward over the Atlantic, down past the southern tip of Ireland, across a narrow strip of England, until at last it ends sharply at the little dot inside of France marked 'Paris.'"[153]

Lindbergh would never forget how he had run out of fuel on the mail routes between St. Louis and Chicago; he was determined not to encounter the same problem over the Atlantic. Fonck's crash, however, had taught him an overloaded fuel tank could spell doom on takeoff. Lindbergh understood both sides of the calculus—too little fuel and he would die in the Atlantic; too much and he would die in New York. He told Hall to design the plane with a single goal in mind: reducing fuel consumption. The only way to conserve fuel was to reduce the weight of the plane. Lindbergh was a fanatic on the weight issue, telling Hall he even planned to tear the margins off his maps.[154] When Hall asked if he was going to bring along a parachute, Lindbergh replied, "No. That would cost almost 20 pounds."[155]

Lindbergh was a stickler for quality on every component installed on the Spirit of St. Louis. He thought, "Every part of it can be designed for a single purpose, every line fashioned for the Paris flight. I can inspect every detail before it's covered with fabric and fairings."[156] Lindbergh paid special attention to what he considered to be the most critical components of his plane—the engine and the fuel distribution system. He insisted Hall install a reliable 220-horsepower engine, called the "J-5 Whirlwind," made by the Wright Aeronautical Co.

In most planes built in the 1920s, a gasoline tank was placed behind the cockpit. Lindbergh, however, insisted on a radical change, putting an 88-gallon nose tank in front of the cockpit, just behind the engine. He told Hall, "I don't like the idea of being sandwiched in between the engine and the gas tank ...If you crack up you haven't got a chance in a place like that."[157]

Putting the main fuel tank in front of the cockpit meant that Lindbergh would not be able to look directly forward. In order to see where he was headed, he would have to lean over and peer out either side of the plane.

One of the Ryan workers had experience working on submarines, and he installed a periscope on the instrument panel that gave Lindbergh a small view forward.[158]

Lindbergh and Hall decided to include five fuel tanks in the plane, holding a total of 425 gallons. In addition to the 80-gallon forward tank, they placed a main tank, big enough to hold 200 gallons, in the middle of the fuselage, just under the wing, and three tanks in the wing, with a total capacity of 145 gallons.[159] Lindbergh planned to use the 80 gallons in the forward tank first. Once the front tank was empty, the plane would become less stable in the air, but more importantly to Lindbergh, it would be less likely to nose over in the event of a forced landing.[160]

Lindbergh knew he would have to continually re-balance the amount of fuel in each of the five tanks as his flight progressed, so he could keep his plane level. He and Hall planned to connect each of the five tanks to what they called a fuel "distribution system" in the cockpit, where Lindbergh could manipulate valves to transfer fuel from one tank to another.[161]

Wayne Biddle has explained that "Aviation was still a very small circle" in 1927.[162] Nearly all the business transacted in the industry was based upon friendships. Most of the pilots knew each other, as well as the men running the handful of American aircraft manufacturers. After meeting Klamm at the Cleveland airport, Lindbergh had asked his friends Glenn Martin and Donald Douglas about the Parker Appliance Co., and both vouched for the quality of its design and manufacturing processes. Hall, who had worked closely with Douglas at his Santa Monica plant, readily agreed with Lindbergh's request to take a closer look at Parker's fuel distribution system. At Hall's request, Mahoney sent a letter to Art Parker asking him to design a fuel distribution system that could handle the 425 gallons of fuel that would be on board the Spirit of St. Louis when it took off for Paris.

Mahoney wrote in his letter, "Glenn Martin tells me you have a nice primer pump, the plug valves to build a fuel feed system, and a new kind of fitting to keep the system dry. Can you design a fuel distribution system to get a 5,000 pound Ryan airplane with a Wright J-5 Whirlwind engine and 3,000 pounds of fuel from Long Island to Paris?"[163]

Art and Klamm understood they would be taking a risk with Lindbergh. They wondered whether the young airmail pilot had what it would take to survive the trip across the Atlantic, and whether he could supervise the construction of a plane that could make the journey. If Lindbergh disappeared over the Atlantic, their fuel distribution system might be blamed for the tragedy, and they would almost certainly lose the business of their most important customers—Glenn Martin, Donald Douglas, and Bill Boeing. Both Art and Klamm were convinced, however, that the prospects of success were too great to pass up. If Lindbergh made it across the Atlantic with their fuel system on board, the Parker Appliance Co. would become known the world over as one of the companies that helped bring New York and Paris closer together.

Art sent a letter back to Mahoney, promising to send Klamm to San Diego with the fuel distribution system Mahoney had requested.

Klamm arrived at the Ryan factory in early April with a truckload of special flared tube fittings and valves that he had designed and built for the Spirit of St. Louis out of a combination of copper, stainless steel, and regular steel made at a mill in Cleveland's Flats. With a bit of bravado, he told Hall and Lindbergh he would personally guarantee that Parker's flared tube fittings would not leak during the flight to Paris. After carefully inspecting the parts, Hall and Lindbergh gave Klamm the go-ahead to fasten the Parker fuel distribution system into the front of the cockpit, at the base of the instrument panel.

Klamm was surprised when he saw how cramped the cockpit was going to be. Lindbergh would be sitting on a hard wicker chair, with barely enough room to sit upright. Just a few inches in front of his seat, Klamm installed a dense array of Parker fittings, connected to 14 valves that controlled the distribution of fuel among the plane's five tanks. Lindbergh would be able to re-balance fuel in the tanks simply by leaning forward slightly in his seat and adjusting the valves.[164]

Lindbergh and Hall looked over Klamm's shoulder as he installed the fittings. Lindbergh realized his life depended upon how well they worked. If the fittings allowed even the tiniest leak, he would die over the Atlantic. Unlike his mail runs in the Midwest, there would be no places to bail out over the ocean. Klamm reassured Lindbergh that he had tested the fittings at high pressures for extended periods, and they had performed perfectly. He also mentioned that just a few weeks earlier, on March 1, the Patent Office had approved Art's patent for the flared tube fitting.[165]

For the rest of his life, Klamm would be asked how it felt to play a role in aviation history during that day on the San Diego waterfront. He usually replied, in his typical modest way, "I was just doing the best job I could for a customer."

The cockpit of the Spirit of St. Louis, with Parker's fuel system below the instrument panel.

Charles A. Lindbergh in 1927 with his plane, the Spirit of St. Louis.

Associated Press Photo

Lindbergh knew he was in a race with other contestants who were likely to attempt an Atlantic crossing as soon as the winter weather cleared. He spent a part of every day on the factory floor, driving the workmen to complete the plane as quickly as possible. He was desperate to get to New York to begin his flight by the end of April, when he expected the weather to improve.

On April 26, Noel Davis and Stanton Wooster, two experienced naval aviators, flew a test flight of the three-engine plane they were planning to fly to Paris. They took off from Langley Field in Virginia, but were unable to clear the treetops at the end of the runway. Their plane plummeted nose-first into a marsh, killing both men. Lindbergh believed that, if the fuel tank had been in front of the cockpit, as in the Spirit of St. Louis, it would have saved Davis and Wooster.[166]

Two days later, Hall pronounced the Spirit of St. Louis ready for a test flight. It had taken him just 60 days from start to finish, more quickly than even Lindbergh had dared hope. The aircraft Lindbergh and Hall had designed and built was virtually a flying bomb, nearly all engine and fuel tanks.

On April 28, 1927, the Ryan workers towed the silver plane to the closest airfield, located at the Dutch Flats along the Pacific. On the nose was emblazoned "Spirit of St. Louis," and on the tail "Ryan NYP," standing for "New York to Paris." Lindbergh had never felt a plane leave the runway so quickly—in less than 100 feet. He took the plane up to 2,000 feet and flew over San Diego Bay, looked down at Hall, Klamm, and the workmen waving from Ryan's factory, then put the plane through a variety of spins and turns. After 10 more days of rigorous testing, Lindbergh believed his plane was ready for the cross-country flight to Long Island.

On May 8, Lindbergh prepared to fly the plane to St. Louis, on the first leg of his trip to Long Island. He read in the paper that morning that two French World War I aces, Charles Nungesser and Francois Coli, had lifted off from Paris' Le Bourget Airport, bound for New York, in a seaplane they named l'Oiseau Blanc ("The White Bird"). Emblazoned on the fuselage was a black ace of spades with a coffin, skull and cross-bones. Thousands of people gathered in New York's Battery Park, hoping to see the French flyers land near the Statue of Liberty. Five hours after takeoff, observers reported the plane had passed over the coast of Ireland, and that it was encountering rain, snow, ice and 25-mile-per-hour headwinds.[167]

Lindbergh departed from San Diego at 3:55 p.m. on May 10 for a 14-hour, 25-minute overnight flight to Lambert Field in St. Louis, where he met the businessmen who had financed the construction of his plane. After landing, he asked about Nungesser and Coli. A reporter replied, "There's a report that a British ship picked them up at sea, but we can't get confirmation."[168]

The next morning, on May 12, Lindbergh left St. Louis on a flight to Curtiss Field on Long Island. As he circled the airport late in the afternoon, he noticed that an adjacent airport, called "Roosevelt Field," had a longer runway, nearly a mile long, and he decided it would give him the best chance for a successful takeoff to Paris with a full load of fuel.

Lindbergh was surprised to find 300 people waiting to greet him at Curtiss Field. After taxiing to a stop, he asked a group of reporters whether Nungesser and Coli had been sighted over North America. He was distraught to hear they had not been seen since they headed out over the ocean from Ireland. He feared they must have exhausted their fuel supply and crashed into the Atlantic or over Nova Scotia or Newfoundland.

Lindbergh stayed at the Garden City Hotel on Long Island, where Fonck and his crew had stayed before their tragic flight. Lindbergh awoke the next morning to headlines in the New York tabloids calling him a "young flying fool" and characterizing his attempt to cross the Atlantic as a "suicidal venture."[169]

For an entire week, Roosevelt Field remained closed by rain and fog. Lindbergh waited impatiently for the weather to clear. He spent his nights tossing and turning at his hotel. In the hallways, he was greeted by another contestant for the Orteig Prize, Commander Richard Byrd, already famous as the first man to fly to the North Pole. Byrd had been planning to fly to France in a Fokker Trimotor, but his plane had crashed in April during a trial takeoff from Roosevelt Field.

Every day, to Lindbergh's dismay, he was receiving more attention from the New York reporters. Suddenly he had become their favorite contestant. Some were hailing him as a hero for attempting the flight on his own.[170] As Lindbergh later wrote of those days of impatient waiting: "These have been the most extraordinary days I've ever spent; and I can't call them very pleasant. Life has become too strange and hectic. The attention of the entire country is centered on the flight to Paris, and most of all on me—because I'm going alone, because I'm young, because I'm a 'dark horse.'"[171]

On May 19, the weather was so bad Lindbergh was convinced he would not be able to take off anytime soon, so he spent his time visiting the Wright Aeronautical factory in New Jersey. He planned to join his mother and a group of friends that night at a Broadway show, but at the last minute, his meteorologist told him to hurry back to Long Island. According to the meteorologist, a high-pressure system was clearing the clouds over the Atlantic and should lift the fog by morning.

The lobby of the Garden City Hotel was filled with reporters that night. Lindbergh did not get to his room until almost midnight. One of his friends waited in the hall to guard his door from autograph seekers. Lindbergh kept thinking over his plans for the flight until 2:15 a.m., when he gave up trying to sleep and headed to Curtiss Field for a dawn takeoff.

At the airport, workers tied the Spirit of St. Louis to a trailer and towed it across a tree-lined gully to nearby Roosevelt Field. Two of Renee Fock's crew had died in that gully just eight months earlier. Lindbergh thought, "My plane lurches forward through a depression in the ground. It looks awkward and clumsy. It appears incapable of flight—shrouded, lashed, and dripping. Escorted by motorcycle police, pressmen, aviators, and a handful of onlookers, the slow, wet trip begins. It's more like a funeral procession than the beginning of a flight to Paris."[172]

Several handlers positioned the Spirit of St. Louis at the western end of the narrow, muddy rain-soaked runway, its nose pointing east, toward Paris. Klamm was there to shake hands with Lindbergh and wish him luck just before he jumped into the cockpit. Another onlooker, a former Yale football star named Juan Trippe, possessing what Harold Evans has called the "dark good looks of a Rudolph Valentino,"[173] had recently bought a small airline delivering mail in the Northeast. A few years later, Trippe would buy another airline flying mail between Havana and Miami, hire Lindbergh as a consultant, and name the airline "Pan American Airways."[174]

At 7:52 a.m., Lindbergh climbed into the cockpit, stuffing into his jacket three letters addressed to Myron Herrick, the American Ambassador to France.[175] Typed on the outside of the letter packet was the phrase "By First Aerial Non-Stop Route, New York-Paris." Charles Lawrence wrote Herrick from his home at 969 Park Avenue in New York, saying, "I am writing you a few lines which I am sending you by Lindbergh, in the hope that if his efforts are crowned with success, which I have every reason to hope will be the case, you will have in this letter a precious souvenir of the greatest feat of our time... I feel it is only fitting that I should send a letter to you through this most modern means of conveyance... to say that anything that brings New York closer to Paris is a great pleasure to me."

Sidney B. Veit, the president of the Paris chapter of the National Aeronautic Association, wrote his letter to Herrick from the Hotel Belmont, at Park Avenue and 42nd Street in New York: "This extraordinary aerial achievement will change the time tables from weeks to hours, and mark the shortest route from the heart of America to the heart of France." Theodore Roosevelt's oldest son, Ted, wrote Herrick from his home at Oyster Bay, Long Island: "This will introduce you to Captain Charles A. Lindbergh, who is a real sportsman. I sincerely hope he is successful in his flight and delivers this letter to you after having landed in Paris. Like the best type of sportsman, Captain Lindbergh is modest. He won't ask you to do anything for him. If I were you, however, I would insist on seeing something of him, for I know you will like him."[176]

The wind had shifted from east to west, promising an even more difficult takeoff. With no headwind, Lindbergh would have to reach a speed of at least 60 miles an hour to leave the runway. He thought of how earth-bound his plane seemed to be: "I'm conscious of the great weight pressing tires into ground, of the fragility of the wings, of the fullness of oversize tanks of fuel. There is in my plane this morning, more of earth and less of air than I've ever felt before."[177]

Five thousand feet away, a line of telegraph wires stretched across the end of the runway. Along the way waited men with fire extinguishers, ready to respond if the plane crashed. Klamm, Trippe, and several other bystanders pushed on the plane to start it moving through the mud. The plane fishtailed down the runway and slowly gained speed. Halfway down the runway, the Spirit of St. Louis was not even close to lifting off; it bounced into a puddle, spraying mud over the spectators. Past the point of no return, Lindbergh kept his eyes on the telegraph wires at the end of the field.

Twice the plane left the ground, then suddenly eased back down. The telegraph wires were only 1,000 feet away.

Finally, the plane lifted off and gained altitude, clearing the telegraph wires by 20 feet. Lindbergh looked out sideways from his cockpit and saw a group of golfers at a nearby course, waving as he headed toward the Atlantic.

The crowd at the airport cheered as Lindbergh took off.

"God be with him," Richard Byrd said, standing by his own plane on the runway. "I think he has a 3-to-1 chance."

Bert Acosta, a member of the Byrd team, said he thought Lindbergh was "taking a long chance. You must remember he is alone and has only one motor. If I were inclined to be superstitious, however, I might say that he has a good chance, for he is above all things a lucky flier."

From London, news came that Lloyds' underwriters were refusing to insure the Spirit of St. Louis, because they believed "the risk is too great."[178]

Back at Parker's Berea Road plant, Art, Helen, and Parker's other 35 employees were listening to radio reports of Lindbergh's lift-off from Roosevelt Field. They were relieved his plane made it off the ground. Art was confident Lindbergh's fuel system would function just as he and Klamm had designed it. If the Spirit of St. Louis faltered, it would not be because of a problem with Parker's valves, fittings, or connectors.

Fifteen minutes after takeoff, Lindbergh reached forward to close the Parker valves to shut off one of the fuel tanks in a wing and open the tank in the nose. For 12 hours, he followed the Eastern coastline to Newfoundland. At twilight, he deviated slightly from his Great Circle Route to fly low over the city of St. John's. Lindbergh wanted the world to know he was about to head out over the Atlantic. He waved to a group of sailors looking up from along the waterfront, and then began his two thousand mile leap across a wide and stormy ocean.[179]

As Lindbergh flew over St. John's, crowds began to congregate in Times

Square, awaiting bulletins on his progress. For the next 15 hours, the world would hear nothing from the Spirit of St. Louis. For Lindbergh, there would be no emergency-landing site, no copilot, no radio—just himself, his plane, the night sky, and the endless sea. One of Lindbergh's biographers, A. Scott Berg, explained, "Nobody had ever subjected himself to so extreme a test of human courage and capability as Lindbergh. Not even Columbus sailed alone."[180]

Gazing at the coast of Nova Scotia, Lindbergh thought, "I look back again at the lowering silhouette of the mountains, still sharp against the western sky. That is America. What a strange feeling—America at a distance!... I've given up a continent and taken on an ocean in its place—irrevocably."[181]

The next 12 hours would be the worst of Lindbergh's flight, as he encountered a sleet and rain storm. Lindbergh tried to fly over the storm, ascending to more than 10,000 feet, and under it, descending to just 10 feet above the waves, but he was unable to break free of the weather. At one time, he became so concerned with the sleet accumulating on his plane that he almost decided to turn back.

As Lindbergh traveled across the Atlantic, he was encased in a tiny world. The instrument panel and the Parker fittings and valves for his fuel system were in front of him, within easy reach. The roof of the cockpit was just high enough to leave clearance for his helmet. Lindbergh could touch both sides of the fuselage with partly outstretched elbows. As he explained, "my cockpit has been tailored to fit me like a suit of clothes."[182]

Lindbergh was already sleep-deprived when he took off from Roosevelt Field. As he cruised over the Atlantic, he had to fight an almost irresistible urge to nap. The constant instability of the Spirit of St. Louis kept jerking him awake. At one point, he nodded off and then awoke just in time to recover control of his plane. Several times, Lindbergh brought the plane down until his wheels were just a few feet above the whitecaps. He was able to recover his alertness when the spray from the ocean slapped his face.[183] He even resorted to using smelling salts from his first aid kit. Several times, Lindbergh began to hallucinate, believing he was seeing family and friends riding along with him through the clouds.

Lindbergh was constantly aware of the complex fuel distribution system just in front of him. As he gazed at the maze of Parker valves and fittings, he thought "my plane and my life depend on the slender stream of liquid flowing through the battery of fuel valves, like blood in human veins."[184] After passing the halfway mark of his Atlantic crossing, Lindbergh decided to open the valves to exhaust the main fuselage tank, leaving fuel in the wing tanks for balance. Using the valves to shift the fuel in the tanks had another advantage—it helped keep him awake.

After flying through the night for a thousand miles, Lindbergh sensed a growing light in the sky ahead. Twenty-seven hours after his takeoff from Roosevelt Field, he spotted a porpoise in the ocean below, a sea gull, and soon thereafter, several fishing boats. He breathed a sigh of relief, as he realized the Irish coast must not be far away. Circling one of the boats at 50 feet, Lindbergh yelled out as loudly as he could, "Which way is Ireland?"

Lindbergh received no response from the fishermen, but within a few minutes, he spotted a purplish blue band on the horizon, and then a jagged coastline with fjords topped by green fields.[185] Consulting his map, he realized he had arrived at Dingle Bay on the southwest coast of Ireland. He was only three miles from where he had intended to meet the coast, and just 600 miles from Paris.[186]

As Lindbergh flew low over Ireland, he began to notice people running out into the streets and looking up and waving. He thought to himself: "I've never seen such beauty before—fields so green, people so human, a village so attractive." He had been "to eternity and back," and thought, "I know how the dead would feel to live again."[187]

The sun set as Lindbergh flew toward the continent of Europe. His spirits were soaring as he saw the fields of England slipping away beneath him in the twilight and listened to the reassuring steady roar of his engine; but suddenly his engine coughed erratically, and the plane began to shake. He started to lose altitude. Lindbergh was afraid he might be forced to make an emergency landing in England. He wondered, "Have I grown too confident, too arrogant, before my flight is done?" He soon figured out his fuselage tank was running out of fuel, as he had intended it, and all he had to do was close a Parker valve to shut off the fuselage tank and open another valve to get the gasoline from a wing tank flowing through the Parker fittings to reignite his engine.[188]

Lindbergh flew over Plymouth, the same harbor from which the Mayflower had sailed to the New World, and then across the English Channel and into France over Deauville. Below him lay the sandy beaches of Normandy. He thought of how, just 13 days ago, Nungesser and Coli had taken off from Le Bourget and then set out from this very point for their westward flight over the ocean. He wondered how far they had flown, and whether they had been lost over the Atlantic.[189] Neither the two men, nor the remains of their plane, would ever be found.

Lindbergh followed the Seine up stream until he spied the air beacons that led him toward Paris. Not a drop of fuel had escaped from his Parker fittings and valves. He had enough fuel to continue all the way to Rome. He considered it briefly, but decided not to take the chance of running out of fuel over the Alps. One hour from Paris, he reached under his wicker seat and pulled out one of the five wrapped sandwiches he had brought from New York. One sandwich was enough. He stuffed the wrapping back in the bag, thinking "I don't want the litter from a sandwich to symbolize my first contact with France.'"[190]

As Lindbergh flew over the Paris suburbs, he believed "From now on everything will be as simple as flying into Chicago on a clear night."[191] He made a grand and graceful circle around the Eiffel Tower and looked down upon the lamps of Paris, the River Seine, the avenues, and the grand pathways of the Champ de Mars. Then he made his final turn northeast toward Le Bourget.

Lindbergh could not find the beacon for the airport. Remembering the night he flew into Cleveland and could not locate the darkened airport, he thought to himself, "Maybe the French turn out their beacons when no planes are due, like that air-mail field at Cleveland."[192] He saw what he thought was a black patch where the airport should have been, but he was confused by a string of lights stretching all the way back to Paris. He finally realized they were from the headlamps of automobiles stuck in traffic, attempting to reach the airport in time to welcome him to France.

Lindbergh shut the Parker fuel valves to the wing tanks, swept his flashlight over the instruments for a final check, fastened his seat belt, and nosed the Spirit of St. Louis down in a gradually descending spiral.[193] He landed at 10:22 p.m. Paris time, on May 21, 1927, 33 hours and 30 minutes after he took off from Roosevelt Field. He had 85 gallons of fuel remaining in his wing tanks, enough to fly another 1,040 miles.[194] Twenty-four years after the Wright Brothers had flown 852 feet at Kitty Hawk, Lindbergh had flown 3,600 miles to Paris.

As Lindbergh taxied down the runway, he wondered how he would find his way to the center of Paris, and he worried he would not be able to obtain a visa for his stay in France. He had no idea he was about to become the first hero of the age of flight, and the first true international celebrity. He was shocked to see the crowd of 150,000 gathered to cheer him. After he came to a stop, he was greeted by half a dozen French workers from the airport. One said, "This time, it's done." Concerned about the state of his plane after the long flight, Lindbergh simply asked, "Are there any mechanics here?"[195]

The crowd broke through the steel fences at the edge of the field, rushed the Spirit of St. Louis, and carried Lindbergh on their shoulders for nearly half an hour. Lindbergh described the sensation as "like drowning in a human sea."[196] He was rescued by two French soldiers. They took him to a hangar at the edge of the field, where he was congratulated by Myron Herrick.[197] Lindbergh gave Herrick the letters entrusted to him at Roosevelt Field.[198] Herrick, a former Clevelander, was proud to hear Lindbergh recount that several Cleveland companies, including Parker Appliance, had helped bring him safely across the Atlantic. At one point in the conversation, Lindbergh had to ask Herrick to speak louder, saying "I can't hear very well. The sound of my motor is still in my ears."

Lindbergh told Herrick that during the ocean crossing "we flew over fog." Raising his voice so that Lindbergh could hear better, Herrick asked, "What do you mean when you say 'we,'" and Lindbergh replied, "Why, my ship and me."[199]

Lindbergh pulled out a scrap of paper from his pocket and asked, "Do you know this Paris hotel? I understand it's quite reasonable."[200] Herrick told Lindbergh, "Young man, I am going to take you home with me and look after you."[201] He was referring to the American Embassy on the Champs Elysees, in the middle of Paris. The soldiers who had rescued Lindbergh from the crowd agreed to take Lindbergh to the Embassy. They drove on back roads in a small Renault, so that no one would recognize them.

When Herrick arrived at the Embassy at 3:00 a.m., he found Lindbergh sitting on the edge of a twin bed in the guest room in a bathrobe, pajamas, and slippers. Herrick's dog Max, who had always slept in the Ambassador's bedroom, must have sensed they had a special visitor. Max slept all that night with his head on Lindbergh's pillow.[202]

It was late afternoon in Cleveland when Lindbergh landed at Le Bourget. After Lindbergh's take-off from Long Island, Klamm had hurried back home on the Twentieth Century Limited to join Art and Helen. They had been huddled around a radio in Art's office on Berea Road ever since mid-morning. When the news broke that Lindbergh had made it to Le Bourget, they gave out a great sigh of relief. They could hear factories in the Flats and boats on Lake Erie and the Cuyahoga River blowing their whistles in celebration.[203]

Lindbergh sent a cable to the New York Times the day after he landed at Le Bourget. He concluded that trans-Atlantic air travel could become practical: "I look forward to the day when transatlantic flying will be a regular thing. It is a question largely of money. If people can be found willing to spend enough to make proper preparations, there is no reason why it can't be made very practical."[204]

Art took out an advertisement in the June 20, 1927, edition of the Cleveland Plain Dealer, which stated, "Captain Lindbergh's fuel flowed safely through Parker tube couplings. We express our sincere appreciation and gratitude for his masterful performance. In the period of commercial aviation just ahead … Parker tube couplings, fittings, and fuel line equipment will keep pace with the demand." From that day on, the Parker name began to stand for something special—a company that made products that perform well even under the most challenging conditions.

Lindbergh returned to Washington on an American cruiser with his plane strapped to the deck. It took him seven days to cross an ocean he had just flown over in 33 hours. A few weeks later, he embarked on a three-month, 82-stop nationwide tour, to promote the reliability and safety of air transportation. The tour proved that an airplane could fly to predetermined stops at scheduled times, paving the way for regular passenger air travel. During a stop in Detroit, Lindbergh gave Henry Ford and his mother, a Detroit schoolteacher, a ride above the city in the Spirit of St. Louis. Ford said, "This was the finest ride I ever had. Why, it is just like going on a picnic."[205] Lindbergh also stopped in Dayton, where he paid his respects to 56 year-old Orville Wright.[206]

On April 30, 1928, Lindbergh flew for the last time in the plane that had made him famous, circling Lambert Field in St. Louis, dipping his wings to thousands of spectators and then pointing his plane east toward Washington D.C. At Bolling Field in Washington, he presented the plane to the Smithsonian Institution. It was hard for Lindbergh to give up his plane, but he believed it now belonged to the American people. For several years thereafter, he secretly visited the Smithsonian, standing quietly in a corner and staring at the plane he had flown over 40,000 miles.[207]

The Spirit of St. Louis hangs today in a place of honor high above the atrium at the Smithsonian's Air and Space Museum on the Washington Mall, next to the Wright Brothers' Flyer. Visitors who walk up to the second level can peer into the cockpit and see Art Parker's fuel distribution system still in place, right in front of Lindbergh's wicker seat.

The Spirit of St. Louis hanging in the atrium of the Smithsonian Air and Space Museum,
with Art Parker's fuel system still inside.

PART 2

# CREATING A SUSTAINABLE CULTURE

### 1927 TO 1945

---

*"I congratulate you on the alert and enthusiastic cooperative spirit that prevails among our Parker people...the ability to get a hard job done and done quickly. It is in the knowledge of this employee spirit that we can optimistically face the future unafraid. I am sincerely proud of you all. Our success is founded upon fair dealing, hard work and coordination of effort."*

Art Parker, addressing a meeting of employees
at the Hotel Carter in downtown Cleveland,
October 12, 1944

# CHAPTER 7

# The Lindbergh Effect

Wvhen Lindbergh landed at Le Bourget, Art had been in business for 10 years. During that time, the Parker Appliance Co. had forged a reputation for providing quality products to the most important figures in the aviation business—Glenn Martin, Donald Douglas, Bill Boeing, and Charles Lindbergh. Prompted by the excitement from Lindbergh's flight, aviation was about to embark upon its Golden Age, a period of expansion that would last through World War II. Art would ride that expansion's coat-tails, providing fuel system valves and fittings for nearly every American air-craft developed over the next two decades.

Lindbergh's biographer, A. Scott Berg, explained that "Celebrity without purpose seemed pointless to Lindbergh; and commercial aviation became his crusade."[208] As Lindbergh wrote, "When I became convinced that man had a great destiny in the air—that planes would someday cross continents and oceans with their cargoes of people, mail and freight...I devoted my life to planes and engines, to surveying airlines, to preaching, whenever men would listen, the limitless future of the sky."[209] Lindbergh's advocacy of air travel created a boom in aviation stocks. In 1928, the market value of all air-craft companies on the New York Stock Exchange reached $1 billion, even though the aggregate earnings of those companies was only $9 million. Sud-denly, businesses like the Glenn L. Martin Co., the Boeing Co., and the Doug-las Aircraft Co. found it easier to secure capital to expand their operations.[210]

Lindbergh's flight to Paris brought air travel into the public's consciousness in much the same way as Alexander Winton's automobile ride from Cleveland to New York in 1899 focused attention on the automobile. In the year after the flight of the Spirit of St. Louis, despite the primitive conditions of air travel, the number of Americans taking to the air quadrupled.[211] Aviation author Sam Howe Verhovek explains: "Most sat on sacks of mail or stacks of wood, enduring freezing conditions over the mountains and scorching temperatures over deserts."[212] Passengers suffered through bone-rattling vibrations when planes hit turbulence; many ended up with bruises and broken bones when their wicker chairs broke loose from the floor.[213]

As the number of passengers increased, the airlines began to demand planes that could fly higher, faster, more comfortably, and with greater passenger loads than ever before. As Harry Bruno, an early public relations expert for the aviation industry, wrote, "The decade after the Lindbergh flight to Paris saw practically every new airplane rendered virtually obsolete within six months of its creation."[214] Art and Klamm had to keep up with that unprecedented period of innovation, constantly improving their fuel valves and fittings to meet the airlines' demands for better planes.

Art had become known throughout the aircraft industry as the man who built Lindbergh's fuel system. His aircraft valves and fittings were regarded as the world standard for quality and performance. With the patent for the flared tube fitting, which was fast becoming the indispensable seal for all fluid power applications, Art had the entire market for aircraft fuel system fittings to himself. The patent was so broad that competitors could not design around it. To Art, his success with the flared tube fitting was a lesson in the value of being the first to innovate in a particular market, and protecting the resulting intellectual property with a patent.

In the late 1920s, Art obtained the patent for a critical improvement in his two-piece flared tube fitting. He developed a three-piece fitting, adding a sleeve, which allowed the fitting to seal more highly pressurized systems. This new three-piece fitting would become a standard part for the high pressure fuel systems being installed in new aircraft, where it could withstand the intense vibration from piston engines.

The Spirit of St. Louis became the model for the new airplane—made of metal, with a single wing, and the ability to fly long distances without refueling. Art planned to use his new-found reputation to convince aircraft manufacturers to use Parker fuel systems on their planes. Once Art's valves and fittings were installed, he was guaranteed the replacement business for parts that wore out in service, creating a barrier to entry no competitor could surpass. At stake was a large potential market among aircraft makers gearing up to make enough planes to meet the increasing demand for passenger air travel.

Over the next 17 years, Art's ever-increasing sales to the aircraft makers allowed him to achieve his dream of reaching economies of scale to enhance his profitability. Just as Rockefeller had with Standard Oil, Art started taking advantage of efficiencies in mass production that would make him one of the industry's lowest cost producers. Unwittingly, however, as Art became dependent upon his aircraft customers, he was laying the groundwork for a crisis that would nearly destroy his company after World War II.

Art's first customer for fuel valves and fittings for passenger aircraft was Henry Ford, a man Art admired for changing the world. When Ford started his automobile company, his dream had been to produce an automobile affordable by the American middle class.[215] Before Ford, automobiles had been made slowly, one at a time, by teams of workers. The process was so expensive that only the wealthy could afford a car. In 1908, Ford told his attorney, John Anderson, how he planned to mass produce affordable cars on an assembly line: "The way to make automobiles is to make one automobile like another, and then to make them all alike...just as one pin is like another when it comes from the pin factory."[216] Ford launched his car for the masses, the Model T, in October 1908, with the advertisement, "Even You Can Afford a Ford."[217] By 1912, thanks to the economies of mass production, Ford was able to reduce the price of a Model T, originally $825, to just $575.[218]

Shortly after Lindbergh's flight, Ford began building the Ford Tri-Motor, a three-engine plane nicknamed the Tin Goose, after its metallic covering, which allowed Ford to claim it was "the safest airliner around."[219] With interchangeable parts, Ford could produce the Tri-Motor on an assembly line, as he had with the Model T. Ford looked at his Tri-Motor as a way to get the American middle class into the air, just as his Model T had put Americans into the automobile.

Every American airline which began passenger service in the late 1920s and early 1930s used Tri-Motors for its fleet. Ford made 199 Tri-Motors from 1925 to the mid-1930s. Art produced a primer to start the Tri-Motor's engines, as well as valves and leak-proof fittings for the plane's fuel system, similar to those Klamm had installed on the Spirit of St. Louis. Art's main selling point to Ford was that with five fuel tanks in its wings, the Tri-Motor, like the Spirit of St. Louis, would require frequent re-balancing of fuel, which could only be accomplished with a fuel distribution system like Lindbergh's. In November 1929, Commander Richard Byrd captured the world's attention when he flew a Ford Tri-Motor over the South Pole, with Art's fuel system on board.

The Tri-Motor carried a pilot, copilot, flight attendant, and nine passengers seated in wicker chairs, outfitted with blue seat cushions and set in one row on each side of the plane.[220] Every Tri-Motor was equipped with a bathroom, which the writer Patrick Cooke called "a much underrated milestone."[221] The interior was modeled on the luxurious Pullman cars of the time, with wood paneling decorated with gold filigree.[222] The Tri-Motors flew many of the city-to-city routes first established by airmail pilots such as Lindbergh. On July 1, 1925, Ford Commercial Airlines inaugurated 100-minute flights from Cleveland to Detroit. A one-way ticket cost $18, a round-trip $35.[223] The airline touted the route in an advertising brochure, promising passengers "You are always in sight of land as you soar over our beautiful Lake Erie islands and watch lake steamers crawling beneath you."

Lindbergh was one of the founders of Transcontinental Air Transport (TAT), which later evolved into TWA. The airline touted itself as "The Lindbergh Line." In 1929, TAT bought a fleet of 10 Tri-Motors. Lindbergh was pleased to learn the planes were equipped with Parker fuel system components similar to those that had brought him safely across the Atlantic. He spent nearly a year putting in place the infrastructure needed to support TAT's transcontinental flights. He would not let the airline start those flights until he had established landing fields and weather stations at regular intervals along the route. Those stations became the foundation of the future National Weather Service. TAT contracted with the Radio Corporation of America (RCA) to put pilots in direct communication with the weather stations, which could warn them of dangerous flying conditions.[224]

Lindbergh inaugurated TAT's "East to West" trans-continental airline service on July 7, 1929, as he stood at the Glendale, California airport, and pressed a Western Union circuit that signaled a Pullman train to depart on an overnight trip from New York City's Pennsylvania Station to Columbus, Ohio. The passengers traveled by train in the evening because night flying was considered too dangerous. The next morning, the passengers transferred to a TAT Tri-Motor in Columbus. The plane landed in Waynoka, Oklahoma, where the passengers took another train to Clovis, New Mexico. There they climbed aboard a second TAT Tri-Motor.

The passengers were thrilled when their pilot came into the cabin to greet them before they took off from New Mexico. It was Lindbergh, who had flown in from Los Angeles the day before to take them on the last leg of their trip. Lindbergh's wife Anne proudly showed the passengers how she and her husband had outfitted the plane's interior. Green curtains shaded the windows, and every seat was equipped with a blue reading lamp. A white-uniformed flight attendant provided the passengers with stationery, maps, postcards and lavender linen tablecloths.[225] The plane arrived in Glendale, a few hours after leaving Clovis, and 48 hours after the passengers left New York—20 hours faster than the transcontinental trip would have taken in an express train.[226]

THERE WAS NO such thing as a "test pilot" in the late 1920s. Daring young men, called "barnstormers," were pushing the limits of aviation at air shows all around the country by performing high-risk maneuvers such as loop-to-loops, dive bombing in corkscrew patterns from high altitudes, close formation flying, and wing-walking. Crowds gathered to anticipate the thrill of a crash, much like those who attend automobile races today. One of the most popular barnstormers was Lincoln Beachey, known for such death-defying stunts as the Corkscrew Twist. The press dubbed him the "Man Who Owns the Sky." By the time he died in a crash at the Panama-Pacific International Exposition in San Francisco in March 1915, he had been seen by 20 million Americans. When a reporter asked Beachey how to explain his popularity, he coolly replied, "People come to see me die."[227]

A billboard advertising the 1929 National Air Races in Cleveland.

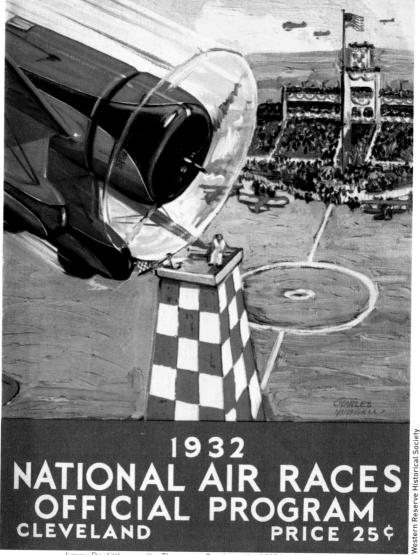

Western Reserve Historical Society

Jimmy Doolittle won the Thompson Trophy at the 1932 National Air Races in Cleveland, flying his "Gee-Bee" 10 laps on a 10-mile course.

Beginning in 1929, the greatest air show of all, called the National Air Races, was held in Cleveland. The show would remain in the city until 1949, with visits to Chicago and Los Angeles in 1930, 1933 and 1936, and a hiatus during World War II. The races were designed to push the limits of aviation. Each year, contestants flew in faster and more maneuverable planes. This led to improvements in the design of fuselages, wings, engines, cockpit ventilation, retractable landing gear, engine cooling devices, and a lighter metal covering, leading the press corps to call Cleveland "the Air Laboratory of the World."[228]

The National Air Races were sponsored by a roster of the most famous aviation companies in America, including Boeing, Martin, Douglas, Thompson Products, Cleveland Pneumatic Tool (a Cleveland manufacturer of aircraft landing gear components that today is part of the Apex Tool Group), Standard Oil of Ohio (which made airplane fuel), American Steel and Wire, the Austin Co. (a Cleveland airport hangar manufacturer), The Sherwin-Williams Co., and three Akron aircraft tire manufacturers, General Tire and Rubber, B.F. Goodrich, and Firestone. Art joined the roster of Cleveland's most important business people as a director of the Cleveland Air Show.

The Cleveland Women's Air Derby was designed to promote women's role in aviation. The cross-country race from Santa Monica to Cleveland served as the opening event for the 1929 National Air Races.[229] Art and Helen watched Amelia Earhart land in Cleveland at the end of the race. Cliff Henderson, the race's managing director, said, "If there ever was a question as to women's ability to fly and to take a significant part in this great industry it is now definitely and finally settled, and their important role in future development will be an accepted fact."[230]

To the delight of 100,000 spectators, Lindbergh flew by in a Boeing F2B-1 bi-plane fighter. A team of Navy flyers called the High Hats (a formation team that preceded the Blue Angels) flew with their wings tied together by ropes.[231] The men's cross-country race, called the Bendix Trophy Race, began in Burbank, California, and ended in Cleveland. Ten days of contests and exhibitions ended with the most prestigious race of all, the Thompson Trophy Race, described as "a Roman chariot face for the modern age."[232] The race took place on a 10-mile closed oval course, with turns marked by 50-foot high bright-red pylons. Crowds in the grandstands could easily see most of the spectacle. The race was named for its sponsor, Thompson Products—a company which became better known for the race than for supplying Lindbergh with the cylinders for the engine of his Spirit of St. Louis.

Just like the Indy 500, the Thompson Trophy Race kept spectators coming back every year, attracted by the thrill of watching contestants who risked their lives during every trip around the oval. The winner's name was telegraphed around the world, and he was regarded as just an important a celebrity as the winner of the "Green Jacket" at the Masters Golf Tournament.[233]

SINCE THE DAY Helen Fitzgerald walked through the front door of Parker's office on the Superior Viaduct, Art had become more and more fascinated by her. By February 1924, five months after she was hired, Art was paying her a bonus for her excellent work. Over time, she took responsibility for bookkeeping, stenography and keeping track of every visitor who came through the door. Art watched how graciously she treated her most difficult visitors, suppliers waiting to be paid, the landlord waiting for his rent, and board members anxious to receive a return on their investments. Art was impressed by how unflappable Helen remained in difficult situations, especially when she had to testify in the company's bankruptcy proceedings.

Most of all, Art, a natural introvert, appreciated Helen's friendliness, good nature, and sense of humor. She was the only one of his colleagues willing to give him unsolicited advice on business matters, and she never hesitated to make him laugh when he seemed weighed down by difficulties.

Art found himself missing Helen more and more in the evenings, when he returned to his parents' home. He envied Klamm, who went home to his wife and children every night. His envy increased when Klamm told him of his evenings out with his wife at Playhouse Square, on Euclid Avenue, where the Loew's State Theatre Co. had constructed five opulent vaudeville and movie theaters, each capable of seating hundreds of spectators for the new movies being produced in Hollywood.

In the fall of 1926, Art had found a note from Helen in his desk drawer, saying how much she enjoyed working for him. Art wondered if perhaps Helen was beginning to think, just as he was, that their professional relationship was evolving into a friendship. He thought she might enjoy going to see 23-year-old Bob Hope's vaudeville group at Playhouse Square.[234] It took him several days to summon up the courage to ask her. Art was 42, Helen only 23. He feared she would have no interest in going to the theater with a man his age. He eventually blurted out the invitation early one day as she walked into the office. He was relieved when Helen accepted without hesitation. Art enjoyed the evening out with Helen. It was one of the few times he let himself relax and forget about everything at the office.

Art was eager to ask Helen to join him again at Playhouse Square. Several times during the next several months he came close to asking her, but every time he stumbled at the last minute. He finally summoned up the courage to invite her to a movie at the State Theater. He was devastated when she turned him down. Most hurtful of all was the reason she gave for her refusal: the nearly 20-year difference in their ages was so great that she could not seriously consider entering into a romantic relationship with him. Helen did not mention to Art another factor that might have influenced her decision. Her parents were adamantly opposed to her marrying a man who was nearly 20 years her senior, and a Protestant to boot.

Helen's doubts failed to stop the burgeoning attraction between the two, as they were drawn ever closer together through their work at the office. It did not take long before they both independently came to the conclusion that they were not going to let their age difference—nor Helen's parents' attitudes—interfere with their happiness.

One day in December 1927, Art asked Helen to come into his office. Looking down at his notes, Art began to dictate a letter to Glenn Martin. Suddenly, he stumbled over a word and dropped his papers.

Surprised, Helen looked up at him. It was the first time she had ever seen him flustered.

Art finally burst out with the words, asking her if she would marry him.

Without hesitation, Helen stood up, threw her arms around Art, and said of course she would.

Art simply said, "Get your coat, Miss Fitzgerald, we're taking the train to Pittsburgh, and we're going to get married there."

Art had been planning to attend an industrial show in Pittsburgh that next week. Now his business trip was becoming a honeymoon. Art and Helen vowed to tell no one, not even Klamm, of their plans. After they arrived at their hotel, Art sent Klamm a letter delivering the surprising news: "If Glenn Martin's check comes in...wire me fifty dollars at Wm. Penn. Hotel in Pittsburgh... Otherwise do not bother. You will probably be a little surprised, but I have taken possession of Miss Fitzgerald for good—you can arrange for another girl in the office—we will be home after the first of the year."

Art Parker and Helen Fitzgerald's 1927 wedding photo.

In an apparent reference to the accident on the Lincoln Highway, Art added that "Mrs. Parker is frightened and worried for fear this shock may be fatal to you. I told her that you are quite familiar with the unexpected and that it would take more than this news to shake you up."[235]

Helen attached a postscript to Art's letter, saying, "Mr. Klamm, I'll let you kiss the bride when we return."

In business as well as in family matters, starting with Helen's hiring as the fifth employee of the Parker Appliance Co., Art and Helen would become partners who complemented each other. As Pat Parker once explained, Art was "a highly creative, inventive, entrepreneurial sort," while Helen was "reliable, stable, persistent, from a strong Irish family, and possessed of strong common sense. Her calming influence kept his decision-making process in perspective."[236]

Art asked Klamm not to divulge the marriage to anyone else. He and Helen had agreed the Fitzgeralds should first hear of the marriage from her when she returned from Pittsburgh. Helen feared how her family would react to her marrying outside their Catholic faith. In 1927, it was unusual for a child (and particularly a daughter), reared as a Catholic, to marry a Protestant. Helen's decision to marry Art demonstrated her independent spirit and willingness to break boundaries.

Helen met with her parents, three brothers, and three sisters at the Tremont house shortly after she returned from Pittsburgh. Her siblings said very little, but her mother and father made it clear she should never have married a Protestant. Even though Helen had expected such a reaction, she was heartbroken. She would never sleep in her parents' home again. She and Art moved into a house at 1470 Lewis Drive in Lakewood, within walking distance of the Berea Road plant.

Despite her parents' disapproval of her marriage, Helen remained close to her brothers and sisters. She and Art made an effort to drive to her parents' home on Sunday afternoons to have lunch with the Fitzgerald family. When Parker became more prosperous in the mid-1930s, Helen set up trust funds for each of her siblings, giving them the opportunity to enjoy a lifestyle they never could have afforded on their own.[237]

As the 1920s drew to a close, the Glenn L. Martin Co. had become the largest American aircraft manufacturer. The Cleveland Press named Martin one of Cleveland's "thirteen most eligible bachelors."[238] His popularity in Cleveland, however, was not enough to convince him to remain in the city. In the fall of 1929, Martin moved his company and its 250 employees to Middle River, Maryland, near Baltimore.[239] Martin was lured away by favorable financing from Baltimore banks and a discounted price for a tract of land next to an inlet of Chesapeake Bay.[240] With easy access to the Bay and the Atlantic Ocean, Martin could be assured of year-round use of open water for testing his seaplanes and carrier-based torpedo planes. Baltimore's proximity to the Army and Navy procurement offices in Washington was also an advantage Cleveland could not duplicate. Martin's company, however, in its successive incarnations as Martin Marietta and later Lockheed Martin, would remain one of Parker's largest customers well into the 21st century.

On October 16, 1929, Art and Helen welcomed their first child into the world. They named him Patrick Streeter Parker, after Helen's father, Patrick Fitzgerald, and Art's mother, Margaret Streeter Parker. Pat's name reflected the continuing love and respect Art and Helen had for their parents. Art and Helen were pleased with the world Pat was joining. America was at peace, and it looked like the economic good times would not end anytime soon.

Helen with the Fitzgerald family at their home in the Old Brooklyn neighborhood
in the early 1930s. Helen is pictured in the front row at the far left, Pat is in the front
row at the far right and Helen's parents are in the middle of the back row.

Nearly every day, Art sat at his desk wondering how he could satisfy all the
new orders coming in to his company.

Art was not alone in failing to foresee the economic calamity on the horizon. In fact, few others appreciated the dangers lurking beneath the good
times. The continuation of the economic expansion was dependent upon
circumstances that could not last forever—the upward climb of the stock
market, low interest rates, easy credit, consumer confidence, and a continued willingness to invest.

On October 29, 1929, a day that would forever be known as Black Tuesday—
just 13 days after Pat Parker was born—the good times abruptly came to an
end. The stock market collapsed, and along with it all confidence in the economy. The stock market crash spawned a deflationary spiral in all asset classes that brought the U.S. economy to a halt. Rockefeller tried to reassure the
American public that good times would soon return. He bought an additional
million shares of Standard Oil and issued a press release saying, "These are
days when many are discouraged. In the ninety years of my life, depressions
have come and gone. Prosperity has always returned and will again."

When the comedian Eddie Cantor heard Rockefeller was buying stock, he
cracked, "Sure, who else had any money left?"[241]

# CHAPTER 8

# The Great Depression

After Black Tuesday, consumers and businesses began to draw back their spending. As prices for most goods declined, investors tried to sell off many of their assets. They hoped that if they held onto cash, they could buy back into the market when prices reached even lower levels. Their actions created a vicious cycle which accelerated the drop in demand. Many banks failed, victims of their unwise investments in the stock market, causing confidence to fall even further. As merchants canceled orders, manufacturers who had been the mainstay of the economy in the 1920s laid off most of their workers. In mid-1933, the unemployment rate in America rose to 25 percent. Nine million people were without work, and 40 percent of American families had annual incomes of less than $1,000.[242]

As a center of American manufacturing, Cleveland was one of the cities hardest hit by the Depression. Biographer Douglas Perry wrote, "In 1929, a hefty forty-one per cent of Cleveland's workers had been employed in manufacturing related jobs helping to build America into the greatest economic force in the world. The city...had almost no unemployment. But following the stock market crash...businesses suddenly began to shut down.... The city was falling apart. Streets and sidewalks pitted by freezing weather remained unfixed. Blocks of apartments, vacant save for squatters, dissolved into kindling."[243]

Crime seemed to be the only business thriving in Cleveland. The city had the second highest murder rate in the country, due chiefly to a corrupt police force that looked the other way as mobsters engaged in gang warfare. In 1935, Cleveland's mayor, Harold Burton, hired as his Safety Director Eliot Ness, who had led the "Untouchables," a small band of Prohibition agents in Chicago who brought Al Capone and other Chicago gangsters to justice. Ness was just as successful in Cleveland, where he jailed the mobsters responsible for corrupting the Cleveland police department.[244]

Art watched several Cleveland businesses much larger than Parker slide into bankruptcy. As economic conditions worsened, he worried he might lose his company again. Just when he had attracted a solid base of customers, demand for his industrial valves and fittings was plummeting. He hated to lay off his skilled workers in the plant, or reduce their wages, but he feared he might have no other alternative. Art realized he could only make it through the Depression by staying close to his customers. He started to spend more time outside the office, traveling to learn his customers' needs firsthand. Art heard the same refrain from every one of them. In order to retain its customers, Parker would have to cut its costs, reduce its prices, and enhance the quality of its products.

During the winter of 1930, Art called his 40 employees together and told them of the crisis they were facing. He said his last resort would be cutting employment. He asked his employees for suggestions on how they could overcome the crisis. They turned in hundreds of ideas, many of which he adopted. The most prevalent suggestion was that, to preserve employment levels, all employees, from Art on down, accept a 10 percent reduction in pay for as long as the economic hard times continued. In the spring of 1930, Art announced the 10 percent pay reduction for everyone, including him and Klamm. He planned to use the savings to attract new customers with lower prices. He promised his employees their pay would be restored as soon as customer orders returned to a reasonable level.

Art and Klamm realized the best way to obtain additional business was by improving the performance of their products. After months of research and testing, Klamm and a team of engineers developed a new type of copper tubing that could seal high pressure steam conveyance systems more effectively. They found a ready market for the tubing from utilities such as Detroit Edison and Cleveland Electric Power. Klamm and his team of engineers also continued to improve Parker's pneumatic braking system for trucks and buses. As more roads were paved, trucks began to rival railroads as the prime movers of goods in America. Companies such as Ford, General Motors, Mack, and

Cleveland-based White Motor were making larger and heavier trucks every year, and those vehicles required more sophisticated and reliable braking systems. Klamm's team was able to develop a more robust system that would meet the needs of the truck manufacturers, and sell it for a lower price.

Klamm began traveling the country, displaying Parker's products at trade shows. Art told him, "Just get the order, and we'll find a way to design and make it."

A Parker display of tubing and fittings at Cleveland's Public Hall in 1933 proudly proclaimed that "every airship produced by the Glenn L. Martin Company and virtually every plane made by every other company manufacturing American aircraft carries Parker tube couplings and fittings." The display included pictures of Parker tube couplings and fittings not only in planes, but also in power plants, trains, trucks, buses, oil refineries, mines, steamships, and machinery in steel and other manufacturing plants.

As Klamm installed Parker's valves and fittings in critical industrial applications, he noticed Parker's customers were buying lubricants to help those components fit together more smoothly. Klamm passed this information on to Art, and together they decided the company could supply the lubricant market for its own products better than anyone else. Art began writing out formulas for different grades of lubricants in a small leather book he carried around in his pocket. He showed the book to Helen several evenings after dinner, and she laughingly began to call it his "recipe" book. She volunteered to type up the recipes, and in the process, suggested several changes to the formulas that Art readily adopted. In 1933, he obtained a patent on a lubricant called "Sealube," and he credited Helen for its success.

Klamm also worked to develop a valve line and a line of fabricating tools for tubing systems. However, until after World War II, the largest portion of Parker's business would remain in its lines of couplings and fittings.[245]

Fortunately, Art and Klamm's most important customers—the aircraft manufacturers—were one of the few businesses that continued to expand during the Great Depression. Art's kindness in extending credit to Glenn Martin in the 1920s was about to be repaid many times over. Martin convinced his friends Bill Boeing and Donald Douglas that they should also buy their fuel system fittings and couplings from Art for the aircraft flying increasing numbers of paying passengers across America.

In April 1930, Postmaster General Walter Folger Brown awarded exclusive airmail contracts to the new airlines—United, TWA, and American. The con-

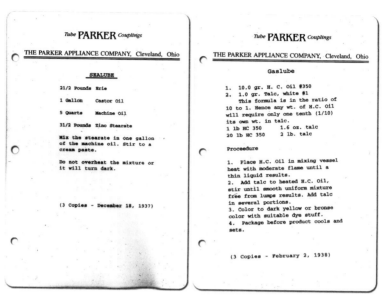

Helen's "recipes" for Parker's lubrication products.

tracts gave those airlines a guaranteed base of revenue that allowed them to survive their first difficult years.[246] During the 1930s, passenger service became just as important a source of revenue for the airlines as the U.S. Mail, and they began to pay more attention to their passengers' comfort.[247] The airlines were demanding safer, larger, faster and more comfortable aircraft for their passengers.[248] As the aircraft makers developed more sophisticated planes, they evolved into that era's high technology companies. Art and Klamm kept pace, continuously innovating to enhance the quality of Parker's aircraft valves and fittings. The airlines wanted lighter planes so they could fly farther on a single load of fuel. To meet the demand, Art and Klamm introduced a new aluminum alloy fitting for aircraft fuel systems that weighed less than traditional steel fittings.

In 1933, Boeing rolled out its model 247, a 160-mile-per-hour, 10-passenger, twin-engine plane, which featured the first retractable landing gear, autopilot and de-icing boots. Bill Boeing agreed to buy Art's valves and fittings for the fuel and de-icing systems of the B247. The plane could fly coast-to-coast in 20 hours, with six intermediate stops—11 hours faster than the Ford Tri-Motor.[249] Long-distance flights in the 247, however, were arduous. The plane's wing ran right through the cabin; passengers had to step over it on the way to and from their seats. The 247 cruised between 4,000 and 6,000 feet, where turbulence was the worst.[250] A passenger described settling down with "ear plugs, blankets and pillows to endure...hours of punishment from noise, vibration and buffeting in rough air at lower altitudes."[251] Another flyer said, "When the day was over my bones ached, and my whole nervous system was wearied from the noise, the constant droning of the propellers and exhaust."[252]

The revolutionary Boeing Model 247, developed in 1933, was the first modern passenger airliner.

Art and Klamm had maintained their friendship with Donald Douglas, ever since Glenn Martin brought him to Cleveland in 1917 to be his chief engineer. After Douglas started his own aircraft manufacturing company in 1920 in Los Angeles, Art and Klamm made frequent trips to update him on the latest innovations in their fuel system components. During a visit in the summer of 1935, Douglas told Klamm that Lindbergh had asked him to design a new plane for TWA, one that would be roomier, quieter, and faster than Boeing's 247. Confident in the quality of Parker's products, Douglas decided to purchase Parker's fuel system valves and fittings for his new airliner, which he called the "DC-3" (short for "Douglas Commercial 3").

Douglas, a master airplane designer ever since collaborating with Glenn Martin on the MB-1, had created an iconic passenger plane.[253] The DC-3 would popularize air travel in America.[254] It had room for 21 passengers seated three abreast—more than twice the number of people who could travel on Boeing's 247. The plane was roomier, quieter, and flew faster and smoother than the 247. With its two powerful propeller engines, the DC-3 flew 207 miles an hour, cutting the coast-to-coast flying time to 15 hours. The historian Kevin Baker was written that "The DC-3's burnished silver skin was arranged in squares that flowed into each other, creating a new standard of machine beauty."[255] By 1939, the plane was carrying 90 percent of the world's airline passengers.[256] With successive versions of the DC brand aircraft, Douglas would dominate the commercial airline market for the next 25 years. An estimated 400 DC-3s are still flying regular passenger routes around the world. The plane may become the first aircraft to last for 100 years in service.[257]

The new orders flowing into the Parker Appliance Co. from Boeing, Douglas and Glenn Martin allowed Art to revoke the 10 percent pay cut and start hiring again. His was one of the few companies in Cleveland posting job openings. By 1933, the annual sales of the Parker Appliance Co. reached $228,000.

As Art's work force expanded, he had to make a greater effort to stay in touch with all his workers. He realized much of his success had been due to the collaborative culture he had established, which was based upon his ability to remind each of his employees how much he valued their ability to turn out quality products for their customers. They reciprocated his regard, referring to him not only as "Mr. Parker," but as "A.L." They called Klamm "The Chief" or "Mr. Micrometer," in recognition of his unwavering standards for making products to exact specifications.[258]

As Art's production runs increased with his volume of business, he was able to adopt many of Henry Ford's techniques of mass production, standardizing the work, separating it into discrete steps, and training each of his workers how to carry out each step most efficiently. Art, however, made it clear he would not accept any shortcuts in the manufacturing process that affected quality. Art agreed with Walter Reuther, the president of the United Auto Workers' Union, who believed "if labor could be seen as something more than skill and brawn hired by the hour, if the workers could be given a level of responsibility for generating new ideas, then there was no limit to the productivity of the American economy."[259] Art was confident his factory workers could decide better than anyone else how best to perform their jobs. It was all a matter of trust. He looked upon each of his workers as talented individuals with something valuable to contribute to the business.

The Douglas DC-3.

Art realized that, as the number of his employees increased, it would be impossible for him to maintain day-to-day contact with each of them. He sought to devise a way in which he could continue to correspond directly with all of them, and in which his employees could continue to communicate with each other.

To accomplish this, Art appointed a committee of employees from all ranks of the company. Together, they began a newsletter called the *Fitting News*.

The first edition, printed in October 1934, included a list of births, deaths and illnesses among employees' families, several corny jokes, the averages of company bowling teams, and parties celebrating company milestones. On the first page, Art wrote of his hope that the new publication would foster a sense of teamwork and mutual support among all his employees, encourage an atmosphere of continuous improvement, and avoid the dangers of complacency, as together they faced the challenges that lay ahead:

> *"I have often contemplated ways and means for promoting a closer fellowship and better understanding of mutual events and problems among this group of men who spend nearly a third of their time here at the Plant...[the* Fitting News] *may mean much to the progress and prosperity of members of this organization...through its columns new talents and abilities may be discovered, new confidence may be inspired and your daily tasks may be less arduous.... Conditions such as we have successfully encountered and waded through during the existence of this business are an inspiration to face the future with a confidence that greater opportunities are ahead."*

By the end of 1934, Art was beginning to feel confident his company could continue to grow through the Depression. His message to his employees in the December 1934 edition of the *Fitting News* struck an upbeat tone: "We have prospered, one and all—and we greet this new year—'35'—with our house in order and ready for whatever may be our destiny."

Art's regular communications created a bond between him and his employees. Parker's men and women began to think of themselves as part of a team that was helping make the world a better place. They became passionate about their work, and willing to put in the extra effort necessary to make their company succeed.

In 1935, the Parker Appliance Co.'s annual sales reached $500,000. It employed 250 people. Art's company was swiftly outgrowing its 50,000-square-foot building on Berea Road. Undaunted by the Great Depression, the ever-optimistic Art noticed that the Hupp Motor Car Co. was offering for sale a four-story automobile manufacturing plant, with 283,200 square feet of rentable floor area.[260] Called the Euclon Building, it was located eight miles east of Public Square, at the corner of London Road and Euclid Avenue. The building was in Cleveland's Collinwood neighborhood, an area filled with factories and the modest homes of Irish, Italian and Slovenian immigrants. At various times since the factory was built in 1919, it had turned out three of the most popular automobiles made in Cleveland—the Chandler, the Cleveland, and the Hupmobile.

The Collinwood Yard, a switching point for 22 New York Central freight trains a day, was near the Euclon Building. Lured by the proximity to rail transportation, several other large manufacturers—General Motors, Thompson Products, General Electric, Lincoln Electric, Eaton Axle, National Acme, and Bailey Meter—built plants in Collinwood. Art knew the neighborhood well. His first employer, the Willard Storage Battery Co., was located on East 131st Street, less than a mile west of the Euclon Building. Glenn Martin's Cleveland factory and adjacent airfield had been only seven blocks northwest, on East 168th Street.

Founded in 1908 in Detroit by two brothers, Robert and Louis Hupp, the Hupp Motor Car Co. made a touring car with the first all-steel body. Hupp became well-known in 1910 when it sent three men on a 14-month, 47,777-mile around-the-world driving tour in a Hupmobile.[261] Hupp acquired the Euclon Building in 1928 when it bought the Chandler-Cleveland Motor Car Co. In the early 1920s, an 18-year-old aspiring entertainer named Bob Hope had filled out orders in Chandler's service department at the plant. Chandler fired him after he and a few friends used a company Dictaphone after hours to practice singing and left it on a desk where their boss discovered it the next morning.[262]

Hupp began to make cars at the Euclon Building in 1928. Assembly lines stretched the length of the four-story building, and large elevators lifted chassis from one floor to another. Railroad spurs ran directly to loading docks on the side of the building, from which cars could be shipped anywhere in America.

Hupp's president, DuBois Young, made a grievous error when he decided to raise the price of the Hupmobile in the midst of the Great Depression. Demand for the automobile plummeted. The last Hupmobile was made at Euclid Avenue in 1934, and in 1935, Young decided to sell the plant to raise badly-needed cash.

Early one Saturday in March 1935, Art stopped by the offices of Thompson, Hine and Flory, a law firm in downtown Cleveland. One of Art's friends had recommended the firm for its expertise in real estate and other corporate transactions. Art was disappointed when the receptionist told him none of the firm's partners were in the office. She did mention, however, that a 25-year-old associate named James A. ("Jim") Weeks was working in the library. Art asked the receptionist to call him.

Weeks was engrossed in reading a recent case decided by the Ohio Supreme Court when his telephone rang.

The receptionist was on the line. She said, "Mr. Weeks, there is a man here in the lobby who says he needs to see a lawyer."

Realizing the receptionist had only called him because no one else was in the office, Weeks hesitated for a second, but then recovered himself, and said, "Well, then send him in. I'll be happy to talk to him."

A few seconds later, Art was standing next to Weeks in the library. He looked down at the pile of books surrounding the young man and guessed he just might know something about the law.

Art asked, "Are you Mr. Weeks?"

Weeks replied politely, "Yes, sir, I am, and I understand you need a lawyer."

Art smiled and said, "Well, I have a job for you. I want to buy a building here in Cleveland. It's the Hupmobile plant on Euclid Avenue. I have an appointment on Monday in Detroit with DuBois Young, the president of Hupp. We can catch a flight on Monday at 7 in the morning and be in downtown Detroit by 10. Would you be able to accompany me?"

Without hesitation, Weeks replied, "Well, yes, certainly I can."

On Monday morning, Art and Weeks flew to Detroit on a Ford Tri-Motor. On the plane, Art told Weeks that Parker had supplied the valves and fittings for the plane's fuel system.

When they arrived at the Hupmobile offices in Detroit, a receptionist told them to take a seat in the lobby. Two hours went by and still Young did not appear. Art told Weeks they should go out and grab a sandwich at a nearby delicatessen. As they walked down the street, they noticed a young man selling The Detroit News. The front-page headline proclaimed in large letters "Hupmobile Stops Production." Art and Weeks quickly glanced through the article, which explained that Hupp was closing several of its factories to conserve cash, and was on the verge of bankruptcy.

Weeks said to Art, "Sir, I think we should just go home. If we wait a few weeks, I believe they will be willing to sell that plant to you for a lower price."

Art looked at Weeks, paused for a few seconds, and then replied, "Let's give it a try."

They flew back to Cleveland that afternoon.

The Euclid Avenue plant, circa 1935.

Two months later, Young called Art and agreed to sell the building for $250,000, a price substantially lower than the amount he had originally proposed. Weeks helped Art form a separate sole proprietorship called the Euclon Corp. to purchase the building on May 23, 1935.

After helping Art negotiate the purchase of the Euclid Avenue building, Weeks became Art's lawyer. In 1936, Art arranged to elect him a director of the Parker Appliance Co. Every year, the partners at Thompson Hine & Flory told each new class of associates how Art had found Jim Weeks in the firm's library on a Saturday morning. For years, young associates would show up on Saturdays, hoping to meet another Art Parker looking for a lawyer. None of them, however, would ever be fortunate enough to find a client like Art.

The October 1935 edition of the *Fitting News* described a company picnic held in August, with a mention of six year-old Pat Parker:

*"Mr. and Mrs. Parker put in a most welcome appearance in the afternoon and were accompanied by their three small children. Little Patrick will have to practice up on his running so that at the next picnic he will be able to win a few races."*

In the same edition of the newsletter, Art reassured his employees that they would enjoy working at the new location on Euclid Avenue:

*"I know that our growing work force have been anxious to get the lowdown on Management's plans for expansion. We all know and have known for a long time that we need more room...and everyone is aware of the fact that our destination is to be the EAST—towards the rising sun.... As we round out this year of '35 let us look forward to the new home— more work and bigger things and hope we may be all snug and comfy in the new plant by New Year's Day."*

Like Parker's business, Art's family had been growing, with the addition of Tom in 1931, and Joyce in 1933. Art and Helen began looking for a larger home. They decided to move to Cleveland's East Side to be closer to the new plant. Art was confident enough in his company's future to pay $26,000 in cash for a four-bedroom home at 2985 Falmouth Road in Shaker Heights, a Cleveland suburb developed by the Van Sweringen brothers in the 1920s, which had become one of the wealthiest suburbs in the country, known for its Tudor-style homes occupied by the leaders of the Cleveland business community.

Art and Helen Parker's home on Falmouth Road in Shaker Heights.

Courtesy of Kitty McWilliams

Designed as a bucolic escape from the industrial inner city, Shaker Heights featured winding, tree-lined streets with generous amounts of open space set aside for churches, schools, libraries and recreational facilities. In the midst of the suburb sat an area of parkland donated by Rockefeller, which included a brook and two lakes.[263] The Van Sweringen brothers had built a "rapid transit" rail line to connect Shaker Heights to their 52-story Terminal Tower in downtown Cleveland. When the building was completed in 1930, it was the fourth tallest building in the world. It contained the brothers' private suite, complete with bedrooms, a dining room, balcony and fireplace.[264]

The Parkers' Falmouth Road home had a large living room with a connected library lined with dark oak paneling. There were four bedrooms on the second floor. A large ballroom occupied the entire third floor; Art and Helen turned it into a playroom for the children. On weekends, Art could walk a few blocks to the Shaker Heights Country Club and play a round of golf. He also enjoyed ice skating at the Shaker community center. Always a formal dresser, he skated in a gray three-piece suit with a gray hat.[265]

Pat Parker retained strong memories of growing up on Falmouth Road. As he later recollected, Helen taught him, his brother and sisters "to pay attention to details, stay with a project until completion, treat negative events as a challenge to work through and stand tall when corrected." As a boy, Pat "learned to take 15 minutes of hell from a stern mom" whenever he violated her strict code of proper behavior.[266] Pat's experiences at home in Shaker Heights would help prepare him to pass on similar values to those who reported to him as he worked his way up through the ranks at Parker.

The Cuyahoga River divides Cleveland into two cities, much like the Mississippi divides Minneapolis and St. Paul. In the 1930s, Clevelanders defined themselves by their neighborhood, their church, the company they worked for, and the country from which they or their parents came—but mostly by whether they lived on the East Side or the West Side. Art, Klamm, and Helen were all native Westsiders, and so were nearly all their employees. For them, the East Side was a foreign land. Most Parker employees eventually decided to relocate to the East Side for the easier commute to the Euclon Building, but it would not be an easy move.

To alleviate his employees' anxieties about the move, Art hired a real estate firm to help them find new homes. After the move, many looked back nostalgically to their days on Berea Road. One of the few remaining employees at Berea Road, assigned to clean out the plant, wrote in the *Fitting News*:

Art and Helen with Tom, Joyce and Pat (far right), circa 1933.

*"Now that the old plant is practically vacated, we cannot help looking back at the many happy hours we have spent in this grand old building. Sometimes we never realize how much we will miss a thing until it has been taken away.... Mr. Parker, remember when we had so much room you used to park your Buick inside the building where the stockroom now is? Mr. Klamm, remember when you were running the shop?"*

From his desk on Berea Road, surrounded by packing boxes, the employee wrote about the dark days of 1924, when Art, Klamm, Helen, and 10 of their factory workers restarted the company at Berea Road after its bankruptcy:

*"Eleven years ago, Mr. Parker moved with a dozen of his loyal workers into this building on Berea Road. The going was rough and tough. It was an uphill pull, until the last couple of years. Then the sun could be seen shining over the hill a little bit. All this was due to the conservative business mind that Mr. Parker applied to all the matters that came up. Like every other growing family, the Parker Appliance Company grew until we became quite crowded at this place."*

Art used only 10 percent of the floor space on the second floor of the Euclid Avenue plant. He was enough of a dreamer to believe his 250-person company, with just $500,00 in annual sales, would grow to occupy the entire facility. In the meantime, he decided to lease three floors to Picker X-Ray, the Rotor Tool Co., and Superior Die Casting.

It took Parker's employees a while to get used to the spacious quarters on the second floor of their new plant. Concerned that the adjustment might affect productivity, Art reminded his employees in the January 1936 edition of the *Fitting News* that they had to continue to keep their focus on improving customer service:

> *"Here we are in the new plant...and all we have to do is make the new place go efficiently. In the past we have built a FAIR reputation for prompt deliveries and attention to customers' requirements. If we are to hold our performance even to past standards (we are, however, bound to improve our past performance) we must revise our methods to meet the new conditions encountered in this larger plant."*

Art realized that in order to build a lasting culture of premier customer service, he would have to continuously emphasize the importance of quality to his employees. In the next edition of the *Fitting News*, published in February 1936, Art once again reminded his employees that the success of the company depended upon its reputation for reliable products:

> *"The Parker Appliance Company serves important industries where precision is absolutely necessary. Our growth will depend to a great extent upon the ability of our organization to maintain a higher degree of precision.... It is our obligation to improve our production methods and the quality of our products to the very highest standards.... Our products go into the most exacting industrial services and in many instances failure of our products can result in material damage and even fatalities."*

BY THE END OF THE 1930S, the airline business was poised to expand beyond the U.S. to international markets. Henry Ford had brought America closer together with his Model T. Now the airline owners had a greater dream—to bring the entire world closer together with the airplane.

Standing next to Carl Klamm in 1927, Juan Trippe had watched Lindbergh take off from Roosevelt Field on his way to Paris.[267] Later, as Trippe watched the reaction to Lindbergh's flight, he realized the young man had eliminated the oceanic barrier to flights between the continents. Shortly after Lindbergh's flight, Trippe bought two small airlines, Pan American and Florida Airways, and merged them to form Pan American Airways. Trippe began passenger service between Key West and Havana, which had become a popular vacation spot for Americans during Prohibition.[268] His advertisements stated, "Fly to Havana and you can bathe in Bacardi Rum two hours from now."[269] Al Capone flew to Havana on Pan American on Valentine's Day of 1929, so he could have an alibi when his hit men carried out the "Valentines' Day Massacre" of several members of a rival Chicago mob family.

In 1929, Trippe asked Lindbergh to help plot Pan American's routes to Europe, the Far East, the Caribbean and Central and South America. Through intensive lobbying, Trippe had convinced Congress to grant him a monopoly on all overseas passenger flights. In March 1929, Lindbergh piloted Trippe and his wife on a Ford Tri-Motor on Pan American's first flight from Brownsville, Texas to Mexico City. Trippe's wife wrote in her diary that, during the five-hour flight, "The clouds were so thick, it was like flying in a milk bottle. The air was so rough, the airplane sometimes dropped hundreds of feet in air pockets."[270]

The industrial historian Harold Evans has explained that Trippe was "always ahead of the makers of...[airplanes], always pressing them for advancements in performance."[271] With his longer routes and expanding passenger loads, Trippe dreamed of using "flying boats" for international flights. He went to the New York Public Library and discovered the logs of the tall-masted "China Clipper" trading ships that clipped so much time off voyages across the oceans in the 1800s.[272] With five or six billowing sails, the ships transported spices from Shanghai to New York at two or three times the speed of previous sailing ships.[273]

Trippe and Lindbergh asked Glenn Martin to make a flying boat for Pan American that could carry 36 passengers along the old sailing routes to Europe and the Far East. Lindbergh insisted Martin make the fuel system for his flying boats with the same leak-free Parker fittings and valves that had kept him safe on his trip across the Atlantic. On November 22, 1935, Martin's four-engine "M-130" flying boat, christened Pan American's "China Clipper," took off from San Francisco Bay for its first trip across the Pacific Ocean, to

Manila. Twenty thousand spectators lined the Bay, while millions tuned their radios to a broadcast of the takeoff. Donald Burr has explained they were "listening as they would listen and watch the Moon landing thirty-four years later."[274] Nearby on the Bay sat one of the original Clipper Ships, the Star of New Zealand, which had taken months to cross the 8,000 miles of ocean the China Clipper was about to cross in just six days.

The plane, filled with 100,000 letters weighing nearly 2,000 pounds, rose slowly from the Bay. Unable to gain altitude, it flew under the cables of the San Francisco-Oakland Bay Bridge, which was still under construction. As the plane rose, it reversed course and headed across the Golden Gate Bridge to the Pacific, on a six-day journey that would include overnight stops at Honolulu, Midway, Wake Guam, and finally, Manilla.[275]

Even while Martin was building flying boats for Pan American, Trippe and Lindbergh began talks with Boeing about an aircraft larger and more powerful than the world had ever seen. They wanted a plane with twice the power of the Martin M-130 and the ability to carry 74 passengers at speeds of close to 200 miles an hour. Boeing was able to produce the plane—designated the 314—in just two years. Boeing agreed to purchase Parker's valves and fittings for the fuel systems on the 314, and Art sent Klamm to Seattle to supervise the installation of the parts. Boeing assembled the plane at its Plant 1 on the Duwamish River. In June 1938, Klamm watched as a tug towed the enormous aircraft to Elliott Bay for flight tests. The pilots revved the aircraft's four propellers and the gun-gray, whale-shaped plane began moving over the water, slowly at first, and then faster and faster, finally rising steeply into the sky.

Pan American began its 314 Clipper flights in 1939.[276] The Clippers flew passengers in a more luxurious style than first-class passengers on today's jumbo jets. On two separate levels, they had access to private sleeping bunks, a cocktail lounge, a dining area where white-jacketed stewards served six-course meals cooked by chefs from four-star hotels, and separate dressing rooms where men changed into black ties and women into evening gowns for dinner.[277]

Pan American's Honolulu Clipper (flying from Los Angeles to Hawaii in eight hours), its Pacific Clipper (flying from San Francisco to Hong Kong in six days), and its Yankee Clipper (flying from New York to Southampton, England in 24 hours) became iconic symbols of luxury travel, like the Pullman cars of the late 19th century, the passenger liners of the early 20th century, and the wide-body 747's and supersonic Concordes yet to come. Boeing would, in fact, copy the shape of the Clipper's nose when it designed the 747 for Pan American in 1969. The Clippers brought the world closer together, making San Francisco a sister city of Hong Kong, and New York a one-day hop from England.[278]

A Pan Am Clipper, circa 1939.

Western Reserve Historical Society

As Art's workforce grew through the 1930s, he had tried to maintain the feeling of a family business by writing regularly to his employees in the *Fitting News*. Now, with his workers spread out over an entire floor of the vast Euclid Avenue plant, he decided to encourage his employees to write back to him about their concerns, and he promised to begin publishing their correspondence in the newsletter.

Art was proud the Parker Appliance Co. had so many long-term employees. By the late 1930s, many of his employees had been with the company for more than a decade. Art realized many of his older employees were finding it harder to keep up with their younger colleagues on the production line. He told his supervisors to be understanding of the older workers, to make sure they were assigned tasks that required less strength and stamina. The more difficult, more physical tasks, he said, should be reserved for the younger workers. Art believed he was sending all his employees an important message in the way he treated his older, longer-term employees. He understood that if the company demonstrated its faithfulness to them, all employees would feel a greater sense of loyalty to the company.

In 1937, Art asked his employees to write in the *Fitting News* about why they liked working at the company. Anna Mikula, the wife of one employee, wrote that her husband had never thought of leaving the company because of "the interest of Mr. Parker in the welfare of the Parker employees and their families, the open door to the superintendent's shop office for all employees, where any and all technical mechanical troubles, grievances, and even personal feelings are given unbiased personal thoughts...the continued employment assuring a steady income...the formation of a Welfare Committee that arranges for evening programs plus a family picnic that breaks up and offsets any dull moments in Parker routine."[279]

By the end of the 1930s, most of Parker's sales were to the Glenn L. Martin Co., Boeing, and Douglas Aircraft, each of which had benefited from the rapid expansion of their own customers—United, TWA, American, and Pan American. Two thousand of Parker's fittings flew on every one of the airlines' passenger planes.[280] Since aircraft sales accounted for most of Art's business, he adopted a pair of wings as the logo of the Parker Appliance Co. To aircraft customers all over the world, the logo represented a reputation for quality and a pedigree that dated back to Lindbergh's flight in 1927.

Parker was one of a few American companies that experienced growth in sales during the Depression. In 1933, the company's annual sales were $228,427. By 1936, sales grew to $824,445, and in 1940 Parker sold $3.1 million of products, 15 times the amount sold seven years earlier. Art's earnings rose along with his company's revenue. In 1939, he received $30,000 in salary, $750 in a bonus, and $80,000 in royalties under the patents he had licensed to the Parker Appliance Co., giving him total earnings of more than $100,000, enough to make him a wealthy man in the late Depression years.[281]

The Parker Appliance Co. had survived a depression that destroyed many of its competitors. Art had succeeded because he had been able to convince his employees they could only survive the hard economic times by working together as a team to provide customers with the best possible products. Art's belief in the value of customer service would resound through succeeding generations of Parker employees, as they learned how the company helped its customers survive the Great Depression.

There was, however, danger lurking beneath Parker's apparent success. The company had become dependent upon sales to the aircraft manufacturers. In 1938, sales to the aircraft industry amounted to 54 percent of the company's total sales; in 1939, 65 percent, and in 1940, 69 percent.[282] Unwittingly, Art was sowing the seeds for a disaster that would befall his company at the end of World War II, when it became a captive supplier to one customer—the U.S. government—for fittings and valves on military aircraft.

The 1930s had been good to Art. He had a loving wife, three children, and a growing company he hoped to pass on to them. Art, his company, and his family would not be as fortunate in the next decade. Just as Pan American's Clippers were bringing the world closer together, another war was about to stop the revolution in passenger air travel in its tracks. For 20 years, Art had enjoyed the fruits of peacetime, helping build a world where people could live in harmony, and a business that could sustain his family for years to come. He was, however, about to be called once again to be a warrior, to face a conflict that would require him to make the supreme effort of his life.

# CHAPTER 9

# Storm Clouds

D uring the first week of August 1936, Art, along with most other Americans, reveled in the triumphs at the Berlin Olympics of an African-American athlete from Cleveland named Jesse Owens. Art first heard of Owens in 1933, when as a student at East Technical High School in Cleveland he equaled the world record for the 100-yard dash. In 1934, Owens entered The Ohio State University. In a span of 45 minutes on May 25, 1935 at the Big 10 Track and Field Meet in Ann Arbor, Michigan, he set three world records and tied a fourth. Richard Rothschild of Sports Illustrated called Owens' feat "the greatest 45 minutes ever in sport."[283]

In an attempt to demonstrate the Nazis' technological superiority in aviation, Adolf Hitler arranged for the largest airship in the world, the dirigible Hindenburg, to hover over the Berlin Olympics' opening ceremonies. He was confident the games would validate his belief in "Aryan" racial superiority. Because of Owens, however, the Berlin Games were about to become something entirely different—a demonstration of the Olympic ideal of a pluralistic society in which men and women of different races and ethnic backgrounds could compete on an equal basis.

Grim-faced, Hitler watched from the stands as Owens won four Gold medals in track and field events. After each of Owens' victories, the Germans in the stands stood and applauded him. Hitler turned to an aide and said, "The Americans ought to be ashamed of themselves for letting their medals be won by Negroes. I myself would never shake hands with any of them."

When the aide suggested it would be good for propaganda purposes for the Fuhrer to be photographed with Owens, Hitler walked out of the stadium.[284] After the Olympics, Owens became known as "the world's fastest human" and "the ultimate symbol undermining Hitler's myth of Aryan superiority."[285]

During the Olympics, Lindbergh and his wife Anne flew to Berlin at the invitation of the German Air Ministry. They attended the opening of the Olympics in Berlin, catching a glimpse of Hitler at his reviewing stand atop the stadium.[286] The Pentagon authorized Lindbergh's trip, hoping he could learn more about Germany's growing air force. Lindbergh had heard about the advancements the Germans were making in aircraft technology, and he was eager to see the results for himself.[287] While Anne enjoyed a week touring Berlin, Lindbergh accompanied Hermann Goring, Germany's Air Minister, on a tour of military installations and aircraft factories.

Lindbergh's life had been devoted to making airplanes a force for bringing the world closer together. Before their trip he told Anne, "The thing that interests me now is breaking up the prejudices between nations, linking them up through aviation."[288] During the last week of July, Lindbergh gave a speech to a crowd of aviators and diplomats at a luncheon in Berlin. His words were reminiscent of Glenn Martin's prophesy before World War I about the destructive potential of aircraft in war: "We who are in aviation carry a heavy responsibility on our shoulders, for while we have been drawing the world closer together in peace we have stripped the armor of every nation in war. It is no longer possible to shield the heart of a country with its army... Our libraries, our museums, every institution we value most, are laid bare to our bombardment."[289]

Upon his return to America, Lindbergh became a staunch advocate for keeping the U.S. out of a European war. He met with General Hap Arnold and warned him the Germans were building a long-range bomber that could destroy nearly every city in Europe. Lindbergh speculated the Germans' new bomber might even be able to reach the U.S. He urged Arnold to consider developing an American "super-bomber" that could counter the new German plane.[290]

In December 1936, just a few months after Lindbergh's visit to Germany, Goring met with several German industrialists and told them in confidence, "We are already on the threshold of mobilization and we are already at war. All that is lacking is the actual shooting."[291]

HELEN HAD SURPRISING NEWS for Art in early 1937: she was expecting another child. The two were overjoyed; they had believed their days of growing their family had been over. A few months later, Cynthia Parker was born. Soon, the third floor of the Parkers' home was filled with an electric train set and toy soldiers for Tom and Pat, and doll houses for Joyce and Cynthia. Art was so busy at the office that he had little time to spend with Helen and the children. He left the task of child-rearing to Helen, who passed on to her children the values her immigrant mother had taught her—to treat others with respect, regardless of their station in life, to see a project through to completion, no matter how difficult, and to see hard times as challenges to overcome, rather than as circumstances to fear.

In November 1937, Art took Helen and the children on a trip to Los Angeles in his Cadillac Fleetwood Town Sedan. The family was celebrating Parker's sales breaking $1 million in the latest fiscal year, to $1.3 million. Art believed it might be his last chance to spend a vacation with his family before he became immersed in preparing his company to produce war materiel. While in California, he wanted to take a look at a small office for sale at 757 Venice Boulevard, near the Hollywood-Burbank Airport, the main airfield in the Los Angeles area. The city was fast becoming the center of America's aviation industry, and Art believed he needed to establish a sales office close to his growing aviation customers.

The Parkers made the trip in 10 days, traveling for long stretches in the Midwest along the Lincoln Highway. The children loved to watch the miles go by from the rumble seat at the rear of the car. After arriving in Los Angeles, Helen and the children spent much of their time in two bungalows at the Chapman Park Hotel on Wilshire Boulevard while Art arranged to purchase the sales office. One day, the family took their first airplane ride together—a 15-minute flight in a Martin boat plane from the Hollywood-Burbank airport to Catalina Island. Shortly after Christmas, Art completed the purchase of the Venice Boulevard property and proudly placed a sign on the door announcing the presence of the "Pacific Division" of the Parker Appliance Co.

Art was interested in expanding his sales to Germany—which, after the U.S., had become the second-largest market for aircraft parts. In the mid-1920s, Glenn Martin had introduced Art to several German aircraft executives when they visited Cleveland. They worked at Germany's most important aircraft companies—Junkers, Messerschmitt, Heinkel, and Focke-Wulf. Shortly after Lindbergh's 1927 flight, Art started corresponding with those executives, who were building planes every bit as sophisticated as the ones being made by Martin, Douglas and Boeing.

In the spring of 1938, several German aircraft executives sent Art a letter indicating they might be willing to consider committing to some large orders for his fuel valves and fittings. Art was concerned about how the Germans might use those parts. He asked the War Department if he should take the trip. The generals agreed he should and asked that he report back to them on the preparations Hitler was making for war.

That summer, Art and Helen embarked on a three-month tour of Germany's aircraft plants. They made the trip to Europe in five days on the Queen Mary. It had been less than 20 years since Art had served in Europe. Along with most other Americans who had fought in France, he had believed President Wilson when he said World War I was "the war to end all wars." Now his generation was facing the possibility of another worldwide conflict.

Helen toured Cologne, Berlin, Dresden and Nuremberg with Art and the German aircraft executives. Having learned German from her mother at an early age, she was able to help Art by translating the comments of their German hosts. As Art traveled through the Junkers, Messerschmitt, Heinkel and Focke-Wulf factories, his hosts confided they were receiving large orders for fighter planes and bombers from Goring. Art was convinced Hitler was preparing to use those planes against his European neighbors.

The German aircraft executives were well acquainted with the quality of Parker's aircraft valves and fittings, and they were eager to purchase them for their new planes. Art, however, was non-committal. He liked and respected the German executives, and he hoped the time would come when he could do business with them. But now was not that time. Art did not believe the German executives were evil men, but he knew they were under the thumb of an evil man and would be forced to do his bidding.

When Art returned to America, he told the generals at the War Department of his concern about the growing power of the Luftwaffe. He also sent a letter to his German hosts, declining their requests for aircraft parts.

Throughout his years at Parker, Klamm had been keeping a detailed record of his contacts at Parker's customers in a small, black, spiral-bound notebook he liked to call his "little black book." The lists in the book Klamm created during the 12 months preceding America's entry into World War II paint a clear picture of the breadth of the company's customer base before it converted to wartime production for the U.S. government. The book was a roster of the most successful aviation companies in America, including Boeing, Martin, McDonnell, Bell Aircraft, Northrop, North American Aviation,

United Aircraft, Bellanca, Woodward Governor, Beech, Cessna, Vickers, Consolidated, Wright Aeronautical and the most successful airlines—Pan American, Delta, United, American, Braniff, Northwest, and TWA.

Klamm's little black book reveals that, even though most of Parker's sales were to aviation customers, the company had developed a large number of industrial customers that held promise for future growth. Some of the most successful American manufacturers were buying Parker fittings and tube couplings, valves, fabricating tools, and lubricants for their in-plant machinery. These included General Electric, General Motors, B.F. Goodrich, Firestone, Goodyear, DuPont, International Harvester, Bendix, Studebaker, Bethlehem Steel, Continental Motors, Square D, and Ingersoll-Rand.

Parker was selling its products for uses beyond factories. The New York Central Railroad was buying Parker couplings and fittings to protect steam, internal combustion, and electric power systems on locomotives. Utilities such as Detroit Edison and American Gas & Electric of New York were sealing steam piping with Parker fittings in their power plants. Standard Oil of Ohio, Standard Oil of New Jersey and Shell Oil were using Parker fittings, tube couplings and valves to control the flow of oil in their refineries. Celanese and DuPont were using those products to guide the transmission of dangerous chemicals in their plants.

Art and Klamm were convinced they would have to leave their promising industrial customers behind when the time came to convert their plants to go all-out in making parts to fight the war they now believed was inevitable. Art had granted an exclusive license to the Parker Appliance Co. for all his patents covering hydraulic tube coupling components, valves and fittings. In fact, approximately 90 percent of the products being manufactured by the Parker Appliance Co. embodied one or more inventions covered by patents owned by Art.[292] The Army and Navy adopted this group of Parker products as the official standard for its aircraft, submarines, and other ships, calling it the "Army-Navy Standards," identified by the abbreviation "AN." Art's company was thus the only one in America capable of supplying those essential parts for the war effort.

Art knew America was not prepared to produce war materiel in the quantities that would be necessary to defeat Germany. The Great Depression had gutted America's machine tool industry, the key to effective mass production. Machine tools perform the vital task of cutting and forming raw steel, cast iron, brass and aluminum into manufactured goods of all kinds. During the Great Depression, the annual sales of American machine tools had plummeted from $185 billion to less than $22 million.[293] By contrast, Germany had a healthy machine tool industry, already helping the Nazis build their war machine.

Art decided he would have to start to prepare for war by retooling nearly all his machinery to make aircraft parts. He was fortunate one of the largest and most respected machine tool companies in the world was located in Cleveland. In July 1939, he placed the largest single order for machine tools ever received by the Warner & Swasey Co. Art was about to violate the oath he had made to Klamm after the accident on the Lincoln Highway—never again to become dependent upon a single customer.

Art had already bet his company on the fortunes of the aircraft industry. Now he was preparing to bet not just on a single industry, but also on a single customer—the U.S. government. Art remembered how Glenn Martin had nearly gone bankrupt when the government canceled its orders for the B-1 bomber after World War I. He understood the risks, but he saw no other way to do his patriotic duty.

On September 1, 1939, less than two months after Art ordered the machine tools that would allow him to make materiel for war, Hitler began his "blitzkrieg" attack on Poland. It was the start of a war that would claim

27,600 lives every day for 2,174 days. Within four weeks of the opening salvos, the German army killed 100,000 Polish soldiers and 25,000 civilians.

"Take a good look around Warsaw," Hitler told journalists during a visit to the smoldering Polish capital. "That is how I can deal with any European city."[294]

Most German civilians, remembering the casualties at Verdun and the other battles along the Western Front, dreaded the start of another war. Upon reading of Germany's attack on Poland, Jochen Klepper, a writer from a Berlin suburb, wondered, "How can a people cope with a war without any enthusiasm whatever, so downcast?"[295]

The German army, however, was primed for war by Hitler's propaganda speeches. In May 1940, the Wehrmacht swept into the Netherlands, Belgium, Luxembourg and France. Unlike 1914, there would be no stopping the Germans at the Marne in this second World War. On June 14, the Germans marched into Paris and unfurled an enormous swastika flag from the top of the Arc de Triomphe. Hitler told a Hearst reporter that England would be "finished" by the middle of August.[296] In September, Germany and Italy signed a treaty with Japan, and Hitler told Mussolini, "The war is won. The rest is only a question of time."[297]

England's new Prime Minister, Winston Churchill, sent a telegram to President Franklin D. Roosevelt, saying, "As you are no doubt aware, the scene has darkened swiftly. If necessary, we shall continue the war alone, and we are not afraid of that. But I trust you realize, Mr. President, that the voice and force of the United States may count for nothing if they are withheld too long."[298]

On May 10, 1940, Roosevelt met with Army Chief of Staff George Marshall in the Oval Office.[299] Marshall warned Roosevelt the U.S. was not prepared to fight Hitler. Congress had reduced the budgets for the Pentagon throughout the Great Depression. The U.S. had the world's 17th-largest army, just behind Portugal. Germany had 6.8 million men prepared for war; America had only 190,000 on active duty, one-tenth the size of the German force that marched into Poland.[300] The U.S. did not have even close to enough tanks, artillery, planes or ships to fight Hitler. Marshall warned, "If five German divisions landed anywhere on the East Coast, they could go anywhere they wished."[301]

Three months later, Roosevelt witnessed the weaknesses of the American military firsthand, during Army drills near his home in Hyde Park, New York, where he watched soldiers drilling with drain pipes in place of mortars and broomsticks instead of machine guns.[302]

The U.S., Roosevelt concluded, must re-arm, first, to assist England in its fight against Hitler, and then, to insure America could defend itself against Hitler and his allies, the Italians and Japanese. In June 1940, William Knudsen, the president of General Motors, agreed, for a salary of one dollar a year, to chair a new agency with broad powers to reorganize American industry for the war effort. Knudsen's expertise was in mass production. He ran Henry Ford's plants from 1911 to 1921, when he was able to increase production speed for the Model T from one every twelve and a half hours to one every minute.[303] The industrial historian Arthur Herman has explained that Ford and Knudsen "had found the key to the economy of scale underlying all industrial manufacturing."[304] Knudsen resigned from Ford after arguing with Henry Ford that he should diversify into making vehicles other than the Model T. Alfred P. Sloan, the president of General Motors wasted no time in hiring Knudsen to run his plants.

Knudsen believed the route to defeating Germany lay in the principles of mass production he had implemented at Ford and General Motors. At a meeting in the White House, Knudsen said to Roosevelt, "Everyone knows that America is the greatest mass producer in the world. Not everyone knows that mass production takes time to get started. But once you get going, the momentum takes you a long way—all the way to victory."[305] The Nazis were skeptical of America's ability to mass produce aircraft. In November 1940, the American reporter William Shirer asked Goring how he felt about American industry's attempts to convert to war production. Goering replied, "Your planes are good. But you don't make enough of them fast enough."

Shirer responded, "Despite what happened last time? [meaning World War I]"

Goering snapped back, "Ja, despite that," and then he broke into a laugh.[306]

Knudsen, Roosevelt and Marshall knew the Allies were going to need thousands of bombers that could make the long trip from English air bases to the German plants turning out war materiel. Knudsen asked Glenn Martin to gear up to make a new long-range bomber, called the "B-26," at his Baltimore plant.[307] Orders began flooding in to Art Parker for fittings and valves for Martin's bombers. Due to Art's foresight, he was able to meet those orders; he had received the machine tools from Warner & Swasey just in time to retool the Euclid Avenue plant to produce aircraft parts.

The real breakthrough in the mass production of bombers occurred when the automobile manufacturers converted their assembly lines to make aircraft. The industry was the country's largest employer. Its engineers and machinery operators understood how to make rapid changes in production and design. Walter Reuther pledged to Kundsen the support of the United Automobile Workers, saying "England's battles, it used to be said, were won on the playing fields of Eton. America's will be won on the assembly lines of Detroit."[308]

Henry Ford built the largest manufacturing facility in the world, a mile-long plant in Willow Run, Michigan, a Detroit suburb, to mass produce Consolidated Aircraft's B-24 "Liberator" bombers in the same way he had made Model Ts. Ford hired Lindbergh to test fly the bombers coming off the plant's assembly line. The workers at Willow Run learned to produce one plane every hour. They would make 9,000 B-24s before the war was over. Each one contained approximately 5,000 fittings made at Parker's Euclid Avenue plant. Every day, several railroad cars filled with fittings left the sidings at Euclid Avenue for the six-hour trip to Willow Run.

At the height of the war, Willow Run employed 42,000 workers who united in a collective production effort unlike any seen in industrial history. One-

Parker employees visiting the Willow Run plant.

third of the Willow Run workers were women. One of them, Rose Monroe, an attractive, determined worker, caught the attention of a government publicist looking for the right woman to encourage others to join the war effort. She became "Rosie the Riveter," a symbol of all women working in American war plants.

Klamm had maintained his friendships with the group of Glenn Martin's Cleveland engineers who had gone on to found their own aircraft companies. He traveled to meet those men at their new companies to discuss how Parker could help them in the war effort. They included Donald Douglas at Douglas Aircraft, Lawrence Bell of Bell Aircraft, and Dutch Kindleberger at North American Aviation. Klamm reassured each of them that Parker would find a way to make enough aircraft valves and fittings to meet their wartime needs.

The government offered to finance the purchase of machinery and construction of expanded facilities for critical suppliers like Parker, but Art insisted on obtaining his own financing. He feared becoming a debtor to the government after the war. He knew his decision to remain self-sufficient would require him to make an enormous capital investment, but he was convinced it was necessary to protect his company's future.

PAT PARKER WAS A TYPICAL 10-year-old during the summer of 1940. He liked to escape with his friends into boyhood adventures, riding his red Schwinn bicycle around his Shaker Heights neighborhood, and exploring the woods, ponds and fields in the Shaker Lakes area Rockefeller had donated to the city. On weekends, Art would strap Pat's bike to the roof of his Buick and take him over to the Euclid Avenue plant. On their rides to and from the plant, Art would tell Pat stories of his travails in the company's early years. Pat's favorite was of the disaster on the Lincoln Highway, and he asked his father to tell it over and over again.

While Art worked in his office, Pat rode his bike up and down the long hallways that, just a few years earlier, had been assembly lines for the Hupmobile. He especially enjoyed walking out onto the floor of the plant and talking to the workers at their machines. They knew he was the boss's son, but they treated him in the same friendly, informal way they treated the children of other employees at the plant.

On special Saturday mornings, Pat pocketed his 10-cent allowance and rode over to the local drugstore, where he could buy a Nehi Orange Soda and something interesting to read. The newspapers were full of stories of the Luftwaffe's bombing of London, Japan's war with China, the first Americans registering for the draft, Franklin Roosevelt's campaign for re-election to an unprecedented third term, and the Chicago Bears' 73-0 drubbing of the Washington Redskins in the NFL championship.[309]

Pat was more interested in reading a comic book that had recently appeared on Cleveland newsstands. All his friends at school were talking about it. The creators of the comic book, Jerry Siegel and Joe Shuster, were sons of Jewish immigrants. They grew up and attended high school together in Glenville, a Jewish neighborhood on the east side of Cleveland, three miles northeast of Pat's home in Shaker Heights, and less than a mile west of Parker's Euclid Avenue plant. Siegel wrote for Glenville High School's newspaper, The Torch, and his friend Shuster was one of its cartoonists. Both boys were idealistic, shy and awkward around girls. Siegel wrote a love poem to a classmate he admired from a distance, a "girl-next-door" type named Lois Amster. On the day the poem was published in The Torch, Jerry dressed up to impress Lois. She, however, paid him no attention.[310]

Siegel and Shuster had always been fascinated by stories of heroes. They rooted for Cleveland's Law Director, Eliot Ness, who was fighting crime and reforming the corrupt Cleveland police department. They read of the athletic triumphs of Jesse Owens. The Cleveland newspapers were calling him the "world's fastest human," as they described him "leaping through space."[311] At the State and Ohio theaters in Playhouse Square, they watched newsreels of Franklin Roosevelt, who was saving the country from a Great Depression and preparing to fight Hitler and Mussolini.

In their free time after school, Siegel and Shuster began to imagine a hero they called "Superman," who possessed the best traits of their own heroes.[312] In the boys' imaginations, he would embody the toughness of Ness, the strength of Owens, and the idealism of Roosevelt. Superman upheld the traditional virtues of truth, justice, and honesty, and he made it his business to protect the weaker members of society against criminals, crooked politicians, and other "strongmen," like Hitler and Mussolini.

With his superhuman strength, ability to fly and X-ray vision, Superman possessed all the qualities the shy and unathletic Siegel and Shuster lacked. What made Superman so special, however, was not his unique powers, but something more subtle—his ordinary human weaknesses, revealed through his alter ego, Clark Kent. When the times demanded it, Kent was able to overcome his weaknesses and summon his super powers to defeat evil in the world. Like Siegel and Shuster, Kent had doubts, fears and failings. He wore heavy glasses to convince others of his poor eyesight, and he shared Siegel's inability to attract a girl such as Lois.[313]

Despite his superpowers, Superman had his own handicaps. Like Owens, a black man who was not allowed to live in The Ohio State University dormitories or eat in a restaurant on team trips, Superman was treated as an alien; like Roosevelt, who hid the fact he was crippled from polio, Superman never revealed he was vulnerable to kryptonite; and like Elliot Ness, who had three marriages and a drinking problem, Superman could not sustain a normal home life.

For boys of Pat's age, Superman seemed a great American hero. As Brad Meltzer, a novelist and host of The History Channel's series Decoded has explained, "When World War II encroached on our shores, America starts getting scared and here comes [Superman] this giant, almost straight-from-the-flag character who's come to save us."[314]

Pat would soon learn he need not look beyond his own front door to find a hero of the American war effort. While Pat enjoyed his Saturday morning idylls, his father sat behind his desk, worrying about how he could afford the costs of retooling for war. Art's conversion of his company to meet the demands of war was about to test his stamina, will power, resiliency, and willingness to sacrifice himself for others. The World War II historian Rick Atkinson has described how the character of leaders like Art was being laid bare by the demands of war: "More than any other human enterprise, war revealed the mettle of men's souls.... War, that merciless revealer of character, uncloaked these men as precisely as a prism flays open a beam of light to reveal the inner spectrum."[315]

Having served as a supply officer on the Western Front, Art understood how critical the military supply chain would be in winning the war that had started in Europe. He reluctantly decided he would have to offer stock to the public to pay for converting his plants to making war materiel. It was not an easy decision, as he remembered the days prior to the 1924 bankruptcy, when he had argued continually with his investors over the direction of the company. He knew that after the stock offering was completed, he would have to contend with a much larger group of independent shareholders—but it was a price Art was willing to pay to defend his country.

In October 1940, the Parker Appliance Co., newly formed as a corporation which succeeded to all the assets and liabilities of the company Art had incorporated in 1924, offered 100,000 shares of stock to the public at a price of $14 a share, netting the company $1.2 million after underwriting commissions. The cash proceeds allowed Art to repay the debt incurred to buy the Warner & Swasey machine tools and to reconfigure the Euclid Avenue plant to devote all its capacity to military aircraft parts. At the time of the stock offering, Art transferred the title to the plant from his Euclon Corp. to the new Parker Appliance Co. After the offering, the Parker family's interest in the company dropped from 100 percent to 67 percent.

Historian and author William Klingaman wrote that "many Americans would remember December 25, 1940, as one of the happiest Christmases of their lives."[316] The country was still at peace, and employment and wages were booming, as factories operated extra shifts, preparing war materiel for England. The New York Times reported "an orgy of spending as if customers were determined to show there was at least one country that enjoyed peace and good will."[317]

Parker's business was prospering, with $3 million in annual sales. A few days before Christmas, Art took Helen and his four children—11-year-old Pat, 9-year-old Tom, 7-year-old Joyce, and 3-year-old Cyndi—to the Euclid Avenue plant, where they served lunch to the workers in the cafeteria. On Christmas Eve, Carl Klamm, his wife, and his 10-year-old daughter Carol came over to the Parkers' Shaker Heights home. Klamm donned a Santa Claus outfit and sat each of the children on his lap, asking what they wanted for Christmas.

By the end of 1940, President Roosevelt had become convinced America would have to join the fight against Hitler—sooner rather than later—if it hoped to prevent the Nazis from dominating the world. Roosevelt knew the American people were not yet prepared for another world war. He realized he would have to educate them in stages, starting with an appeal for the country to unite around gearing up its industrial base to supply the European democracies with the materiel they needed to fight Hitler.

On the evening of December 29, 1940, Art asked Helen and Pat to join him in the library to listen to a radio address by Roosevelt. Unlike today's politicians, who are overexposed on 24-hour cable news channels, Roosevelt appreciated that "less was more" when it came to speech-making. He wisely decided to limit the number of his Fireside Chats so the American public would perceive each one as a major event, and take time to tune in. When

Roosevelt began to speak at 9 p.m., the whole country seemed to stop what it was doing. As the historian Doris Kearns Goodwin has explained, "theater owners noticed a decided drop in attendance: thousands of people who would otherwise have gone to the movies stayed home to listen to the president's speech."[318] Like Art in his letters to his employees in the *Fitting News*, Roosevelt, in his Fireside Chats, was able, as David Brooks has written, "to cultivate a deep sense of unity, responsibility, and sacrifice" among his audience.[319]

Pat was happy to listen to the radio rather than do his homework. He sat on an oriental rug, looking up at the Philco radio sitting atop Helen's oak desk. Made of dark brown wood, the Philco had a carving of Snow White and the Seven Dwarfs along its curved top. Art told Pat and Helen the president was going to send a serious message to the country. Most of Europe had been overrun by the armies of Hitler and Mussolini, and the Japanese had invaded China. England was hanging on by a thread as Hitler was sending hundreds of bombers to destroy London and other English cities. Art explained to Helen and Pat that Roosevelt realized England was the only country standing between Hitler and America.

Art, Helen, and Pat listened quietly as Roosevelt spoke:

> *"The people of Europe...ask us for the implements of war, the planes, the tanks, the guns, the freighters which will enable them to fight for their liberty and for our security.... American industrial genius, unmatched throughout the world in the solution of production problems, has been called upon to bring its resources and its talents into action."*

The president said he expected that soon the country would be able to produce 50,000 aircraft a year and concluded with the statement, "We must be the Great Arsenal of Democracy."

Roosevelt's promise to produce 50,000 planes a year—more than 10 times what the country was currently producing—was brave, to say the least. U.S. Steel Chairman Edward Stettinhus would later say "it seemed at first like an utterly impossible goal; but it caught the imagination of Americans, who always had believed they could accomplish the impossible."[320]

After Roosevelt's talk, Art told Pat that if America did not oppose Hitler, its own sovereignty, and the future of all democracies, would be threatened. Art said he was committed to doing whatever was necessary to support the war effort. Glancing at Helen, Art said, "Pat, as the president just said, these are desperate times. So I've decided to retool all our factory space to produce parts for the planes we're going to need to win this war."

As Helen looked over at Art, he took a deep breath and continued, "Son, there's something else you have to understand. I've hoped our company would always remain in the family. I've expected this call from Roosevelt for the last several months. I've thought a lot about it, and I've decided there's no way our family can afford the investment we would have to make to retool the company to produce the airplane parts our country is going to need."

Art went on, "There's only one way we could afford to do what the president is asking of us. We've sold one-third of our company's stock to outside shareholders, in order to give us more than a million dollars to invest in retooling the plant for war. That means, from now on, you, your brother and your sisters are going to have to share the ownership of the company with a lot of other shareholders."

Not fully understanding the implications of what his father had just said, Pat replied, "Well, Dad, if you think it's the right thing to do for our country, it's OK with me."

# CHAPTER 10

# Another World War

December 7, 1941, was a clear, warm day in Cleveland, with temperatures in the mid-60s. The Parkers, in keeping with their normal Sunday routine, drove to have lunch with Helen's parents, her brothers and sisters, and their children at the Fitzgerald family home on the West Side. When the Parkers arrived back at Falmouth Road in Shaker Heights, Art retired to the library and turned on the radio to hear the latest news. Reports of the Pearl Harbor attack had moved over the Associated Press wire at 2:22 p.m. Eastern Time, and the radio stations began breaking into regular programs to report the news at 2:30 p.m. Art asked Helen and the four children to come into the library, where he told them the country would soon be at war. He mentioned how thankful he was that he had started preparing for the war a year earlier. With the funds received from his stock offering, he had bought the machines needed to make parts for the fighters and bombers America was going to need to fight a war in both Europe and the Pacific.

The next day, America declared war on Japan. Germany responded by going to war against the U.S. Just as in World War I, Germany was fighting against Russia, England and the U.S. Churchill later wrote of his initial thoughts after he heard America had declared war on Germany: "I knew the United States was in the war, up to the neck, and in to the death. I went to bed and slept the sleep of the saved and thankful."[321]

Roosevelt realized American air power would be critical in winning the war. In his January 6, 1942, State of the Union address, he told Congress that

America would produce 60,000 warplanes in 1942 and 125,000 the following year. "These figures," the president said with dripping irony, "will give the Japanese and Nazis an idea of what they accomplished at Pearl Harbor.... The militarists of Berlin and Tokyo started the war. But the massed, angered forces of humanity will finish it."[322]

When Hitler heard about Roosevelt's promise to build 60,000 planes in the next year, he scoffed, "What is America but beauty queens, millionaires, stupid records, and Hollywood?"[323] Even America's allies knew the country was not prepared to fight a three-pronged war against Germany, Italy and Japan. Churchill's chief military representative in the U.S., Field Marshall Sir John Dill, told him American soldiers were "more unready for war than it is possible to imagine."[324]

The world was about to discover just what Roosevelt's Arsenal of Democracy was capable of producing. A good portion of the war production would come from Cleveland factories. Eighty Cleveland aviation components makers would produce 25 percent of all the parts needed for America's military aircraft.[325] More than 300 Cleveland defense plants would produce a variety of war materiel. A worker in a Cleveland factory making diesel engines for submarines said, "If Hitler could've stood on the Detroit-Superior High Level Bridge over the Cuyahoga and looked down on the Flats, he never would've started World War II."[326]

By the time the war ended, two-thirds of the ships afloat and planes flying in the world would be American-made.[327] Parker fittings and valves would protect the fuel systems of the bombers, fighters, and military transport planes that would dominate the skies over North Africa, Italy, France, Germany, the Pacific Islands, and Japan: Boeing's B-17 "Flying Fortress," Consolidated Aircraft's B-24 "Liberator," North American Aviation's B-25 bomber and P-51 fighter, Bell Aircraft's P-39 fighter, Glenn Martin's B-26 "Marauder" bomber, the Curtiss C-46 transport and P-36 and P-40 fighters, Lockheed's P-38 fighter, Republic's P-47 fighter, the Grumman "Hellcat" fighter, Douglas Aircraft's C-47 "Skytrain" transport (a modified version of its DC-3 passenger plane), and the most advanced and deadly bomber of them all, the plane that finally ended the war, Boeing's B-29 "Super-Fortress."[328]

North American Aviation would make nearly 10,000 B-25 bombers before the war ended—all of them flying with Parker fuel valves and fittings. On April 18, 1942, Jimmy Doolittle led a squadron of 16 B-25s from an aircraft carrier in the Pacific on a bombing mission over Tokyo. Seventy-nine airmen

Douglas C-47 "Skytrains" on the cover
of the *Fitting News*, March 1943.

volunteered for the mission, knowing their chance of survival was slim at best. After bombing Tokyo, most of the planes crash-landed in China when they ran out of fuel. The "Doolittle Raiders," as they came to be called, gave Americans a much-needed boost in morale four months after the attack on Pearl Harbor. Doolittle, already famous as the winner of the Thompson Trophy at the Cleveland Air Races in 1932, became the perfect poster child for the American war effort.[329]

Many of the American heroes of World War II fought in the deserts of North Africa, the mountains of Italy, the beaches of Normandy, and the islands of the Pacific. Others, like Art Parker and his employees, fought on the home front, but their efforts were no less important in winning the war. Even Superman stayed home. After Pearl Harbor, Siegel and Shuster, working in their Cleveland offices on new Superman episodes for DC Comics, had to decide whether to send their super-hero overseas to fight the Nazis and the Japanese. They realized that, with his superpowers, he would "win" the war in comic books years before it could ever be won in reality. All around them in Cleveland, Siegel and Shuster were watching companies such as Parker (whose Euclid Avenue plant was three miles east of their office) retool for the war effort.[330] They decided to make Superman, like the workers in Cleveland's factories, a hero of the home front.

In a comic book issued shortly after the Japanese attacked Pearl Harbor, Clark Kent failed his Army vision test, because he accidentally turned on his X-ray vision and read a chart hanging in another room. Superman had to remain in America, where he led scrap metal drives and other initiatives that helped American industry tool up to fight Germany and Japan.[331] Pat loved to read those stories, and to think about how his father, in his own way, was doing everything he could to help America win the war.

When the Japanese attacked Pearl Harbor, they already controlled more than 90 percent of the rubber plantations in Asia. Art realized he would need an assured domestic source of rubber to make seals for his aircraft fittings. Fortunately, B.F. Goodrich, in nearby Akron, working with funds provided by the federal government, had been able to develop a synthetic form of rubber for the war effort. Art knew he would have to develop his own proprietary process for transforming the synthetic rubber into seals.

Art rented the basement of a luncheonette across the street from the Euclid Avenue plant, and turned it into a chemistry lab, where Parker's engineers developed a means of taking the raw rubber compound and cooking it in a way that would form a reliable seal. The seals Art's team produced were of such high quality that many of his competitors began buying seals from the Parker Appliance Co.

Art had to ask his three tenants at Euclid Avenue to leave to make way for the expansion of his plant to the entire 283,200-square-foot facility. Workers started ripping out offices and building assembly lines to make fittings, valves, and connectors for the planes that would soon be heading to the war zones. By the time they were done, the Euclid Avenue plant contained a pattern shop, plating and heat treating departments, tool room, welding shop, foundry, research laboratories, offices and a large production area filled with machinery.[332]

By the fall of 1942, 2,600 Parker workers at Euclid Avenue were turning out products 24 hours a day, seven days a week for the Allies' war machine.[333] Many of the workers lived in the neighborhood and were able to walk to work. Jobs at Parker were so plentiful that neighbors in Collinwood liked to say you could apply for a job in the morning and start work before supper. Family members were welcome at the plant. They often stopped by to drop off lunches and dinners for the workers, so they could keep aircraft parts for the Allies' bombers and fighter planes moving out the door.

To keep track of all his workers, and meet government requirements for wartime secrecy, Art implemented a badge program for all employees. The badges were numbered consecutively, based upon the worker's hire date. The earliest employees were assigned the lowest numbers, and the most recent employees the highest numbers. Art was employee No. 0-1, Klamm was 0-2 and Helen was 0-5.

In 1942 alone, 350 of Parker's employees left to fight in the war. Young men who had been operating lathe machines and designing aircraft valves and fittings were now heading to the South Pacific to fight the Japanese and to Africa and southern Europe to fight the Germans and Italians.

Most of Art's remaining employees were either immigrants or sons and daughters of immigrants. Determined to climb the ladder of success, they had grown up as underdogs, fighting to improve their place in the world.

They took nothing for granted, and were thankful for what they had achieved in America. All were eager to fight for their country, either on the field of battle or the home front—making fittings for U.S. fighters, bombers, destroyers, aircraft carriers, and submarines. Accustomed to hard work, they were ready to take on the challenges and sacrifices Art was asking of them in the war effort.

In November 1942, Art bought a manufacturing plant from the Black & Decker Corp., located at the corner of St. Clair Avenue and East 72nd Street in Cleveland, approximately two miles northwest of the Euclid Avenue building. Soon 300 employees were turning out thousands of fittings a day at the new St. Clair Avenue plant.

Parker's annual sales increased exponentially, from $3 million in 1940 to $20 million in 1942. The Parker Appliance Co. had become the world's largest producer of aircraft-connecting and flow control devices. The empty automobile plant Art had bought seven years earlier was now filled with the sounds of 2,600 workers turning out parts to win the war. The company had become a captive supplier to the Allies' war effort. Parker now had only one customer—the U.S. government.

In 1942, with the Euclid Avenue and St. Clair plants at full capacity, Art decided to lease a plant in Los Angeles to make aircraft parts. The red brick plant, located at 6506 Stanford Avenue, replaced the sales office Art had purchased in 1937 for the Pacific Division. With this new plant, Parker gained a manufacturing foothold at the center of the American aircraft industry. Soon the employees at the Pacific Division were producing ten percent of Parker's total shipments of aircraft fittings.

Before 1942 was out, American industry would make more war materiel than Germany, Italy and Japan combined. Each of the nearly 50,000 warplanes produced in 1942 contained a large complement of Parker parts. Each bomber flew with an average of 4,000 to 5,000 Parker fittings, and each fighter plane carried an average of 500 to 700 fittings.[334] By the time the war ended, 4,500 different types of Parker's valves and fittings would fly on nearly all 324,750 American-made planes, as well as aircraft carriers, destroyers, troop ships, landing craft, cruisers, PT boats, submarines, tanks, and earth movers.[335] Parker components protected critical fuel, oil and hydraulic systems on all those planes, boats, and vehicles, sealing and interconnecting complicated fluid power systems, just as they had on the Spirit of St. Louis.

Producing the fittings and valves for all those applications required extraordinary effort and teamwork among thousands of Parker's men and

*Fitting News* cover, September 1943.

women. In the Pattern Shop on Euclid Avenue, five women turned out more than a million patterns between April 1942 and April 1943.[336] At peak production, Parker's factory workers had to make 10 million valves and fittings a month, and yet they never sacrificed quality in their race to get products out the door. Parker's men and women on the factory floor were continuously implementing new means to ensure the most efficient flow of products. Foremen were empowered to order improved tools directly from the Tool Room, without seeking prior approval from supervisors. As the *Fitting News* reported in April, 1943, "Suggestions from the shop are welcome, and any foreman can originate a tool request for an entirely new design. In fact, his request is a mandate to find a solution for the shop's problem."[337]

In 1942, 13-year-old Pat Parker began spending more time with Art at the Euclid Avenue plant. It was the only way he could see his father for an extended time. Art had been working at the plant most evenings and weekends ever since the attack on Pearl Harbor. Pat noted how Art established personal ties with his employees. Walking through the factory with Pat at his side, he often paused at a machine and asked the operator about his work and his family. Pat watched as Art listened respectfully to his workers, treating them as colleagues rather than subordinates.

Pat had many opportunities to sit next to his father when he and Klamm discussed the challenges of the war effort. Pat heard their biggest problem was in meeting the U.S. government's ambitious delivery times. Plants like Willow Run were churning out hundreds of bombers every month; if Parker was just one day late in delivering valves or fittings, entire bomber assembly lines would have to shut down. Pat overheard his father and Klamm discussing how to implement efficiencies in their manufacturing process in order to get their products out the door on time.

Pat noticed that, above all, his father and Klamm were concerned with ensuring the quality of their products. Parker's aircraft valves and fittings had to be made to within a tolerance of just 1/10,000th of an inch—50 times smaller than a human hair and 100 times smaller than the width of sewing thread.

Art and Klamm never forgot that the crews of America's bombers were relying on them to keep their planes safely in the air; they were not about to let those brave boys down. They were proud that, during the war, not one of their valves or fittings failed on an Allied aircraft. Art and Klamm asked the Tool Room to produce 1,500 new measuring gauges every month, and assigned extra inspectors to use those gauges to magnify parts up to more than 60 times their size to ensure they were within the 1/10,000th of an inch margin of error.[338] One of the dedicated inspectors was Evelyn Parish, who had to determine whether a 1/1,000th of an inch diameter spring within a valve was coiled the right number of times to produce the exact amount of tension to control the flow of aircraft fuel.[339]

Art was convinced it would take years for the Allies to defeat Germany, Italy and Japan. They would have to make a full-scale invasion of Europe, and perhaps of the Japanese islands, before the Axis powers would surrender. Millions would lose their lives, and many would be former employees, or family members of current employees. Patrick K. O'Donnell has written that "Elite warriors throughout history have believed that willpower and determination can overcome all odds."[340] Art knew he had to find a way to inspire his employees, giving them a reason to persevere in making war materiel through the difficult days that lay ahead, much as generals were trying to inspire their men not to give up on the battlefield. As the war historian Rick Atkinson explained, "There is a soul to an army as well as to the individual man, and no general can accomplish the full work of his army unless he commands the souls of his men, as well as their bodies and legs."[341]

Art saw a revitalized *Fitting News* as a way to appeal to the hearts and minds of his employees. He had discontinued publishing the newsletter in 1937 because orders for aircraft parts had started to increase so fast that he and his employees were working night and day just to keep up with the demand. Art re-introduced the *Fitting News* in January 1943 in a new format, upgrading it to a glossy, full-color monthly magazine rivaling a national publication in sophistication. He believed the investment in publication costs was worthwhile. His employees were working all out—night and day—to produce the hundreds of millions of fittings required for the planes coming off assembly lines all over America. Now more than ever, he needed to remind them that they had a higher purpose for their work: freeing the people of Europe and Japan from the dictators.

Many of Parker's employees would look back upon their wartime experience at Euclid Avenue as the most meaningful period of their working lives. The economics author John Lanchester has explained how manufacturing workers gain a sense of purpose in making products that change the world.[342] Nothing could have been more world changing than the 500 million fittings Parker's men and women would produce for the Allied aircraft that would win World War II.

In March 1943, Art hired an accomplished artist named Don Paul Brown to draw the covers of the *Fitting News*. In a span of 15 months, from March 1943 to May 1944, Brown created seven iconic covers for the *Fitting News*. It was the height of the "Golden Age of Illustration," as accomplished artists like Brown were designing illustrated covers for national magazines like Life, Look, and Collier's. Many of the *Fitting News* covers, in the fashion of an illustration by Norman Rockwell (who was at the peak of his career, drawing covers for the Saturday Evening Post), depicted the everyday challenges of employees at work and at home. Deborah Solomon believes Rockwell realized "the war wasn't just about killing the enemy. It was also about saving a way of life."[343] Like Rockwell, Don Paul Brown showed everyday events in a way that dramatized the character of his subjects. One magazine cover showed a long line of employees trudging to work at night through a heavy snowfall; another depicted a mother weeping in the bedroom of a son who had died in combat, with his high school graduation picture hanging behind her on the wall.

*Fitting News* cover, July 1943.

Art sent copies of the magazine to every one of his employees serving in the Army, Navy or Air Force. Each received a bonus check along with the *Fitting News*. The magazine was a lifeline to employees fighting on the front lines, as it provided them with a connection to their colleagues at Parker. It also gave the soldiers a chance to explain their wartime experiences to the folks back home.

Twelve million Americans were in the Armed Forces; 10 million of those were serving overseas. To replace the men in the armed services—and to meet continued growing demand—Art placed advertisements in the Cleveland newspapers for new employees. Many of those who applied were women who had never before worked in an industrial setting. Art was proud when he discovered how quickly his female employees learned how to operate complex machinery. Other American business leaders doubted the wisdom of hiring women for their plants, saying they would distract the men, were not strong enough, would require their own rest rooms, and could never learn to operate complex machines. Art, however, had no doubts about how well women would operate his factory. He had, after all, hired a woman as one of his first employees, and after he married her, she became a trusted confidante on business as well as personal matters.

*Fitting News* cover, June 1943.

Sherma Gluck conducted a survey of female employees' attitudes toward working in plants during World War II. [344] She concluded that "Finally valued by others...[women] came to value themselves more" as they became involved in the war effort.[345] Seventy-nine percent of the women in Gluck's survey reported they enjoyed working more than staying at home. Some liked the companionship of their fellow workers, and others valued their financial independence. The welder Lola Weixel recalled, "At the end of the day, I always felt I'd accomplished something. It was good—there was a product, there was something to be seen."[346] One woman commented that women were better than men at operating complex machines, because "they were not afraid to ask for directions."

The *Fitting News* described Parker's women workers in admiring terms: "Averaging between 28 and 30 years of age, the women at Parker...have brothers, husbands, sons, and sweethearts in the nation's armed forces at home and abroad...a far greater reason for wanting to do their share in America's victory drive than just the wage incentive.... For example, that mother in the burring department who joined Parker a month after her son joined the Army Air Corps is intent on seeing that every fitting or valve part that goes through her hands is machined carefully and to precision instruments.... Her son may be flying that plane someday."

Milna Kulber was studying at Western Reserve University to be a teacher. Her husband was serving in the Army. During the summer of 1942, she worked the 3:00 p.m. to midnight shift at the Euclid Avenue plant, where, as she recounted 55 years later in an interview with the Western Reserve Historical Society, her "job was to take little stainless steel fittings and count them, examine them to make sure they were smoothly finished, put them in a pan and put the pan on a conveyor belt that would go to the next department." Milna had to take three different streetcars, in stifling summer heat, to get to and from the plant from the home where she was living with her parents.

One day a "very tall, handsome young Russian" who worked next to Milna at the Euclid Avenue plant offered to give her a "cool ride home" on his motorcycle. Milna always made sure the man dropped her off a few blocks from her home. She explained in her 2007 interview, "If my parents saw me, a married woman, with a handsome young man, on the back of his motorcycle, they'd have had a heart attack." As Milna Kulber looked back upon her wartime work at Parker, she thought, "Remembering those wonderful, frightening days and nights, it was painful, it was depressing, and it was a lifetime experience that I will never forget."[347]

Most of the women who worked at Parker during the war would not remain with the company after the war ended. Their places were taken by men returning from the war. The prevailing feeling among the men in the service was that their sisters, wives and mothers should not continue to work in the plants after the war ended. A 1944 pamphlet published by the War Department quoted a soldier in the South Pacific: "I want my wife waiting for me and I want my job waiting for me. I don't want to find my wife busy with a job that some returning soldier needs. I don't want to find that some other man's wife has my job." Another soldier said, "Where I come from, we don't send our wives to work. If I can't make enough money to support a wife I don't

Parker's recruiting booth for women workers at Loew's State Theatre in Cleveland, Ohio.

expect to get married. My mother had plenty to do around the house. I'm for the good old fashioned way."[348]

The *Fitting News* conducted a survey of Parker's male employees, to learn their attitude toward women in the workforce. The magazine prefaced the results with a summary of all that women were accomplishing in Parker's plants:

"Many jobs previously held exclusively by men are today being handled by women with a degree of efficiency unsuspected by the most optimistic factory employment manager. The lathe, the mill, the grinder, the screw machine have all succumbed to the feminine touch. But is this a permanent condition?"

The men's responses to the survey were harsh by today's standards, reflecting the prevailing views of the time. Ninety-two per cent of Parker's men believed that married women should not continue to work after the war. One man said, as he adjusted a saw at the Euclid Avenue plant, "My wife work when this thing is over? I'll say she ain't. The minute we clean up this mess she's going home—and that's where she's going to stay!" Roy Patrick, working on an airplane wheel brake at Euclid Avenue, said, "My wife is helping the war effort, but I'd much rather see her at home." Paul Seliskar, in production planning, said, "I have nothing against wives working. But after the war mine won't." And Valentine Kaposky, a foundry worker, added, "Just as soon as the boys come back my wife's going home to stay."

Years later, many of the women who helped Parker fight the war on the home front would have a chance to change the prevailing attitudes toward female workers. They proudly explained to their daughters—part of the Baby Boom generation that began making its presence felt in the 1950s—how they helped win World War II during their time at the Parker Appliance Co. Inspired by their mothers, those young women would go on to march for civil rights in the 1960s, and when they entered the workforce by the millions in the 1970s, they would demand fair treatment and equal pay for their work.

In February 1943, the *Fitting News* reported that "Over 650 of our fellow employees have laid down their tools and left their machines to answer our country's call for men to fight for freedom's cause around the world." Women accounted for 30 percent of Parker's workforce, and their numbers were growing at the rate of 125 each month. Parker sponsored a "Women at War" exhibit in the lobby of Loew's State Theatre on Euclid Avenue in downtown Cleveland, the same theater where Art and Helen had watched Bob Hope on their first date. Displays depicted the types of jobs women were performing in Parker's plant. Colonel T.H. Eickhoff told a crowd in the State Theater lobby, "As more men are called to battlefields, the burden will fall heavily on

WOMEN AT WORK....

The caption in the February 1943 *Fitting News* reads: "Little argument remains concerning the American woman's versatility in the multifarious phases of American life. Pictured on these pages are women devoting their working talents 100 percent to building the tools of battle. Whether or not they will return to their former livelihoods at war's end is another story. But here is proof that they are worthy of the challenge of war."

women who must take the place at home of the men called to service. Someday women of Cleveland will proudly tell their children that they too played their part in World War II."[349]

The April 1943 edition of the *Fitting News* included several letters from the "boys" on the front lines. Private William G. Williams, who had worked in Raw Material Control on Euclid Avenue, wrote, "I realize now how much your continued production of aircraft parts means to the success of our war effort. Airpower will be the decisive factor in the war." Sergeant C.W. Bondurant said, "I'm just one of the guys who put about a year in the third floor stock room, but you and I have a job to do and, by God, we're going to double barrel do it." Nancy Shaw of the Timekeeping Department included a letter from her brother Raymond, a former shop employee, who said, "I have seen so many of Parker's fittings that it seems as though I am still working in the shop. I have been around quite a few planes and about 95 percent of the fittings are from Parker."

One employee, Private G.E. Hargreaves, who had been a member of the Lubricant Department on Euclid Avenue, wrote that he was recuperating in an English hospital after suffering a crushed foot. He said "the English folks have been most hospitable to the American boys" and that he was "amazed how cheerful and still determined to win they were even after three hard years of war." He added, "My only hope is that the American civilian is taking the war in the same way."[350]

In April 1943, the Allies defeated the Axis forces in North Africa. Winston Churchill called the victory "the end of the beginning" of the war. Germany's "Desert Fox," General Edwin Rommel, acknowledged the Allies' superiority in weapons had turned the tide, saying: "The bravest men can do nothing without guns, without ammunition. The battle is fought and decided by the quartermasters before the shooting begins."[351]

The spring of 1943 was especially beautiful in Cleveland. By the beginning of April, the daffodils were up and leaves were budding on the trees. For the employees of the Parker Appliance Co., however, it was a difficult time. More than half the workers at the Cleveland plant were women, and many of them had husbands, sons, and fathers fighting in North Africa. Every morning before coming to work, most of Parker's 3,000 employees in the Cleveland area scanned the Cleveland Plain Dealer, wondering whether the loved one of a friend, neighbor or fellow employee had been reported killed, wounded or missing in action.

The first page of the April 1943 edition of the *Fitting News* set forth one of Art's most fervent hopes, as he looked forward to a time when aircraft would once again become an instrument of peace:

> *"In sweat and blood and tears a world is rising to reaffirm the dignity of man.... Today, we choose to think that the machine is saving civilization.... In the darkness of the hour, American airpower is recording a new chapter in our history.... We believe... the coming of the air age will bind the hearts and minds of the world in a closer sympathy and understanding than ever before. Parker people are proud of the part they are playing in this prelude to a new day. For on every front where war planes fly, their work is represented, as it will be on every air lane traversed by future aircraft of peace."[352]*

The *Fitting News* chronicled how employees were trying to keep up their spirits by participating in bowling leagues, softball games, variety shows, dance competitions, company picnics, and clubs of all kinds. The magazine also passed on its share of bad news. The April 1943 edition mentioned the death of William H. Kidd, a former member of the Valve Scheduling Department on Euclid Avenue:

> *"Kidd was killed in a freak accident on his 22nd birthday at the Army advance flying school at Pampa, Texas, when another plane crashed into his after he had landed following a night training flight... Widowed by the crash was the former Miss Betty Bowes, his bride of five months. The two had been childhood sweethearts, graduating from Collinwood High School. His parents are Mr. and Mrs. Ralph Kidd at 15510 Huntmere Avenue."[353]*

The last page of the April 1943 Fitting News listed 180 Parker employees who had joined the armed services over the previous two months.[354] America was now producing nearly 100,000 bombers and fighter planes every year with critical Parker components. Parker's production reached its peak in 1943, when the company's total shipments were approximately 12 times what they had been in 1940.

On July 9, 1943, the Allies landed in Sicily. The *Fitting News* reported that 26-year-old infantryman Edward Canda, who had worked in the Euclid Avenue foundry, had been killed during the invasion. On the day before his death, he wrote a letter to his wife, Rita, and their 7-year-old son, Kenneth, explaining how excited he was about the success of the invasion and how he looked forward to being reunited soon with his family in Cleveland. John Gedney, who had worked in the Shipping Department, survived the invasion and wrote that he had received his first copies of the *Fitting News*, and that they "made him feel good that the people back home are doing their best to help us over here. Tell them to keep plugging and we'll keep slugging."

Since 1935, the Euclid Avenue plant had been shipping fittings and valves to Boeing for the de-icing equipment, landing gear, brake controls, and fuel systems of the B-17 bomber. Each plane was equipped with 5,550 Parker fittings and 25 valves.[355] The B-17 was the first military aircraft with an enclosed flight deck instead of an open cockpit. The plane earned its name "Flying Fortress" from its 13 machine guns.[356] Pilots loved the plane for its ability to fly up to 35,000 feet, well above enemy "flak," and to keep flying with an exceptional amount of damage. One B-17 pilot said, "To me, the Flying Fortress was, and always will be, the Queen of the Sky. I owe my life to the Queen."[357]

The August 1943 edition of the *Fitting News* included an article by a Boeing employee about Parker's contribution to the success of the B-17. The article described the large group of Parker valves, fittings and "more than a

Boeing's B-17 "Flying Fortress," featured in the August 1943 *Fitting News*.

mile of Parker tubing" that controlled critical functions on the aircraft. By the time the war was over, Parker would send more than 70 million fittings to Boeing, which would allow it to build 12,726 B-17s. Those planes would comprise the core of the air armadas that led to the defeat of Germany. General Carl Spatz, the American Air Commander in Europe, said, "Without the B-17, we may have lost the war."[358]

Walter W. Brass, who had been a Third Shift Grinder in the tool room at Euclid Avenue, was one of the B-17 pilots flying bombing runs over Germany. It took him eight hours to fly to the German targets, and then back to an air base in England. His plane was shot down by Luftwaffe fighters during the bombing of a submarine base in Kiel, Germany. He was badly burned before he bailed out. Soon after landing in a farmer's field, he was captured by German soldiers. The *Fitting News* reported that, in a letter to his mother from a German prisoner of war camp, he wrote that "Since the Germans are good medical men, everything is all right." Brass told his mother that Germany, "with its rolling, slightly hilly country," reminded him of home.

B-17 on the cover of the *Fitting News*, August 1943.

Parker had several parts aboard the Douglas C-47 "Skytrain" a transport plane derived from the Douglas DC-3. Seven Parker executives, including Carl Klamm, attended the rollout ceremony for the plane at a Douglas plant in Chicago. Hundreds of Parker precision valves and tube couplings controlled the flow of fuel and oil to the plane's engines. Nine hundred Skytrains, flying at 500 feet above the English Channel to avoid Nazi radar, would ferry the 101st Airborne Division to landing spots behind enemy lines early on D-Day.

Articles in the June and September 1943 editions of the *Fitting News* reminded Parker's employees why they were helping fight the war. Erwin Abels of the Engineering Methods Department on Euclid Avenue had been arrested by the Nazis in Vienna in 1938 and sent to a concentration camp. Abels had been a well-to-do General Manager of a building company, until the Nazis discovered he was a Jew. They forced him to forfeit all his assets in order to obtain his release from the camp. Soon thereafter he set sail for America, ending up in Cleveland, where he was hired by Parker.[359]

Arthur Kerdemann worked in the Tool Design Department at the Euclid Avenue plant. He was among the 25,000 Jewish men and women arrested in Germany and Austria on the evening of November 9, 1938, which later became known as "Kristallnacht"(meaning "the night of the broken glass"), after the broken glass from 200 synagogues and 8,000 Jewish-owned stores destroyed by the Nazis. Kerdemann was beaten by SS guards at a Vienna prison and then transferred to one of the Nazis' first concentration camps, at Dachau, just outside of Munich. He was forced to help build a factory where the first German jet fighter plane, the Messerschmitt Me 262, would be produced.

Kerdemann was released from Dachau after agreeing to donate all his possessions to the Nazi Party. He found passage on a boat to America, just seven days after Hitler invaded Poland in August 1939. He obtained an engineering degree from Art's alma mater, the Case School of Applied Science in Cleveland, and started working at Parker in 1942. He could hardly wait to return to Europe to fight the Nazis. In 1943, he began his service as an Intelligence officer in Europe. He would survive the war, move to California, start a family, and live to the age of 97, passing away in 2009.

At the December 1943 Teheran Conference, Josef Stalin thanked Roosevelt

Arthur Kerdemann working at Parker, circa 1942.

for the planes that were attacking Germany. Stalin said, "The most important things in this war are machines...[and America is] the country of machines."[360] Stalin, who had already lost millions of his soldiers fighting Hitler on the Eastern Front, was eager for his allies to begin their invasion of Western Europe.

Art wanted to recognize the efforts of his older, long-term employees, who found it the hardest to work night and day to make fittings for the planes that would provide cover for the troops about to invade Western Europe. In February 1944, Art began a tradition that has continued to the present day: he convened an "Old-Timers" dinner at the Cleveland Club to honor 33 of his workers who had been with the company for more than 10 years. The "Parker Appliance Employee Orchestra," featuring a "Big Band" sound, played at the dinner, as it did at most other employee get-togethers.

The bandleader, 31-year-old Frankie Lane, was a lathe operator at the Euclid Avenue plant. He loved to sing while working. Many of those working near him during the summer of 1944, including 15-year-old Pat Parker, silently wished he would give his singing a rest. After the war, Lane became a famous vocalist, whose brash style and insistent beat set the stage for the "blues" singers and rock and roll bands of the 1950s.[361]

In February 1944, the *Fitting News* listed an "Honor Roll" of 1,330 Parker employees serving in the Armed Forces, a contingent that included more than a third of the company's workforce. By the beginning of June 1944, the main topic of conversation on the floor of the Euclid Avenue plant was the timing and location for the invasion of Western Europe. Pat Parker was getting ready to begin high school in the fall, but in the interim he had started his first summer job, running a machine that was making valves and fittings for B-17 bombers. He was proud to receive his first paycheck, at a rate of 45 cents an hour.

By the time Parker's workers arrived at the Euclid Avenue plant on the morning of June 6, 175,000 Allied troops—supported by an armada of 7,000 ships and 2,200 planes equipped with Parker valves and fittings—had been attacking the Normandy beaches for eight hours. Nearly every one of the 2,600 workers at the plant had a hand in designing, testing, or making those parts. As Parker's men and women gathered around radios on the factory floor, they heard the Allied soldiers were clinging to a tenuous foothold in the face of withering fire from German pillboxes on the bluffs above the beach. Watching the carnage at Omaha Beach, General Omar Bradley feared "an irreversible catastrophe."[362]

The *Fitting News* reported:

> *"The predominant emotion welling suddenly through the entire plant was that of release from waiting—escape from the tension that had been mounting steadily as spring wore on... News flashes broke periodically through the steady drone of machines, over the clatter of typewriters. Three members of the purchasing department had a son-in-law, father, and brother who were storming the beaches. They spent most of the day waiting for word of their loved ones, and trying to comfort each other. A member of the cost accounting department worried about the fate of her relatives in the French 'Underground.' ... Lillian Danko, whose paratrooper brother landed in France during the initial hours of the invasion, sadly stuck to her post throughout the long, uncertain day. Ruth Dukes, of Inspection, listened in dazed bewilderment to the invasion news over speakers in the plant. Her husband landed with infantry. Many other women in the plant shared her fears."*

Three days after the invasion, the Allies had established a secure foothold in Normandy. The historian Jay Vinik believes the Normandy invasion was "arguably the most significant battle in history."[363] The Pulitzer Prize-winning war correspondent Ernie Pyle described a group of German prisoners of war on the Normandy beach, looking out at the vast Allied armada sitting offshore: "They stood staring almost as if in a trance. They didn't say a word to each other. They didn't need to. The expression on their faces was something forever unforgettable. In it was the final, horrified acceptance of their doom."[364]

Ruth Dukes awaits news on the fate of her husband who landed at Normandy on D-Day, from the July 1944 *Fitting News*.

Allied air power had been decisive in the success of D-Day. As L. Douglas Keeney wrote, "D-Day must surely be the most important airpower achievement in the history of military aviation. Not a single significant air attack was mounted by the Germans while the invasion forces battled to get ashore, and that may very well be why the infantry finally pushed over the bluffs of Omaha Beach when, by the slimmest of margins, they were very nearly thrown back."[365]

During the latter part of 1944, 100-mile-long columns of B-17s and B-24s, including up to 1,000 aircraft, were bombing German cities, factories, transportation networks, and military installations nearly every day.[366] By the end of the year, U.S. and English forces were on Germany's western border, and the Soviets were on the east. The end of the European war looked to be only a few weeks away. In the Pacific, however, no end was in sight. The U.S. and British were advancing slowly, in an island-by-island slog. On Japan's home islands, women and children were being drilled to prepare for a fight to the last person standing.[367] The Pentagon worried the war with Japan would not end until America invaded Japan's home islands. Fearing the casualties that would occur in such an invasion, military planners hoped to end the war instead in a bombing campaign.

The Air Force's two heavy bombers were not fit for the task of bombing Japan. The B-17 could not carry enough fuel to make the long flight to Japan from American air bases in the Pacific. The B-24 was plagued with so many mechanical problems that pilots had begun to call it "the Flying Coffin."[368] For every B-24 lost in combat, six were lost in accidents. Airmen trying to fulfill their 40 required combat missions had only a 50 percent chance of surviving in a B-24.[369] Ford never bothered to paint the B-24s coming off its assembly line in Willow Run, because it did not believe the planes would last long before they were either shot down or suffered catastrophic mechanical failures.[370]

The Air Force, appalled by the fatalities occurring among its airmen, commissioned Boeing to build a more reliable aircraft that could reach Japan from American-controlled islands in the Pacific. When finished, the plane would fulfill Lindbergh's dream of the "superbomber" that he had proposed to the Air Force when he returned from Germany in 1936. Boeing's B-29 "Super-Fortress" was a wondrous airplane: 99 feet long, nearly half a football field wide from wingtip to wingtip, it could carry more than twice the bomb load of any previous plane and fly higher, faster, and twice as far as the B-17 or B-24.[371] Parker sent hundreds of thousands of fittings and valves across town to the 2.2-million-square-foot Bomber Plant at the Cleveland airport, where 15,000 General Motors Fisher Body workers were assembling B-29s. Parker fittings and valves activated the braking systems, lowered the landing gear, protected the fuel systems, controlled the de-icing systems, and opened and closed the bomb bay doors of Boeing's B-29s.[372]

Engineers from Boeing and Parker solved a problem that had been deadly for the crews on Boeing's B-17. As Arthur Herman has explained, the bomb bay doors of the B-17 "swung wide and open like the doors of a saloon...[and they] had become telltale visual invitations to fighter attack. A savvy fighter pilot knew that opening bomb bays meant a bomber had to slow down and hold course in order to hit its target. So [Boeing, with Parker's assistance] created a new, pneumatically driven bomb bay door that snapped open and shut in less than four seconds."[373]

A B-29 first flew over Tokyo on a reconnaissance mission at noon on November 1, 1944. It was a clear day, and the silver plane, spewing long white contrails, was clearly visible as it circled nearly six miles high. Like an eagle eyeing its prey, it was mapping the path for thousands of B-29s that would devastate Japan.

Louis Zamberini, an American sprinter in the 1936 Berlin Olympics, had been a bombardier on a B-24 that crashed in the Pacific. After surviving on a raft for 47 days, he had been captured by the Japanese, and for 18 months he languished in a series of Japanese prison camps, where he was forced to perform hard labor.

Zamberini was near starvation and had almost given up, but the sight of the B-29 gave him hope. As the plane circled Tokyo, Zamberini and his fellow POWs rushed into the prison compound, pointing upward. "Oh God, God, an American plane," one POW shouted. A recently captured American airman told the POWs the plane was a new bomber called the B-29. A group of POWs began to cheer, and then to yell, "B-29! B-29!"[374]

The Japanese guards looked stricken. One POW wrote in his diary, "Not even bayonet prods could wipe the smiles from the POW faces now."[375]

Like most Americans, Art had grown weary of war by the end of 1944. How long, he wondered, until this conflict ended, and he could return to making products of peace?

# CHAPTER 11

# Casualties

Thirty-five year-old Sergeant Joe Campbell was unhappy when he received his induction notice in mid-1942. He loved his job in Labor Relations at the Euclid Avenue plant, which allowed him to provide a good living for his wife and 1-year-old daughter. The *Fitting News* asked Joe to correspond regularly with the magazine when he was sent overseas. With his training in human relations, he was an acute observer of the men around him. In his dispatches, he proudly described how the men he was leading were gaining confidence during basic training, saying "It's kind of surprising to find that we're all plain GI Joes and all pretty good ones at that." Many of those men died on D-Day when Joe's squadron stormed the Normandy beaches.

In one of his reports from the hedgerows of northwest France after the invasion, Joe explained how he felt about receiving a copy of the *Fitting News* and his bonus checks:

> *"One of the grandest surprises I ever received came in the mail yesterday. Your fine 'Good Luck' message and the oh-so fine checks arrived.... Being in the Army isn't so bad, but leaving one's work and one's friends at work is. Even worse is the possibility of being forgotten. Since your letter of yesterday I don't have that feeling. To hear from the plant in such a grand way is the best morale booster I ever experienced. It makes one proud to have been associated with an outfit of that kind."*

Joe's last letter to the *Fitting News* was dated August 2, 1944, two months after D-Day.

*"Lying under my little pup tent on the thick green sod of this French cow pasture, I muse on the workings of men and the army. We've been alerted a time or so during the short French nights when stray planes have passed overhead. The first time or so we hit the bottoms of our freshly dug foxholes in one scoot from tent to burrow. Now we cast a wary eye. One grows accustomed to the strange and improbable, I guess."*

On August 26, 1944, the French leader, Charles de Gaulle, marched through the Arc de Triomphe and down the Champs Elysees with hundreds of French and American soldiers. More than 1 million cheering French citizens lined the boulevard. Joe Campbell spent his time fighting his way with General George Patton's army across northern France, on the way to Germany. Ernie Pyle wrote that many American soldiers marching into Paris felt guilty about their less fortunate colleagues like Joe, still fighting the Germans on the front lines: "I heard more than one rear-echelon soldier say he felt a little ashamed to be getting all the grateful cheers and kisses for the liberation of Paris when the guys who broke the German army and opened the way for Paris to be free were still out there fighting without benefit of kisses or applause."[376]

On September 6, 1944, one month after Joe Campbell wrote his letter to the *Fitting News*, he was wounded in northern France during a firefight with German soldiers. He died of his wounds five days later. Joe was one of 134,000 American soldiers killed, wounded, missing or captured in France in the three months since D-Day. In an obituary, the *Fitting News* called Joe a "sort of representative of all our G.I. boys who are fighting this country's war."

President Roosevelt was re-elected to a fourth term in November 1944. Harry Truman, a little-known Senator from Missouri and veteran of the Meuse-Argonne Offensive of 1918, was his vice presidential running mate. The press noted how pale and tired Roosevelt looked at his victory party. Twelve years of fighting the Great Depression and a world war had taken its toll.

Helen worried that Art was starting to look the same way. He had exhausted himself in the task of overseeing his company's production of aircraft parts for the military. In the fall of 1944, he was about to turn 60 and he was starting to feel his age. Art came home each night so tired he could barely finish his dinner before falling asleep. Like the soldiers serving on every side, all

Art wanted to do was go home, embrace his family, and regain his strength. As Dwight D. Eisenhower, the Supreme Commander of Allied Forces in Europe, wrote from France to his mother in Kansas, "If I could get home, I could lie down on the front lawn and stay there for a week without moving."[377]

Fritz Probst, a German engineer serving on the Eastern Front, wrote one of his last letters to his wife Hildegarde from an encampment near Stalingrad. He said he was disturbed by the thought that he and Hildegarde "were becoming old and the best years are passing by untapped.... When I once more hold you in my arms and find your mouth to kiss, everything will be forgotten and I know for sure we'll then be the happiest of beings. For now, dreams are the only things that unite us."[378]

One night, Helen found Art in the library, listening to the latest war news on the radio. Art told Helen he was worried about the company's ability to adjust to a peacetime economy. He said he wanted to make sure Helen and their four children would be financially secure, no matter what the future might bring. Helen was taken aback when Art said he had purchased a $1 million life insurance policy with her as the beneficiary. Helen told him that she, the children, and his 3,000 employees were all counting on him and that no amount of insurance could compensate for his loss. Helen told Art he should start to slow down now that the war seemed almost over. She was relieved when Art told her he had passed the physical for the life insurance policy with flying colors.

Art addressed a group of Parker employees on the evening of October 12, 1944, at the Hotel Carter in downtown Cleveland. He wanted them to look forward to peacetime with optimism. The speech would be the last Art would ever make to Parker's men and women. Perhaps he felt an intimation of mortality, for he spoke about the values he hoped his employees would follow after he was gone—customer service, teamwork, caring for each other, and persistence during hard times.

The occasion was a preview of the company's display for a national industrial trade show, scheduled to start October 16 at Cleveland's Public Hall. As he looked around proudly at the exhibits of his company's fluid power products, Art told 400 of his employees:

> *"This is another demonstration of the alert and enthusiastic cooperative spirit that prevails among our Parker people... the ability to get a hard job done and done quickly. It is in the knowledge of this employee spirit that we can optimistically*

*face the future unafraid. I am sincerely proud of you all. Our*
*success is founded upon fair dealing, hard work and coordina-*
*tion of effort."*

Art went on to express his confidence in the future of the company, de-
claring that "we are going to be busier in reconversion than we have been
in the war effort." He predicted the establishment of "a series of separate,
diversified businesses all under the Parker name and tied together with central control." He stated, however, that the company's first priority was "to see
the war through first, there being plenty of time to think about peacetime
production when victory is won."

Art reminded his employees that they had developed an "invaluable asset" in acquiring the expertise to produce aircraft products...to the highest
standards." Their manufacturing expertise, he was convinced, would bring
"higher standards to peacetime products," and continue Parker's reputation
for "premier customer service." Art reminded his audience that the company had a long list of satisfied industrial customers before the war, and that
they would return to Parker after the war ended. He concluded by assuring
his employees that their reputation for customer service would carry them
through whatever challenges lay ahead: "We have no fear of the industrial

Art Parker's last speech to his employees, at the Hotel Carter in Cleveland, Ohio, on
October 12, 1944, with Helen at his side.

future... We have gained the respect of our one great customer, the govern-ment, and we also have the respect of our old customers, a great asset."

Art had little time for family life during the war; he tried to make what time he did have with Helen and the four children something special. He and Helen frequently invited the children's Fitzgerald cousins from the West Side to spend time with them at the Shaker Heights house. Art often took the children to Cleveland Indians baseball games at Municipal Stadium on the lakefront. "Aunt Helen" had a close relationship with all her nieces and neph-ews, but they were somewhat in awe of "Uncle Art." One weekend afternoon in late November 1944, Rosemarie Fitzgerald Hritz, one of Helen's nieces, was playing pingpong with Pat in the recreation room in the basement of the Parkers' Shaker Heights home. Both she and Pat had turned fifteen that year. Suddenly Art appeared in the basement. Pat and Rosemarie were surprised to see him, for he rarely played games with the children. As Art grabbed a pad-dle and started serving from the other side of the table, Rosemarie thought to herself, "I can't believe I'm playing pingpong with Uncle Art."

Two days before Christmas in 1944, Art continued a tradition he had be-gun in 1940, during the last Christmas holiday before America went to war. He took his family to the cafeteria at the Euclid Avenue plant, where he, Helen and the four children helped serve a Christmas dinner to Parker's employees.

The Parkers celebrated Christmas in their traditional way, at home in Shaker Heights. On Christmas Eve, the Parkers' two live-in helpers, Anna, the cook (an immigrant from Poland), and Augie, the housekeeper, nurse-maid and nanny (an immigrant from Hungary), appeared in the doorway of the library, a comfortable room lined with books on wood-paneled shelves, carpeted with a bright oriental rug, and containing two well-stuffed chairs for Art and Helen. The children were sitting on the carpet, playing games before dinner, while Art and Helen drank Martinis and smoked their unfil-tered "Camel" cigarettes. Augie and Anna served the family an Oyster stew in the dining room. Afterwards, the children were allowed to eat several of the Christmas cookies Anna had been baking for the last two weeks. Then Art brought in the tall pine tree that had been sitting out on the patio, and the family decorated the tree in front of the bay window in the living room.

THERE WAS MUCH FOR ART to be thankful for on New Year's Day of 1945. The 101st Airborne, in Bastogne, Belgium, was holding the line against the German's counter-offensive in the "Battle of the Bulge." It was clear the Germans could not hold out much longer. At least 1,000 Allied planes were in the air during every 24-hour period, bombing German railways, airfields and industrial targets. The German aircraft manufacturers Art had visited during his visit to Germany in 1938 had lost their factories, and had to resort to trying to building aircraft underground—Junkers in a mine, Heinkel in a subway tunnel in Berlin, and Messerschmitt in a cave in the German mountains. The Russians had fought their way back to Germany's eastern border, and the Allies were getting ready to cross the Rhine, not far from where Art had ended his duty in 1918 on the Western Front. Eisenhower's armies were preparing to speed more than 6,000 tanks along the Autobahn, directly into the heart of Germany.[379] In the west, 500,000 exhausted Wehrmacht soldiers were facing 3.5 million well-provisioned Allied fighters.

Art had sacrificed much for the war effort. He was relieved an end to the war in Europe seemed to be in sight. Now he planned to turn his efforts in a more positive direction than making war materiel. He was planning on buying a house on a large plot of land, big enough for a horse stable and riding area. He could hardly wait to hear the children's reaction when they heard they were going to own horses. He was disappointed that Helen seemed cool to his idea. She had even refused to go with him to inspect the properties he was most excited about, pleading she was too busy with the children to spend time looking at real estate.

Art decided to start the new year by spending more time with his family. For the last four years he had hardly seen Helen or his four children—all of whom yearned to spend more time with their father. Pat had turned 15, his brother Tom was 13, his sister Joyce 11, and his youngest sister Cyndi had just turned 8. Art had been looking forward to this New Year's Day for a long time, when he would not have to go into the office and could relax at home with his family.

The winter of 1944-45 was shaping up to be the worst in Cleveland since 1918. It had been snowing continuously since Thanksgiving. More than nine inches of snow had covered the ground since the end of November. Intense cold had caused shortages of coal, closing stores, theaters, and schools, and turning off the bright lights at Playhouse Square. Cars in Parker's parking lot on Euclid Avenue were buried under snowdrifts.

A heavy snow fell throughout New Year's Day of 1945, adding another 10 inches to the blanket of white already on the ground. Art looked out the window of his home to see his driveway and front sidewalk covered in drifts. Helen, Joyce and Cyndi were playing Parcheesi in the library, as Pat and Tom looked on. Art asked Pat and Tom to put on their winter coats and go out front to help him shovel snow. As he turned toward the front door, Art noticed that Joyce was arguing with Cyndi about how she was playing the game. He took Joyce's hand, drew her over to him and said in a forceful voice, "Don't be so stubborn."

Outside in the snowstorm, Art decided to make a game out of a necessity, challenging Pat and Tom to see whether they could shovel snow faster than him. There was a lot of good-natured joking and laughter as they hoisted the snow as fast as they could. Suddenly, Art felt winded and told the boys he was going inside to rest on the living room couch.

Joyce, Cyndi and Helen saw Art as he smiled and waved at them from the doorway between the living room and the library. Helen asked him how he was, and he said he was just a bit tired and was going to lie down and rest on the couch. Twenty minutes later, the telephone rang. It was the neighbor from across the street. She had seen Art and the boys out shoveling snow, and she wanted to invite the Parkers over to their house to celebrate New Year's. Helen told the neighbor she would call right back after she checked with Art.

Helen asked Cyndi to go into the living room and wake Art up. She found Art lying on the couch. She thought he was sleeping and kept calling to him to wake up, but he did not respond. Cyndi suddenly became very frightened and ran back into the library, telling her mother she could not wake her father. Helen ran into the living room, and a few seconds later, yelled out toward the kitchen, "Anna, get the brandy!"

Pat and Tom were just coming in from shoveling snow, and Helen told the children to go upstairs to their rooms. The four children sat in their rooms, listening with increasing fear to their mother's frantic cries, as she told Augie to call an ambulance. Joyce was troubled that she had caused her father to become angry a few minutes earlier, and she feared she might have been responsible for his illness. She kept clinging as hard as she could to the post at the foot of her bed, believing that if she could just hold on long enough, her father would be all right. It was not long before the ambulance arrived, and Helen came upstairs and tearfully told the children their father had passed away.

Art Parker, who had worked himself to death in service to his country, was felled by a heart attack at age 60, leaving behind a bereft family and 3,000 employees, most of whom had known no other leader. Art had given his life for his country, just as surely as his fellow employees William Kidd, Edward Canda and Joe Campbell, and the 400,000 other Americans lying in graves in North Africa, Sicily, Italy, France, Belgium, Germany, Japan, and the Pacific Islands.

Art was buried in Cleveland's Lake View Cemetery, at the highest point of the most western foothill of the Appalachian Mountains. His grave sat across from the ridge where John D. Rockefeller had been laid to rest eight years earlier. Other Clevelanders who changed the world lay close by, including Alexander Winton, Jeptha Wade, Samuel Mather, Charles Brush, John Hay, Mark Hanna, and Myron Herrick. From those gravesites, visitors can look down upon Lake Erie, downtown Cleveland, the Cuyahoga River, and the Great Plains beyond.

An anonymous employee wrote a tribute to Art for the *Fitting News* in January 1945:

> *"By nature a shy and retiring individual, he shunned the limelight of public recognition.... preferring to be considered merely as a member of the vast organization which he had founded and struggled so valiantly to build.... He had generally been referred to in inter-employee conversation as 'the old man.' Yet this term was affectionately used in the same sense that the ship's skipper is referred to as the 'old man' by his seamen.... The beginning years of the company were not easy ones...but involved a constant struggle to keep the business alive... Even when things looked darkest, his intense zeal and profound conviction in the rightness of his designs spurred his men on to overcome even the biggest obstacles.... Hence, from a modest beginning, Mr. Parker built up an organization which today is a model for modern mass production methods. Yet at no time would he tolerate any compromise with precision in workmanship or quality of product—a combination which, heretofore, had often been considered impossible."*

Helen never fully recovered from Art's death. She was haunted by regret that she had been so cool to his suggestion they start to look together for a house in the country. She told her friends she had lost the man she called "the love of my life" and never considered remarrying, though she would live on for another 20 years. At Art's funeral on January 4, 1945, Helen fainted several times. For months after Art's death, she took smelling salts frequently to keep from fainting. The children were afraid she might never regain her equilibrium. They wondered whether she could handle the pressure of keeping the company going, and what they would do if she failed.[380]

Photograph of Art Parker, circa 1944.

TWO WEEKS AFTER ART DIED, Hitler confided to his Luftwaffe adjutant that the war had been lost, due to the Allies' advantage in the tools of war. Hitler said, "I know the war is lost. The superior power is too great."[381]

Three months after Art's death, on April 12, 1945, President Roosevelt died. Late in the evening, Vice President Truman was called to the White House. No one had told him why he was being summoned.

Eleanor Roosevelt greeted him, and placing her arm gently on his shoulder, said, "Harry, the President is dead."

Truman, momentarily speechless, finally asked if there was anything he could do for her.

Eleanor replied, "Is there anything we can do for you? You are the one in trouble now."[382]

One of the last B-17 assaults on Germany, in the early spring of 1945, gave a foretaste of the Cold War about to begin between the U.S. and Russia. Thirty-six of the planes took off from Essex, England, bound for Oranienburg, a northwest suburb of Berlin, where a factory was processing enriched uranium for an atomic bomb. As the B-17s reached their cruising altitude north of Amsterdam, the temperature in the planes fell to 40 degrees below zero, and the air became too thin to breathe without an oxygen mask. The exhaust from each of the B-17's four engines formed white contrails, betraying their position to German defenders below. Despite heavy flak, the planes were able to release their bombs and destroy the uranium plant, just days before the fast-approaching Russian army would have captured the plant.[383]

Germany surrendered on April 29, but the Japanese fought on. Knowing the Japanese people believed surrender to be shameful, President Truman feared they would not give up until the Allies conquered their home islands. Marshall told Truman the invasion of Japan would last at least 18 months and cost a million more American lives. He advised the new president, for the first time, of a top-secret weapon that was ready for deployment. It was called the "atomic bomb." Seeing no other way to end the war with Japan, Truman approved dropping the bomb on a Japanese city.

On August 6, 1945, the most famous B-29 ever made, the "Enola Gay," piloted by Paul W. Tibbets Jr., took off from Tinian Island at 2:45 a.m., on its way to Hiroshima, a city chosen for its importance as a manufacturing center, supply depot, and troop embarkation point. In its bomb bay sat an atomic bomb on which was inscribed the name "Little Boy." Six hours later, Tibbets ordered his crew to put on their goggles as he lined his B-29 up over a T-shaped bridge in the middle of the city. He released the bomb from 32,000 feet at 8:15 a.m. on a beautiful summer morning. A few hours earlier, an American reconnaissance plane had flown over the city to confirm the clear weather. Many of those on the ground believed Tibbets' bright big silver plane, which reflected the sun's rays, was also not on a bombing mission, and as a result they did not take shelter from the force that was about to be unleashed upon them.[384]

Knowing it would take 57 seconds for the bomb to reach its detonation altitude of 2,000 feet, Tibbets put his B-29 into a dive to gain speed. Suddenly, the sky over the city exploded in an unbearably white light, 10 times the intensity of the sun. Beneath Tibbets and his crew, 75,000 people lay dead or dying, and 70 percent of the city had been destroyed. Seventy-five thousand more would die later of their injuries or of radiation poisoning.

Tibbets' copilot wrote in his diary, "My God!"

Then the shock wave from the blast shook the B-29, throwing the crew up and down. Tibbets thought they had been hit by flak. After wrestling with the plane for several seconds, he was able to regain control and return safely to Tinian. Three days after Hiroshima was destroyed, another B-29 dropped the second atomic bomb—the "Fat Man"—on Nagasaki. Six days after that, on August 15, 1945, Japan unconditionally surrendered. Boeing's bomber had helped end a war in which 60 million people had died.[385]

A RIFLEMAN FROM the 157th Infantry was present when Dachau was liberated by the Americans. As his battalion approached the camp, SS guards forced prisoners into huts, nailed the doors shut, and set them on fire. After finding a stack of 400 burning bodies, the rifleman said, "I've been in the Army for 39 months. I've been overseas for combat for 23. I'd gladly go through it all again if I knew that things like this would be stopped."[386]

Nearly the same age as Art Parker, Victor Klemperer was a language professor, scholar, writer, and German patriot from Dresden, who earned military honors for his bravery in the trenches of World War I. He had brought supplies to the German soldiers on the front lines, not far from where Art was doing the same for Allied soldiers. Victor was also a Jew. Because of his military record and marriage to Eva, a "full-blooded Aryan," Victor was spared deportation to the death camps for a time, but whenever he left home, he had to wear the yellow star that marked him as a Jew. One day a young man, blond and brutal-looking, noticed the star on Victor's coat and yelled from his car, "You wretch, why are you still alive?"[387] On the night of March 2, 1943, several of Victor's friends were loaded onto cattle trucks at the Dresden train station and taken to the Auschwitz-Birkenau concentration camp.[388]

Victor lived in a continual sense of dread he might be next. The slightest misstep—appearing in a forbidden part of Dresden, buying certain food, or expressing an opinion critical of the Nazi regime—could deliver him to the Gestapo. And yet, despite the years of Nazi propaganda against the Jews, Victor experienced regular acts of kindness from his neighbors: the butcher who gave him extra meat, the housewife who sent him and Eva clothes, the friend who risked death by hiding Victor's diary in a suitcase in her closet, and the lawyer who promised to find him a hiding place if the Gestapo ever came for him. One day, a stranger came up to Victor on the street and said, "I saw your star, and I greet you. I condemn the outlawing of a race, as do many others."[389]

Victor knew he would be executed if the Gestapo discovered his diary, but he vowed, "I shall go on writing. That is my heroism. I shall bear witness to the very end."[390]

After the bombing of Dresden in February 1945, Victor and Eva fled to upper Bavaria, where they were sheltered by generous German families as they waited out the end of the war. Victor realized the war was finally ending one day when he heard the drone of hundreds of Allied bombers heading to Berlin and Munich to destroy the last remnants of the Nazi regime. He wrote in his diary: "the deep hum of the squadrons...formation after formation, flying in every direction, usually visible as silver fish thousands of feet high...day and night the distant banging of falling bombs, the very distant thunder of the front...and meanwhile, we sit in the wood feeling safe."[391]

It was for those like Victor, Eva and the millions of others under the heels of the dictators that Art Parker, William Kidd, Edward Canda, Joe Campbell, and the other Parker employees who died in the war had been fighting. At a terrible price, they bequeathed a better world to those who lived to see the peace.

The Allies prevailed because of what Ben Macintyre called "an American economic juggernaut that produced much, much more of nearly everything than Germany and Japan could."[392] America produced more than 300,000 warplanes for the Allies, nearly all of which flew with thousands of Parker fittings. All told, Parker sent more than 500 million valves and fittings—each made to the most exacting specifications—to the aircraft manufacturing plants which, at their peak of production, rolled one plane off an assembly line every five and a half minutes. Martin van Creveld believes that "Nothing like it had ever been seen before, nothing like it has been seen since, and almost certainly nothing even remotely resembling it will even be seen in any kind of future."[393]

The dictators had been defeated. But Europe and Japan lay in ruins— entire civilizations destroyed by the flying machines the Wright Brothers, Glenn Martin, Lindbergh, Bill Boeing, Donald Douglas, and Art Parker had hoped would bring the world closer together. As 75 year-old Orville Wright said soon after the war ended, "We dared to hope we had invented something that would bring lasting peace to the earth, but we were wrong."[394]

With the war over, the world watched and waited to see whether an integrated community of nations could be rebuilt on the smoldering ruins of the old world.[395] As the worst fears of Art and other aviation pioneers came true, and the Allies' bombs killed millions of innocent civilians in their homes and destroyed the great cities of Europe and Japan, Art had moments of regret about where his efforts during the war had led. If he had lived to see the peaceful Europe and Japan that rose from the ashes of war, he likely would have rested more easily.

Today, travelers can drive in less than two hours from the city of Verdun, the site of one of the bloodiest conflicts in history, into Germany, crossing the long-disputed French/German border without even slowing down, on a superhighway that connects two countries that fought each other for centuries. As Adam Hochschild wrote, "It surely is an extraordinary achievement today that you can walk or drive or swim across boundaries among countries that had fought one another many times over centuries, and not find a fence or border guard in sight. I wish all wars ended thus."[396]

When the Japanese surrendered in August 1945, Parker's plants were still going full blast, producing parts for America's warplanes. The company had more than $17 million in backlog of government orders. Then, ironically, peace suddenly brought the Parker Appliance Co. face-to-face with bankruptcy for the second time in its history. Parker's aircraft valves, fittings and other fluid power components had helped win the war, but after the Japanese surrendered on August 15, there was no longer any need for those products. On August 16, Parker received a call from the War Department, canceling all orders. Within weeks, employment fell from 3,000 to 300, and all the company's facilities were idled.

The government had insisted, right up until the war ended, that aircraft parts makers continue to produce inventory at rates far in excess of the requirements of the aviation industry. Art had appealed to the War Production Board to reduce its orders for spare parts, but the government had refused to do so. Excess inventories of Parker fittings were sitting at the company's plants, in government warehouses, and with the aircraft manufacturers. The inventory would take years to work off. Parker was left with factory space, machines, equipment and mountains of spare parts for which there was not a single customer.

A majority of the company's directors told Helen Parker the company could not go on. They believed their primary responsibility now was to determine how best to liquidate the company's assets in an orderly way, since they saw no market for Parker's machinery, facilities, or expertise. Helen had to make a decision that would determine the future of her four children and her 300 remaining employees. How she wondered, could she ever continue Art's dream to build the greatest fluid power company in the world?

PART 3

# DIVERSIFYING

1945 TO 1957

---

*"Since our old business of making
aircraft fittings was dead…there
were two ways we could look at
the future. One, it was hopeless.
Two, we had a clean slate and a
good vehicle for growth….
We could plan any future we
wished. We took this second view
and…our dream for the future
began to take hold."*

Robert Cornell, writing in Parker's
1976 Annual Report to Shareholders
about the hard times Parker faced in 1945

# CHAPTER 12

# Survival

Pat Parker rarely betrayed his deepest emotions, but Helen could tell how disturbed he had been since his father's sudden death. It was hard for him to watch the company for which his father had given his life head toward bankruptcy. Helen believed the best thing she could do for her son would be to get him involved at Parker so he could play a part, however small, in turning the company around.

Pat's job at the Euclid Avenue plant in the summer of 1945 turned out to be heartbreaking. He was assigned to tag products and equipment that were awaiting sale at rock bottom prices. He had to watch as buyers paid pennies on the dollar for assets that only a few months earlier had been helping the Allies win World War II. After Pat finished his tagging assignment, he worked in the foundry making bronze funeral urns for the remains of American soldiers lying in cemeteries in Europe, North Africa, and the Pacific Islands. The work was exhausting. He had to ladle hot molten metals into molds, burning his hands through his thick asbestos gloves. Pat could not help thinking of the irony that one of the companies that helped America win the war was now relegated to marking its soldiers' graves.

Helen did not want Pat to be shown any favoritism. She told him that if he wanted to be accepted by the company's workers he would have to understand what it was like to perform the most menial jobs in the factory. Remembering what her father had told her of how Cleveland's immigrant Irish worked their way up in the world, she said to him, "Start at the bottom, and work your way up to the top." Pat spent every summer during high school and college at the Euclid Avenue plant, cleaning tools, sweeping the factory floor, and operating lathe machines.

Sixteen-year-old Pat Parker in 1945.

In August 1945, Helen faced an agonizing choice. She could take the proceeds of Art's $1 million insurance policy, a considerable fortune at the time, and be assured she and her four children would be comfortable for the rest of their lives. Or, she could invest the proceeds of the insurance policy back into a company with uncertain prospects at best. Most of Helen's advisors, including every member of the Board of Directors except Jim Weeks, counseled her to liquidate the company. The woman whom one of Art's Directors had called "Miss Fitzgerald, the stenographer and telephone girl," now held the fate of the Parker Appliance Co.—and its 300 remaining employees—in her hands. She was about to become one of the few women in the world at the helm of a significant industrial company.

Weeks had been a trusted counselor to Art and Helen ever since he and Art bought the Euclid Avenue Building in 1935. Helen was about to demonstrate her mettle, to Weeks and the rest of the Board. They would soon discover she was a fighter. She came from an immigrant, working class family that took nothing for granted, working hard every day. She had never expected life to be easy, and she was not about to give up on the dream for which she and her husband had fought for the last 20 years.

In September 1945, during a meeting in the library of the Parkers' Shaker Heights home, Weeks told Helen he was also determined to save the company. He said they would have to come up with a plan quickly, as a Board meeting was scheduled in just a few weeks to determine the company's future. Weeks said she could expect the other Directors to opt for liquidation. He reminded her the Parker family still retained majority control of the company despite offering shares to the public in 1940. Helen held proxies for all the Parker family shares, and by voting those shares against liquidation she could ensure the company would continue to operate.

Weeks made it clear Helen would need to present a plan to the Directors that set forth exactly how she planned to bring back to profitability a company with no usable inventory and no backlog. Helen reminded Weeks she began to work at Art's first company just before it went into bankruptcy in 1925. She remembered how she, Art and Klamm had refused to give up their dreams for their company, even in the face of unanimous opposition from all their directors and investors, who put the Parker Appliance Co. into bankruptcy. Helen believed Art's second company had succeeded because of the faith of its customers in the quality of its products. Now, Helen said, the company had a long list of satisfied customers, which included industrial as well as aviation companies, and she did not believe they would abandon Parker.

While acknowledging the company's strength in customer service, Weeks reminded Helen that Art had no successor who could lead the company. He had continued to run the company until his death in the same way as in 1917—by making all important decisions himself. Weeks told Helen they would have to find an executive team from outside the company to lead the enterprise in the post-war years. The interim president, Herbert L. Markham, an investment banker, who had served on the company's board as a representative of the public shareholders since the 1940 stock offering, had agreed to serve as president only until the company decided whether it would liquidate.[397]

At the October 1945 board meeting, Helen told the Directors Parker's greatest asset was its remaining cadre of 300 long-term employees who had learned the company's culture of customer service directly from her husband. Art had led them through a bankruptcy, the Great Depression, and the war, and they had learned how to survive hard times. Helen was certain Parker's people could face the current crisis with the same will and perseverance as in the past. Above all, she was confident they remained committed to the higher purpose that had sustained them since the company's founding—providing customers with the best possible service. Helen vowed that she would never submit to liquidation.

For Helen, liquidation would have been the easy way out. With her shares in a bankrupt company valued at zero, she would have had to pay no inheritance tax for Art's two-thirds share of the Parker Appliance Co. If the company continued to operate, however, Art's shares would have a taxable value, and she would have to use the proceeds of Art's $1 million life insurance policy to pay inheritance taxes. As a token of her determination, she told the other Directors she was willing to forfeit the $1 million from Art's life insurance policy in order to keep the company alive. Inspired by Helen's commitment (and bowing to the reality that she controlled a majority of the company's voting shares), the Directors voted to continue the company's operations.

Since Art's death, Weeks had been soliciting ideas from Cleveland businessmen on candidates to run the Parker Appliance Co. Charles C. ("Sig") Sigmier was one of the most respected bankers in the city. He had a long career at the Cleveland Trust Co., and had been Art's banker for several years. Sigmier had helped steer the company through the war years, providing financing for the expansion of the Euclid Avenue plant. Sigmier, who knew the top executives of nearly every Cleveland-based company, told Weeks one executive stood above all the rest in his ability to lead Parker back to prosperity. Weeks was immediately sold on Sigmier's recommendation—a man he already knew by reputation—and promised to propose him to Helen as the right person to run the company.

One afternoon in early November 1945, Weeks arrived at Helen's Shaker Heights home. As he sat down in Art's former chair in the library and gazed across at Helen in her chair, he realized how devastated she remained nearly a year after Art's death. She looked pale and drawn, and her voice had lost all the vitality it had possessed over the 10 years he had known her.

Helen perked up when Weeks explained the credentials of the candidate he had in mind to lead the company: S. Blackwell ("Ghost") Taylor. Taylor was a high-ranking executive at the Reliance Electric Co. in Cleveland. Reliance was a quintessential Second Industrial Revolution company, managed by Clarence Collins, a Yale graduate. Collins had led the company for 40 years, and was approaching retirement. For years, Taylor had been the heir apparent to succeed Collins as CEO. He had, however, been passed over in favor of another candidate.

Ghost Taylor.

A manufacturer of electric motors, Reliance was founded in 1904. Like Parker, it was focused on providing engineering-driven solutions to its customers' problems. During the war, the government became Reliance's primary customer, as it built motors for Navy ships and Army tanks. Reliance was facing the same problem as Parker: how to recover from the loss of its most important customer—the U.S. government.

Helen agreed to meet Taylor at her home for an interview early in November 1945. She was impressed with his commanding six-foot-five presence and the seriousness of his demeanor. As soon as she saw his shock of light-colored hair and pale complexion, Helen realized why his friends called him "Ghost." She was surprised when the serious looking Taylor told her that in his free time he liked to play the trombone in a band at the Hermit Club in Playhouse Square.

Sitting in Art's former chair in the library, Taylor told Helen they should not underestimate the challenges Parker faced. He believed, however, they had a good chance of bringing the company back to prosperity by building upon its strengths: the customer-oriented culture bequeathed by Art, which had given the company's employees a sense of purpose. That purpose, Taylor believed, would help Parker's employees survive the crisis that lay ahead— just as they had met the challenges of a bankruptcy, the Great Depression, and a world war over the previous 27 years.

Taylor told Helen that he was convinced Parker should diversify its sales beyond the aircraft industry, so that it would never again be threatened by a single circumstance that might destroy the company. Helen told Cornell that Art had warned her time and again of the mistake he and Klamm had made by loading their entire inventory of brake parts on the trailer that disappeared over the cliff on the Lincoln Highway. She remembered that Art had vowed never again to make his company dependent upon the fortunes of a single market, customer, or stroke of bad luck. As the war was nearing its end in late 1944, Art had made it clear to her that, after the war, the company should return to the diversified markets for its industrial products that it had served before Pearl Harbor. His greatest fear was that his company could not survive if the U.S. government, his only customer, suddenly canceled all its orders.

Helen told Taylor that she would "refuse to commit the bulk of the company's resources to war, which had killed her husband and nearly killed the company."[398]

Bob Cornell.

By the time Taylor finished his presentation, Helen was sold on his ability to lead the company out of its difficulties. Sensing he had made a good impression, Taylor told Helen that if he was chosen as the company's new president, he would like to ask another Reliance executive named Robert W. Cornell to join him as Parker's vice president. At a special board meeting in January 1946, the Directors unanimously agreed with Helen's recommendation that Taylor be elected president and Cornell as vice president. They would be the only leaders of Parker selected from outside the company in its 100-year history.

Taylor and Cornell complemented each other well, much as Art and Klamm had. Like Art, Taylor was the serious minded chief executive; like Klamm, Cornell was the more extroverted and approachable operating officer. Cornell's friendliness, however, did not detract from the image he projected of a man in charge. Tall, handsome and self-confident, he liked to wear French cuffs on his shirts, which he pulled upon whenever he became impatient with long-winded presentations. It was a signal to his subordinates that it was time to move on to another topic.

It was clear to Taylor and Cornell that Helen hoped Pat would someday lead the company that bore the family's name. It was one of the reasons why she invested $1 million from Art's life insurance to ensure Parker's survival. They reminded her, however, that ever since Art's offering of shares to the public in 1940, the company's executives owed a duty not only to the Parker family but also to the company's other shareholders. Pat, they said, would be treated just like any other employee. Only if he demonstrated outstanding executive abilities would they recommend he be promoted to a leadership position.

Pat had begun to learn Parker's business as a child. When he was about to turn 10 in the summer of 1940, Art started to bring him to the Euclid Avenue plant. It was then that Pat first began to become interested in the family business. Pat remembered his father "would take me down to the factory and pretty much turned me loose. So I learned a hell of a lot just by doing. He let me experiment for myself, which is the best way to teach."[399]

From 1945 to 1948, Pat attended high school at University School, a private school in Shaker Heights favored by Cleveland's wealthiest families. It was the beginning of an excellent education designed by Helen to prepare Pat to lead the company. She was pleased that while attending University School, Pat acquired not a trace of the elitism one might expect from the oldest son of the founder of an important Cleveland company. She noted that Pat retained the same down-to-earth personality he had displayed as a child. He had an air of self-assurance, but it was leavened with a self-deprecating humor. Perhaps Pat had learned from the challenges his family had faced that nothing could be taken for granted, that years of success could be wiped away by a single misstep or bit of bad luck.

During the summer of 1946, Helen made sure Pat was assigned to work the night shift in the foundry at Euclid Avenue. She wanted him to appreciate what it was like for the factory workers who had to endure working through the night under difficult conditions. In the foundry, caldrons of molten metal, jackhammers, dangerous liquids of all kinds and large ovens surrounded Pat. The summer time temperatures in the foundry hovered regularly around 111 degrees. As Pat later explained, "As a foundry laborer, I learned more than

I will ever learn about what goes on in the trenches. It was the dirtiest, toughest place to work that you could ever imagine. It was natural for me. I gained from the experience a natural affinity for the guy working at the machine."[400]

The foundry at the Euclid Avenue plant where Pat Parker began his career at Parker.

Helen bought Pat a large black lunch pail and a thermos, and he took them with him every evening so he could enjoy a late snack. Late one evening, the foreman, a man named Sam Brown, noticed Pat was fast asleep on a bench. Sam had no idea who Pat was, and he grabbed him by the arm and took him over to the Human Resources Department to be fired. Pat was good-natured about the whole thing. He told Sam, "Listen, I don't blame you, I was sleeping on the job. You're just doing your job, and I deserve to be fired. But my mother is going to be very unhappy when she hears about this."

After the incident, Pat and Sam became good friends. Twenty-five years later, after Pat became the company's president, he presided at Sam's retirement party and told the story of how Sam discovered his dereliction of duty. As Pat finished the story, he smiled and said, "Sam has the distinction of being the only person ever to fire me from Parker."

TAYLOR AND CORNELL gave Klamm the title of Chief Engineer, but it was a misnomer; he had been working as Parker's Chief Operating Officer ever since Art hired him in 1917. While Art set the company's course in the role of CEO, Klamm had been responsible for overseeing the details of production, sales, and the design of new products. When Taylor took over as CEO, and appointed his own man, Bob Cornell, as Chief Operating Officer, Taylor feared Klamm might resent the downgrading of his job, and might interfere with Cornell's plans for operations. Taylor told Helen it was time for the 56 year-old Klamm to retire. Helen fiercely resisted Taylor's suggestion, telling him Klamm had been an important part of the company's success, and still had much to contribute.

Taylor and Cornell agreed to keep Klamm on in the position of Technical Assistant to the President, and to allow him to continue to design new products and teach Parker's new employees the company's fluid power technologies. Taylor and Cornell soon discovered Klamm was not a man who harbored hard feelings, and he became a valued member of their executive team. Known throughout the company as "the Chief," Klamm became famous among Parker's new employees, who invariably started out as students in his "fittings school." They admired him as the man who had designed products to fit customers' precise needs, and who had maintained friendships with bedrock customers such as Boeing, Douglas, McDonnell Aircraft, John Deere, and Caterpillar.

Taylor and Cornell started sorting through what was left of the Parker Appliance Co., trying to decide what was salvageable. The company's plants

Carl Klamm, standing in the middle, during one of his fittings classes in the late 1940s.

were filled with millions of partially completed pieces lying around the factory floors. Taylor and Cornell tried to convince buyers to purchase the company's surplus machinery and inventory. They received just a few cents on the dollar, but they were able to generate enough cash to temporarily stave off their creditors.

Taylor and Cornell examined the company's books and spent hours talking with Helen, Weeks, Klamm and other long-term employees about its prospects. After several months, they became convinced the Parker Appliance Co. had a chance to survive. They decided to rebuild upon the company's traditional strengths: its reputation for quality products and customer service, its culture of teamwork, its employees' refusal to give in to hard times, and its engineers' in-depth expertise in the technology of fluid power. At Reliance, Taylor and Cornell had learned the company's electrical technology could perform across a wide range of applications. It did not take them long to appreciate that Parker's fluid power technology also had broad potential applications across nearly every type of moving mechanical application.

Helen was determined to continue to take a leading role in the company's management. She held a regular meeting with Weeks at her Shaker Heights home the day before every board meeting, going over the agenda and making sure they were prepared to ensure that Helen's will prevailed on every important issue facing the company. She was particularly insistent on one principle—that the company keep expanding its product lines, despite its precarious financial position.

Somehow, even while Art had been devoting so much energy to the war effort, he had found time to file patent applications for new fluid power products. Just a week before he died, he had filed an application for a new tube coupling, with enhanced sealing properties. In the years after the war, Helen arranged for the filing of 26 more patents based on designs created by Art. At the board meetings, she insisted the company continue to invest in research and development, pointing out Parker had prospered during the Great Depression because it was continually innovating to meet its customers' evolving needs.

At a board meeting, Helen told the directors Art had been determined to diversify the company's customer base as quickly as possible after the war. Helen believed now was the time for the board to support extending the company's reach to new customers and product markets. Taylor and Cornell fully embraced Helen's diversification goal. They vowed to expand the company's sales base beyond the aircraft market, and never again to become beholden to one customer or industry. In the company's annual report sent to shareholders in November 1945, the two men explained why they expected Parker to return to prosperity:

> *"Our products have returned from the war, tested and tempered in the crucible of a world conflict, again ready for their intended use in the field of Fluid Power, the modern method of efficient transmission of power. Our products have been well received during the war, and with our proven ability to develop precision products essential to many different industries, and to manufacture such products in mass precision production, it should follow that the new products contemplated by the Company will find ready acceptance and satisfactory markets."*

Despite the positive faces Taylor and Cornell displayed to the public, the fiscal year that ended on June 30, 1946 was a disaster. The company lost $2.5 million. Taylor spoke to Parker's employees over the loudspeakers at the Euclid Avenue plant, admitting the year had been discouraging. He also said, however, that he was "able to see some light in an otherwise black picture," and predicted the company would return to profitability in the near future, as it sought out new markets for its fluid power products.

Helen, Taylor and Cornell were struggling to hang on to their core of talented fluid power engineers, many of whom were beginning to doubt the company's survival. In an article called "Looking Back," which he wrote for Parker's 1976 Annual Report to Shareholders, Cornell described how they decided to make their way through the hard times they had faced in 1946:

> *"Since our old business of making aircraft fittings was dead— and it looked like it would be for the next five more years—there were two ways we could look at the future. One, it was hopeless. Two, we had a clean slate and a good vehicle for growth. Taking into consideration our assets, reputation and talents, we could plan any future we wished. We took this second view and it was at that time our dream for the future began to take form.*

> *Our dream? First, we had the vehicle of an established corporation, and the equipment and talent to design and make small precision parts, such as aircraft valves and fittings. Second, we*

*had a reputation for quality and service. Third, all of our know-how was related to products which conducted or controlled fluids—air, fuel, gases, and hydraulic oil. Fourth, we had just taken a terrible beating because 90 percent of our business was dependent on government orders which could come or go at the whim of war and politics.*

*So our dream (and later our plan) became: 1. We would stick to fluid components. 2. We would make only high quality products. 3. We would strive to excel in service. 4. We would stay with the aircraft industry and try to develop new products, such as valves which were not in surplus. 5. We would adapt our fittings for industrial use by changing the tolerances and materials. 6. We would try to develop or buy more fluid power products for the industrial market, with a goal of 50 percent of sales to industrial as opposed to aircraft use. 7. The real dream was to fill a niche in the fluid systems industry such as General Electric had filled in the electrical industry. A company whose product lines could do the whole job—and the complete system—pumps, motors, cylinders, tube and hose connections. We wished to become the one-stop shop for the fluid components customer."*

Parker, known since its founding as a "short line" fittings company, was about to embark upon a transformation to a company capable of supplying all the components of a fluid power system. In a retrospective article in that same 1976 Annual Report, Pat Parker explained how his mother, Taylor and Cornell concluded, even in the dark hours of 1946, that Parker could evolve to become to fluid power what GE was to electricity:

*"Parker Appliance looked at itself and said that if one company can provide a total range of electrical components and electrical products, why should this not make sense for a total range of fluid components and fluid products? This was probably the single most important management decision made in the history of this corporation. Perhaps the second most important decision was to stick to this philosophy, and not to be guided away from it.... It became the motto around our organization that we would be 'the GE of fluid power.'"[401]*

Taylor sent a copy of the June 30, 1947 Annual Report to all of Parker's workers, saying in his cover letter, "I want each employee to have this report and to understand it." Before tax, Parker had earned a profit of $314,555. Taylor proudly added, "It is a pleasure now to report that...we did achieve profitable operations; although the amount of profit was quite small."

Despite financial challenges, Taylor and Cornell continued to fund research and development programs for new products. In July 1948, *The Clevelander* described a new Parker valve incorporating "several ingenious operating procedures" that allowed workers to refuel planes from below the wings for the first time, in a process that filled aircraft fuel tanks almost four times faster than the previous 'above-the-wing' method. The article also mentioned "new plastics designs and special synthetic rubber compounds" being developed by the company for various industrial applications.[402]

In an article he wrote for the July 1955 edition of *The Clevelander*, Taylor looked back to the desperate days after World War II and explained how he, Helen, and Cornell were able to save the Parker Appliance Co. Taylor emphasized they rebuilt the company by retaining its foundation—the engineering expertise and culture of customer service that had existed since Art Parker founded the company in 1917—and supplementing it with a new diversification philosophy:

> *"Parker ... 'grew' with the growth in the aircraft industry...Such 'growth' was wonderful—while it lasted. But it didn't last; it couldn't be expected to last because it was founded largely on war-created emergency.*
>
> *But out of its war experience, Parker had acquired more than a large volume of business. A lot more! It had acquired engineering skills and know-how in the development and manufacture of...hydraulic components.... It was prepared - better than was at first recognized—to start on its 'second growth.'... [That growth] has come about not by specialization in the perfection of one product, but by a program of product diversification.... Product diversification must have a common denominator; in Parker's case it is engineering skill and production know-how....*
>
> *We thought, at first, that what we were selling was our products. It was only after trial and error that we realized that what we*

*had for sale was engineering experience as well as products. In short, we were...in the business of assisting an increasing number of manufacturers to solve problems to which our engineers and our production men already knew the answers.... [We realized] our products could be designed to meet related situations, encountered in one industry after another.*

*Our company has based its growth not upon its capacity to make one particular product better than anyone else, but upon the ability to adapt certain skills to the needs of a series of industries. In the course of a year we turn out some 20,000 distinct pieces of merchandise!... The extremely broad range of industrial fields we serve include, for example, mining, marine engines, petroleum refining, instrument manufacturing, power generation, construction, machine tools, motor vehicles, textile equipment, food processing, materials handling, and paper making...Meanwhile aircraft has again returned to be one of our major markets. In spite of our product diversification, we are still just selling one thing—a certain engineering skill and know-how, having to do with hydraulic and fluid systems."*[403]

Taylor and Cornell realized they would have to make certain fundamental changes in the company's operating structure in order to grow the business during the post-war period. Art had operated the company like most other entrepreneurs, making all the important decisions himself. Taylor and Cornell knew that as the company diversified its product lines it would become too complex to be run by a few people. Parker would need a cadre of managers, each assigned to a particular product line, and empowered to make their own decisions on how best to serve their customers.

The two men decided to implement a decentralized operating structure. They divided the company into separate divisions organized around particular product lines, each headed by its own general manager who was empowered to make the critical decisions affecting the division's business. Taylor and Cornell made sure each division remained small enough that each general manager could, like Art, get to know every one of his or her customers and employees. They gave their general managers the autonomy to run their divisions almost like separate companies. The general manager

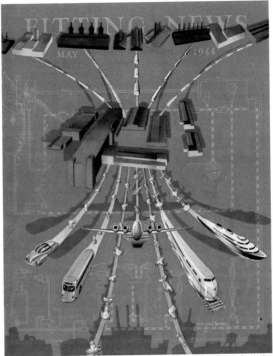

Cover of the May 1944 *Fitting News* depicting
Parker's product diversification.

had complete profit and loss responsibility, reporting the division's results monthly to the corporate offices. Every division general manager was empowered to purchase raw materials, plan his or her production processes, conduct research and development, and determine the sales and marketing strategy for the division's product lines.

Art had anticipated the divisional structure in his last speech to Parker's employees in October 1944, when he said that after the war Parker would establish separate business units, "tied together with central control." Taylor and Cornell believed such a decentralized structure would help retain within each division an entrepreneurial culture similar to that which Art had promoted since the day he started the company. They saw the divisional structure as a way to empower those closest to a customer to solve that customer's problems. They also appreciated that, within their divisions, managers could take risks and learn from their mistakes without putting the entire company at risk. Taylor and Cornell were searching for a delicate balance; each division general manager had to be empowered to run his or her business, but at the same time, the manager had to follow best practices in financial reporting, purchasing, manufacturing, and sales.

In 1948, Taylor and Cornell lured Sig Sigmier away from Cleveland Trust. The board elected him Chairman of the Board and tasked him with the responsibility of overseeing Parker's financial systems. Sigmier wrote a "corporate creed," focused on four basic principles:

*"(1) Parker Appliance Co. was not for sale; (2) management would strive to reduce the percentage of government business overall, while still increasing actual sales to government customers; (3) corporate growth would be through a combination of internal research and development as well as acquisitions; however, Parker had to be the dominant factor in any proposed merger; and (4) acquisitions would be sought principally to expand and fill gaps in fluid power component product lines."*

A Parker Board meeting, with Helen and Pat Parker at far right, Ghost Taylor at the head of the table and Bob Cornell to his left.

Parker eked out small profits of $314,000 in 1947, on sales of $5.5 million, and $289,000 in 1948, on approximately the same amount of sales, but it lost $212,000 in 1949, on sales of $7.5 million. It would be the last year Parker suffered a loss. As the 1950s dawned, Helen, Taylor, Cornell, and Sigmier were about to discover just how well their company was positioned to take advantage of an approaching era of unprecedented prosperity.

In the early 1950s, Parker's executives would have their hands full in meeting the demand for their products in America. International expansion would have to wait until the 1960s. There was more than enough work to be done in the U.S. The country had emerged from the war as an economic colossus. With only 7 percent of the world's population, America controlled 62 percent of its oil, manufactured 57 percent of its steel, and assembled 80 percent of its automobiles. All those industries urgently needed Parker's fittings, valves, and hydraulic cylinders to keep their factories running. Helen could look back to the dark days after Art's death, and marvel that her $1 million investment in the company had given her, Cornell, Taylor, Sigmier and their growing workforce a realistic hope that the company was on a path to long-term prosperity.

Helen's display of courage in keeping the company alive after World War II would become the subject of stories told by Parker's men and women for decades to come, as an example, along with the disaster on the Lincoln Highway, the company's bankruptcy, the Great Depression, and the company's conversion to wartime production in World War II, of how Parker's people summoned the will to overcome hard times. Those stories would inspire future generations of Parker employees to meet their own challenges. The men and women who remained with the company through the post-war crisis would form the core of the group that would help their customers begin the Jet Age, send men to the Moon, and win the Cold War with the Soviet Union. As Collins and Hansen discovered in their study of successful business leaders: "If you beat the odds, you then gain the confidence that you can beat the odds again, which then builds confidence that you can beat the odds again, and again, and again."[404]

# CHAPTER 13

# Boom Times

In the 1950s, just as in the 1920s, Parker had the wind at its back as, buoyed by a resurgent global economy, the greatest economic expansion in history began to take hold. After two world wars that nearly destroyed Europe's civilization, the continent rose from the ashes, in a remarkable economic recovery, led, improbably, by West Germany, which had been partitioned from East Germany after the war.[405] Less than 10 years after the war, economists began to refer to West Germany's "economic miracle." The country's economy would soon be the envy of most of the rest of the world.[406]

The return of Europe to prosperity was due in large part to the integration of the continent into a unified economy. It was a radical concept, creating an economic confederation of countries that had been divided by culture, religion, tradition, and warring armies for centuries. Jean Monnet, a French statesman, drafted the charter for the European Coal and Steel Community, which would evolve into what is now the European Union. As John Lancaster has written, "Monnet's idea was simple…If France and Germany pooled the production of coal and steel… neither community could get a jump on the other…Their essential industries were inextricably linked…The treaty would insure that Europe, a charnel house for the first half of the 20th century, would in the second half become a place of guaranteed peace."[407]

For 15 years, through the Great Depression and World War II, Americans had been deprived of consumer goods. Now they were determined to make up for lost time. They went on a spending spree for automobiles, homes,

furniture, and appliances. Fortune magazine reported, in an article entitled "What a Country!" that "Never has a whole people spent so much on so
many expensive things in such an easy way as Americans are doing today."[408]
The American middle class exploded in the 1950s, creating a consumer culture that would make the 1920s look like child's play. The core of the middle
class—those with disposable incomes between $4,000 and $7,500—grew by
44 percent between 1948 and 1953.[409]

Consumer spending in the 1950s was a boon to American manufacturers
such as Parker. By 1960, America's gross national product was five times what
it had been in 1940. The soldiers that had returned from the war had married and were having babies, creating the generation that would be called the
Baby Boomers. The new families fueled demand for some of the first "name
brand" consumer products. Millions of children began playing with Hula
Hoops, made of a new material called polypropylene, and Mattel's Barbie
Doll appeared on department store shelves.

With its homeland untouched by war, America was in a position to supply
the entire world with its goods. America came to be called the "Breadbasket
of the World," as it began to export half of its wheat to other countries.[410] As
the U.S. began to export food to the rest of the world, American farmers put
more acres under cultivation, and the manufacturers of agricultural equipment—International Harvester, the J.I. Case Co., John Deere and Caterpillar—began to buy Parker's fittings and couplings for farm tractors and har-
vesters that were enhancing agricultural productivity. As Kevin Baker wrote,
"What had been weeks of backbreaking toil by two dozen men (gathering the
harvest) became a few hours' work by a single driver in an air conditioned
cabin."[411]

Helen's refusal to give up on Art's dream was about to be rewarded. Soon
she would have every reason to be proud of how she had carried on what Art
had started. At board meetings, she championed a new compensation plan
she called "Cost Goal." It provided a bonus to employees based upon how
well their division reduced costs to improve its return on assets. Remembering Art's admiration for how Rockefeller achieved economies of scale as he
grew his oil business, Helen was a constant advocate for expanding Parker's
manufacturing footprint. She spoke forcefully in board meetings about the
importance of building a plant in Berea, Kentucky, totally dedicated to the
manufacturing of seals. In 1950, she joined Ghost Taylor in cutting the rib-
bon at the new plant.

By 1950, Parker's sales reached $7 million a year, and it employed 1,000 people on Euclid Avenue, in Los Angeles, and in Berea. The company earned a profit of $457,000 before tax. Helen, Taylor and Cornell looked to the growing post-war economy to help them diversify into industrial markets. Automated processes were beginning to replace the tasks in America's factories previously done by hand. This increased the demand for Parker's fittings, seals, and connectors for the machines that performed the heavy lifting, moving and positioning performed by manual laborers. Fluid power products were transforming factory workers' jobs. Rather than spending their time doing the dangerous tasks of lifting, pushing, pulling or digging, workers were learning to operate complex machines that did those jobs for them.

The new automated machines often ran 24 hours a day, seven days a week, and they required regular servicing to replace their worn-out fluid power components. Parker began to set up warehouses across America to ensure quick delivery of those parts, with the goal of minimizing machine downtime. Taylor and Cornell insisted the company establish a system of independent distributors in every region of the country that could deliver replacement parts at a moment's notice, giving Parker a significant competitive advantage over its rivals in the fluid power industry. Beginning with a warehouse in Holland in the early 1950s, Helen, Taylor and Cornell extended this distribution system to Europe, where Parker's customers were starting to use the same labor-saving machines being used in the U.S.

Speaking to an interviewer in March 2005, Pat Parker remembered "a quiet board meeting celebration in 1952, when, thanks to the company's growing presence in the in-plant machinery market, the directors were able to hail a quarter in which sales to industrial customers equaled the government's 50 percent of Parker's business."[412]

The American automobile companies became important Parker customers, as the company began to supply seals, fittings and connectors for the machines in Detroit, Flint, Toledo, and Cleveland that were turning out Buicks, Fords, Pontiacs, Chevrolets, Lincolns and Cadillacs by the millions every year. The U.S. automobile industry was thriving on the back of low-priced gasoline and prosperous consumers, eager to buy bigger and bigger cars. In 1950, gasoline cost only 27 cents a gallon. Low gasoline prices made it possible for the U.S. manufacturers to make the most profitable type of car, a large vehicle loaded with expensive options. Henry Ford II, the Chairman and CEO of the Ford Motor Co., explained why his company built big, gas-guzzling cars: "Americans like to blast along over interstate highways at 80 miles an hour in big cars with every kind of power attachment, windows up, air conditioning on, radio going, one finger on the wheel. That's what they want, and that's what they buy, and that's what we manufacture. We build the best cars we can to meet the taste of the American people."[413]

By the end of the 1950s, the industry that began in the garages of Henry Ford and Alexander Winton accounted for almost 20 percent of American GNP.[414] General Motors had become a symbol of American industrial power.[415] Henry Ford had begun the first era of the automobile, with his methods of mass production that made the Model T affordable by the middle class. Alfred P. Sloan, the Chairman of General Motors, inaugurated the second stage, in which Americans came to love cars more for their status and style than their practicality. General Motors' top designer, Harley Earl, adopted a jet-age look for his cars, adding fins that copied the wind-swept design of Boeing's 707 passenger jet.[416] Steven Parissien described Earl's 1959 Cadillacs as resembling "futuristic rocket ships, with massive rear fins which stood 42 inches above the ground."[417]

The American automobile manufacturers implemented a strategy of "planned obsolescence," making dramatic changes in the style of their cars every model year, in an effort to convince consumers to keep up with the latest designs. George Walker, who supervised Ford's styling department, said, "The 1957 Ford was great, but right away we had to bury it and start another. We design a car, and the minute it's done, we hate it—we've got to do another one. We design a car to make a man unhappy with his 1957 Ford long about the end of 1958."[418]

Beneath the facade of affluence, unaddressed problems were threatening to humble the American automobile industry. General Motors, Ford and Chrysler, aptly called "the Big 3," were so dazzled by style they neglected engineering advances that could have made their cars safer, more durable, and more energy efficient. During the 1950s, the American automobile companies missed the opportunity to lengthen their technological lead over foreign competitors such as Toyota, Honda, BMW, and Mercedes-Benz. This sense of complacency would haunt the Big 3 in the 1970s, when foreign cars began to make inroads in the U.S. market.

By 1955, Parker was operating four plants—in Cleveland; Eaton, Ohio; Los Angeles; and Berea, Kentucky, with 1,900 employees. The company was divided into two segments with approximately equal sales—Industrial and Aviation. The Industrial Group included the Tube and Hose Fittings, Rubber Products, and Industrial Hydraulics divisions. The Aviation Group included the Hydraulic Valve, Fuel Valve, Check Valve and Fittings, and Cleveland Aircraft divisions.

Parker was selling tube and hose fittings, rubber seals, hydraulic valves, and fuel system valves for a diversified group of applications, including aircraft, automobiles, locomotives, in-plant machinery, submarines, aircraft carriers, oil-field equipment, construction equipment, farm tractors, forklifts, cranes, and processing equipment in oil refineries and chemical plants. The company's sales in 1955 had more than tripled since 1950, to $22 million, and its net income more than quadrupled, to $1 million, the best performance since 1943. At the same time, Parker was diversifying away from its dependence upon the aircraft industry, a goal Taylor, Cornell and Helen had been pursuing since the end of World War II. Thirty-six percent of Parker's sales ($8 million) were for aerospace applications, and the other 64 percent of sales ($14 million) came from a wide variety of industrial customers.

In 1956, nearly 37 years to the day after Dwight Eisenhower set out to cross the country in an Army convoy on the Lincoln Highway, he signed legislation providing $25 billion to construct a national system of interstate highways that would link every large city and region in the country. Eisenhower's travails on the Lincoln Highway had helped convince him America needed better roads.[419] By the late 1950s, the need was even more urgent, as millions of new cars poured forth from American factories every year. After riding Germany's Autobahn at the end of World War II, Eisenhower had a precise vision of the type of road Americans needed. Most of the road graders, dump trucks, and other construction equipment used to build those roads would include Parker fittings, connectors and seals.

From 1955 to 1960, Parker's sales more than doubled, to $50 million, and so did earnings, to more than $6 million. At long last, the company had recovered to the levels of sales and earnings achieved during World War II. In 1960, the company employed 3,000 men and women across the country.

UNTIL NEARLY THE end of the century, U.S. foreign policy would be dominated by the "Truman Doctrine" of containment, designed to oppose Communist expansion anywhere in the world. Remembering how England and France had appeased Hitler in the 1930s, post-war American Presidents believed aggression by the Russians must be resisted, no matter what the cost.[420] The two political parties reached a consensus that America should fight the Communists not in a "hot" shooting war, but in a Cold War, achieving dominance in science, weaponry, technology, and finally, in space, in order to prove the superiority of America's democratic, capitalistic society.

Spurred by concerns about the growing military might of the Soviet Union, Congress kept increasing military appropriations. The U.S. Armed Services began ordering increasing numbers of planes, boats, missiles, and various weapon systems from U.S. industry, in a race to keep pace with the Russians. The expanding Pentagon budget allowed Parker to increase its sale of fittings, valves and connectors for military planes.

The stand off between America and the Soviet Union manifested itself in "proxy wars" in remote corners of the globe. In June 1950, North Korean troops crossed the 38th parallel and invaded South Korea. The Soviet Union supplied the North Korean military with weapons and was extensively involved in its war planning. United Nations troops, most of whom came from the American Army that had occupied Japan after World War II, fought alongside the South Koreans in an attempt to repel the northerners.

Helen, Taylor and Cornell had learned a lesson from World War II: They were determined never again to devote all their production capacity to making war materiel. As Pat Parker later explained, "We did not intend to again be decimated by a huge, short-term customer."[421] During the Korean War, Parker expanded its sales for industrial applications as a way to mitigate the company's reliance on government orders for aircraft parts. As a result, the Parker Appliance Co. emerged from the Korean War with its industrial base intact and its finances secure.

Russia's detonation of an atomic bomb started a nuclear race between the two superpowers. America exploded a hydrogen bomb on November 1, 1952, at a small atoll in the Pacific called Elugelab. The explosion was a thousand times greater than the Hiroshima bomb. Three years later, the Russians tested their own hydrogen bomb.[422] During the 1950s, a phrase evolved to describe the nuclear standoff between America and the Soviet Union: "mutually assured destruction" (aptly called "MAD"). Neither country could seriously consider going to war against the other because it would lead to the destruction of both. As Albert Einstein said, "I know not with what weapons World War III will be fought, but World War IV will be fought with sticks and stones." Robert Oppenheimer, who led the U.S. effort to produce the first atomic bomb, described the U.S. and the Soviet Union as "two scorpions in a bottle, each capable of killing the other, but only at the risk of his own life."[423]

The U.S. aviation industry was one of the principal beneficiaries of America's Cold War military spending. Helen, Taylor and Cornell had predicted the coming boom in military aircraft manufacturing in 1948. In a bold move that signified their confidence in the future of their company, they acquired a 40,000-square-foot plant located on five acres of land at 5827 Century Boulevard, at the corner of Century and Airport Boulevards and within walking distance of LAX Airport. The center of the aviation industry had by then been securely established in Southern California. Aircraft companies had been relocating there for years, lured by the good weather, the comfortable life style, and the talented aircraft engineers graduating from California universities.

In 1948, Parker moved its Pacific Division from the leased premises on Stanford Avenue to the property at LAX. During the 1950s, Parker's aviation business expanded rapidly, as the company supplied valves and fittings for the fuel systems of nearly every American-made military plane. In order to accommodate growing demand, Parker purchased an adjacent five acre plot in 1958 from McCullough Motors. Parker expanded its aircraft valve and fittings plant and built a two-story office building as the headquarters for what the company began to call the "Parker Aircraft Co."

PAT PARKER LEFT Cleveland in 1948 to attend Williams College in Western Massachusetts. He obtained an MBA from the Harvard Business School in 1953, just as the Korean War was ending. Pat nearly missed the chance to attend Harvard, for his grades at Williams did not meet Harvard's standards. During the last of several interviews at Harvard, however, he impressed one of the professors from the business school, as he described how his mother had saved the family company after World War II. He explained to the professor how it felt to watch his parents' company reborn, based upon its culture of customer service and quality products. The professor was convinced that Pat, having experienced Parker's hard times, could add an element of much-needed practicality to the classes he would be attending at Harvard.

During a vacation from his Harvard studies, Pat traveled to New York City for a blind date with a senior from Smith College. One of Pat's friends from Shaker Heights had been rooming with Margaret ("Peggy") Claire Buckley at Smith, and she thought Pat and Peggy would have a great deal in common. Peggy stood out at Smith for her intelligence, wit, kindness toward others, and sophisticated good looks. Pat had met several girls from Smith at various dances. When he first saw Peggy, he thought to himself, "Why, she's by far the prettiest girl at Smith."

For Pat and Peggy, it was love at first sight. They were drawn together by their mutual good looks, intelligence, sense of excitement about the world, and wide range of interests in literature, history, art and culture. Within a month of their first date they were engaged. They eloped five months later. Pat and Peggy moved to Cleveland in 1953 when Pat took an entry-level sales job at Parker. He spent a year traveling to General Motors, Ford, Chrysler, John Deere, International Harvester, Caterpillar, and several other Midwestern customers.

Pat, knowing he was about to be drafted, decided he would prefer to enter the service as an officer rather than an enlisted man. He was accepted to the Officer Candidates School at the U.S. Naval College in Newport, Rhode Island. Peggy moved with Pat to Newport for his six months of training. Spending much of his time at sea on Navy training vessels, Pat acquired a love of sailing that would provide a release from the tensions of his job for the rest of his life.

After graduating from the Naval College, Pat, like his father in World War I, was assigned to work in the military supply chain, where he would learn lessons that would serve him well in peacetime. In 1954, he attended the Naval Supply Corps School in Athens, Georgia, where he began to appreciate the importance of insuring the on-time delivery of critical supplies to servicemen in the field. It was in Athens that the Parkers' first child, Nancy, was born. In 1956, upon graduating from the Naval Supply Corps School, Pat was sent to the Navy's Aviation Supply Office in Philadelphia. The office was responsible for ensuring a reliable supply of spare parts for the Navy's jet fighters stationed on aircraft carriers around the world. Soon after Pat and Peggy moved to Philadelphia, they welcomed their second child into the world. They named her Helen, in honor of Pat's mother, and soon started calling her "Holly."

Not long after Holly was born, the supply officers sent Pat out for a tour of duty on the U.S.S. Forrestal. Pat's mission was to figure out why North American Aviation's FJ-3 "Fury" jet fighters were out of service for long periods of time. He later recalled:

> *"The commanders and captains [in Philadelphia] liked their desks, so they sent Ensign Parker—a flunky, a gopher—out to the fleet to figure out why all this expensive equipment was crapping out. All I did was talk to the troops, the crew chiefs who were under the bellies of these airplanes cursing, swearing, and pulling [defective parts] out."*[424]

Instead of joining his fellow officers for meals, Pat ate with the flight crews, who understood what was going wrong on the flight deck. They confided in him that there were quality problems with the spare parts being delivered to the Forrestal. Once Pat convinced the officers to find better suppliers, the crews were able to keep the fighter jets flying with little down time.

Pat remained at the Naval Supply Office in Philadelphia until 1957. He and Peggy began to think about staying in Philadelphia after he finished his naval service. He had always assumed he would go to work for the family business. Now, however, he began to think about starting his own company, just as his father had.

BY THE LATE 1950s, Taylor, Cornell and Helen found themselves in an enviable position. Their sales had increased to the point where they had enough cash, and a strong enough balance sheet, to start acquiring other companies. They vowed to look for acquisition candidates that would fill gaps in Parker's product lines, helping make the company a full-line supplier worthy of the name "GE of fluid power."

In 1957, Taylor, Cornell and Helen were ready to take a leap into a new fluid power technology—hydraulic and pneumatic cylinders and valves that could perform heavy lifting in industrial applications. Ever since Parker's founding, the company had remained focused upon only a few product lines—couplings, fittings, valves, lubricants, and seals. Now Parker was ready to implement a diversification strategy under which successive generations of Parker's men and women would transform their company into a manufacturer of hundreds of thousands of product lines, changing Parker from a components supplier to a maker of entire fluid power systems.

On September 30, 1957, the Parker Appliance Co. acquired the Hannifin Manufacturing Co. of Des Plaines, Illinois, a leading manufacturer of hydraulic and pneumatic valves and cylinders that controlled the movement of all types of in-plant machinery. Recognizing that the "Hannifin" name had greater recognition in industrial markets than the "Parker" brand, Taylor and Cornell decided to change the merged company's name to the "Parker Hannifin Corp." The merged company displayed a name that stood for quality and dependability in both industrial and aircraft markets.

The Hannifin acquisition was an important step in Parker's goal to supply all the components of a fluid power system. Hannifin's cylinders were strong enough to hold air, water, fuel, hydraulic fluid and other liquids under high pressures. When the fluid was released from the cylinders, the pressure could be transferred through Parker valves, fittings and connectors to move and position parts in machinery in America's plants and mills.

The Hannifin headquarters in Des Plaines, Illinois.

Like the Parker Appliance Co., Hannifin was named after its founder, Michael John "M.J." Hannifin, an inventor, entrepreneur and risk-taker, much like Art Parker. In the 1880s, when he was only 14, M.J. hitched a ride from his home in New Britain, Connecticut, to Cleveland on a freight train, hiding underneath a tank car on a cold winter day. M.J. was going to Cleveland to see a friend who had found him a job at a steel mill in the Flats. A conductor on the train discovered M.J. during a stop and thawed him out by serving him hot food and coffee in the caboose. Shortly after he arrived In Cleveland, M.J. started out sweeping floors in the steel mill 12 hours a day, six days a week, and eventually worked his way up to a skilled position as a machinist.

M.J. moved to Detroit at the turn of the century to take a job in a small machine shop. One day a man came into the shop and asked him to make a few pieces of tooling for his new manufacturing business. The final bill for the tooling came to $1,700, a substantial amount in those days. The man asked if he could pay half in cash and half in stock of his new company. M.J. knew the man had a sullied reputation around Detroit. He had started other manufacturing companies before, and all had failed. M.J. feared the stock the man was offering would soon be worthless. He told the man he would have to pay the entire bill in cash. The man's name was Henry Ford, and the stock M.J. had declined had been in the fledgling Ford Motor Co.

M.J. moved to Milwaukee for another machinist's job, and it was there that he married and had a son named Arthur Vincent ("A.V.") Hannifin. A.V. obtained his engineering degree from the University of Wisconsin, and in 1913, he and M.J. started a small machine shop on the west side of Chicago, which they called the Hannifin Engineering Co. A.V. functioned as the business manager, while M.J. worked as the plant superintendent and production manager. M.J., like Art Parker, was intrigued by the emerging science of fluid power, and he obtained several patents for pneumatic valves controlling cylinders that provided the muscle for in-plant machinery.

In the 1930s, the Hannifins sold their company to two Chicago bankers, Clarence Mitchell and Victor Peterson. They changed the company's name to the Hannifin Manufacturing Co., and in 1957 sold it to Parker. Mitchell and Peterson could have sold their company to any one of a long list of manufacturers, but they chose Parker because they felt comfortable with its culture. For more than 40 years, the Hannifin, Mitchell and Peterson families had operated the company in much the same way as Parker—with a group of dedicated engineers and production workers with whom they maintained a close working relationship. The Hannifin employees, like their counterparts at Parker, were loyal to their company. Many had never worked for any company other than Hannifin.[425]

Taylor, Cornell, and Helen kept their promise to retain Hannifin's 75 employees after the merger. They regarded them as Hannifin's most important asset. Victor Peterson joined Parker's Board. With the Hannifin product line, Parker's sales increased to $30 million. Consistent with their decentralized philosophy, Taylor, Cornell, and Helen kept the Hannifin business in a separate division, called the Cylinder Division. The division was able to take advantage of the growing market for cylinders in the machine tools being used in America's expanding automobile plants. The Big 3 automobile makers became so enamored of Parker's cylinders that each of them instructed the largest machine tool company in America, Cincinnati Milacron, to use those cylinders in its automotive machine tools.[426]

Parker would go on to acquire 250 more companies by the end of the first decade of the 21st century, accounting for 50 percent of its growth and filling gaps in its fluid power product lines. In the 1950s, 60 percent of Parker's motion and control markets were served by hundreds of small companies like Hannifin, with narrowly focused product lines. Many faced the challenges of management succession and of obtaining enough capital to grow their business. Many also found it impossible to match the breadth of Parker's product line and its level of customer service.

From the Hannifin merger, Parker's executives learned a successful template for convincing smaller fluid power companies to merge with Parker. They made a special effort to build friendships with the owners of its competitors that had cultures like Parker's, and products within Parker's fluid power competency. Parker's executives made it clear to those owners that, like Hannifin, their companies could retain their identities as independent Parker divisions, while taking advantage of the ability of a larger company to grow their businesses. When those owners approached retirement, those without a family member willing to take over the business found it natural to reach out to Parker as their preferred buyer.

Each general manager had to convince Parker's board that an acquisition would be successful, and each had to return to the board in three years with a "make good" report proving the acquired company had met their expectations. The general managers had an incentive to integrate acquisitions ef-

**New Era in Fluid Power Sparks Parker-Hannifin Merger**

Victor Peterson, president of Hannifin, with Ghost Taylor, right, in October 1957.

fectively. The greater the synergies they achieved, the higher their bonuses would be under their division's Cost Goal plan.

As a result of this carefully planned process, nearly all Parker's acquisitions achieved the profitability measures the general managers promised to Parker's board. Less than 5 percent of the acquired companies failed to meet their original expectations. Parker's success with acquisitions set it apart from its competitors. A recent study concluded that only "a few companies succeed persistently in M & A," and that, in contrast to Parker's 5 percent failure rate, most companies experience acquisition failure rates of 50 percent to 80 percent.[427]

# PART 4

# BREAKING BOUNDARIES

## 1958 TO 1970

———————————

*"Houston, we have a problem."*

Jim Lovell, reporting to Mission Control on the
explosion in the service module of Apollo 13

# CHAPTER 14

# The Jet Age

The late 1950s and 1960s were a time for breaking boundaries. Just as in the 1920s, innovators intent on changing the world dominated the '50s and '60s. In the '20s, Art Parker, Glenn Martin, Donald Douglas, Bill Boeing and Charles Lindbergh had helped make the airplane a fixture of everyday life. In the '50s and '60s, Wernher von Braun, Alan Shepard, John Glenn, Neil Armstrong, and tens of thousands of engineers at NASA, Parker, Boeing, Douglas Aircraft, North American Aviation, Grumman, TRW, and hundreds of other contractors made it routine to fly on a jet plane, to orbit the earth, and ultimately, to fly to the moon.

The "can-do" spirit of the times even extended to politics. In his acceptance speech at the Democratic Convention in Los Angeles in 1960, John F. Kennedy spoke of a "New Frontier" of technology, space exploration, and the alleviation of poverty. In 1964, his successor, Lyndon B. Johnson, declared that in his "Great Society" people "will see an America in which no man must be poor," an America "in which no man is handicapped by the color of his skin or the nature of his beliefs," and an America "unwilling to accept public deprivation in the midst of private satisfaction."[428]

The aircraft industry was also looking to a new frontier where passengers would be whisked across oceans on planes powered by jet engines. Art Parker had seen such an engine on a test stand at an aircraft factory during his 1938 visit to Germany. The engine was designed by Hans von Ohain, a professor at the University of Gottingen, one of Germany's centers of aeronautical research. An English scientist named Frank Whittle was testing a jet engine at the same time. The Germans, working from von Ohain's design, and the English, using Whittle's, raced against each other during World War II to build the first jet fighter plane. In the summer of 1944, RAF pilots on bombing runs over Germany were attacked by the Luftwaffe's Messerschmitt Me 262 fighter, the world's first jet aircraft.[429] Later in 1944, the RAF flew the first British jet, the "Gloster Meteor," to intercept German bombers.

Realizing the strategic importance of jet aircraft, American military planners added von Ohain and other jet engine scientists to their "Operation Paperclip" list, part of the secret plan to bring German rocket and jet engine designers to the U.S. before the Russians could capture them in 1945. After the war, Von Ohain became the Director of the jet engine research department at Wright-Patterson Air Force Base in Dayton, Ohio.

The jets Pat Parker had watched take off and land on the *Forrestal* operated under Newton's Third Law of Motion: that for every action there is an equal and opposite reaction. After air enters an intake in front of a jet engine, it is compressed in a series of chambers by a group of blades, and then forced into a combustion chamber, where nozzles spray fuel into the compressed air. An electric spark ignites the mixture of fuel and air, causing the burning gases to expand and blast out the back of the engine. The stream of super-charged air exiting a jet engine is so powerful and concentrated that it moves a jet much faster than the airstream from a propeller driven plane. Physicists call this reaction "thrust," Newton's "equal and opposite reaction" to the air being forced into the engines from the front.

Whittle explained the concept of a jet engine in simple terms, saying the engine works "something like a giant vacuum cleaner; it sucks air at the front and blows it out the back."[430] Newton's Third Law of Motion has equal application to the science of rockets. As Sam Howe Verhovek has explained, "Push air behind you and you can make an airplane zoom ahead, equally fast. Figure out a way to push air downward fast enough, and eventually you can rocket your way to the moon."[431]

During World War II, the government's Aircraft Engine Research Laboratory at the Cleveland airport conducted tests on Whittle's jet engine. After the war, the laboratory accelerated its research, and began to work with engine manufacturers such as General Electric and Pratt & Whitney on perfecting jet engines for military and commercial aircraft.[432]

The relative simplicity of a jet engine, with fewer moving parts than traditional piston engines, made jets easier to maintain. Nevertheless, in the early 1950s, many in the aircraft industry were resisting the move to passenger jets. Donald Douglas believed jets would be too noisy, too difficult to maintain, and too large for most airports. A New York Times aviation reporter thought air-traffic controllers would not be able to track fast-moving jets on radar, saying "There is a limit on how many blips a single brain can safely juggle."[433] When Cyrus Smith, the tough Texan who ran American Airlines, placed a large order for the propeller-driven Douglas DC-7, he proclaimed, "We can't go backward to the jet." Ralph Damon, the president of TWA, echoed Smith's sentiment, saying, "The only thing wrong with the jet planes of today is that they won't make any money."[434]

DURING WORLD WAR II, Boeing's CEO, Phillip Johnson had, like Art Parker, driven himself relentlessly to support the war effort. In September 1944, he collapsed in a Wichita hotel room, dead of a cerebral hemorrhage at age 49. As in the case of Parker at the end of the war, there was no clear choice for a successor from Boeing's ranks. The company's Board of Directors turned unexpectedly to one of their own, a Boeing director who was a partner in a Seattle law firm. As a young lawyer, Bill Allen had drafted the legal papers for Bill Boeing's timber business and his new aircraft company.

Shortly after Allen became CEO, the war ended and Boeing, like Parker, lost its only customer, the U.S. government, and was nearly thrown into bankruptcy.[435] Despite massive lay-offs, Allen was able to retain a core group of experienced engineers who would design the military and civilian jet air-craft of the future, and eventually, the first stage of the Saturn rocket that would take Neil Armstrong to the moon. Allen benefited from an extraordi-nary stroke of luck at the end of the war, when one of his engineers happened to be among the advance party of Americans who discovered, in an aban-doned mine shaft in the Hartz Mountains, documents detailing the results of the Nazis' wind tunnel research on jet engines, and a "swept wing" design that kept jet planes stable at high speeds. Boeing engineers in Seattle would later use the Germans' research in designing the company's first jet planes, the six-engine B-47 "Stratojet" bomber and the eight-engine B-52 "Stratofor-tress" bomber.

Allen realized entering the passenger jet market would involve tremen-dous risks, but he believed Boeing had no choice; it had to build a complete-ly new type of passenger plane in order to survive. Boeing's reputation had been built upon large military planes such as the B-17, B-29, B-47, and B-52. In 1950, the company held less than 1 percent of the commercial aircraft market.[436] Allen saw passenger jets as the only way Boeing could break Douglas's domination of that market.

In the summer of 1952, Boeing's board approved building a jet aircraft prototype called the "367-80." The "Dash-80" would be the precursor to the Boeing 707 passenger jet and the KC-135 "Stratotanker" aerial refueling aircraft for the military. The company's business model had always been risky, requiring it to invest substantial funds for new aircraft up front, and then waiting for years, even decades, for sufficient revenue from the airlines or the government to provide a return on that investment. Allen's decision to build a passenger jet was a high-stakes gamble even by Boeing standards. He decided to invest $16 million—four times the amount of profits earned by Boeing in all the years since 1945. John Newhouse has written that "In changing direction [from military to commercial aircraft], Boeing took a gamble on the commercial sector to a degree unmatched by any other American company."[437]

As Boeing worked to develop a passenger jet, England's de Havilland Corp. already had its jet—called the "Comet I"—in the sky. The bullet-shaped plane, which made its inaugural flight in May 1952, could fly at 500 miles per hour, quietly and smoothly, seven miles above the earth, far beyond most storms and turbulence below. The cabin held 36 passengers in the lap of luxury, with a library next to the entrance, separate men's and women's bathrooms, and elegantly clad flight attendants who served "Comet Cocktails."[438]

In May 1953, exactly one year to the day after the aircraft's first flight, a Comet I disintegrated six minutes after taking off from Calcutta. In April 1954, a Comet I tore apart in the sky over the Mediterranean. A coroner noticed something unusual about the bodies of the passengers recovered from the sea. Their faces bore no expressions of shock or horror, indicating their deaths had occurred without warning. The British determined the Comet I's fuselage had fractured and blown apart due to metal fatigue.[439] Boeing was able to learn from the Comet I disasters; it solved the metal fatigue problem by reinforcing the cabin of its new jet with aluminum struts.

As part of his duties as Parker's Chief Operating Officer, Bob Cornell ran the Parker Aircraft Co., making frequent trips to the LAX plant from his office in Cleveland. In 1955, Cornell moved to Los Angeles so he could more closely supervise Parker's growing aircraft business. He traveled to Seattle several times in the early 1950s to meet with Allen, who told him of Boeing's decision to build the world's first passenger jetliner, the 707, a plane Allen believed would revolutionize air travel. Cornell convinced Allen to purchase Parker fittings and valves for the 707's nose wheel brakes and fuel system, and valves for its hydraulic and de-icing systems.

On May 14, 1954, Boeing flew a test flight of the Dash-80 prototype for the 707, an aircraft unlike any ever before seen. It had an elegantly tailored fuselage, swept-back wings and four dangling pods that held the plane's powerful Pratt & Whitney turbojet engines. Instead of hiding the engines in the wings, as on the Comet I, Boeing placed them in full view below, making them easier to repair and replace. The aerodynamic 707, like other emerging American icons—McDonald's swept-back "Golden Arches" and the Cadillac Coup de Ville's tail fins—was a perfect reflection of American exuberance in the 1950s.

The airline executives watching the plane's test flight were instantly sold on the promise of the 707, and it was not long before they began placing

Boeing

The "Dash-80" prototype for Boeing's 707.

orders for the plane.[440] One of those executives, Juan Trippe, was the owner of Pan American Airways. Ever since watching Lindbergh's takeoff from Roosevelt Field with Carl Klamm, he had dreamed of providing international air travel affordable to the middle class. Like John D. Rockefeller, with his low-cost, high-quality kerosene, and Henry Ford, with his affordable Model T, Trippe was developing a new product for the masses—reasonably priced international air travel.[441]

Travel to Europe aboard luxury ocean liners had been designed for the elite; Trippe bought the first production models of the 707 because it could cross the Atlantic non-stop, and carry enough passengers to allow for fares affordable by millions of new passengers. On October 26, 1958, Pan American launched the first commercial flight of the 707 from New York's Idlewild Airport to Le Bourget in Paris. The plane, equipped with Parker fittings and valves for its critical control systems, flew the Atlantic in seven hours—half the time taken by the fastest propeller plane. Following Lindbergh's Great Circle Route almost to the mile, the plane made it to Le Bourget more than 26 hours faster than the Spirit of St. Louis. Trippe proclaimed, "In one fell swoop, we have shrunken the earth."[442]

Within two years, nearly all the world's major airlines switched from propeller planes to jets.[443] Sam Howe Verhovek has written, "The modern-day Magellans who designed and flew...[the 707] really did shrink the world, in the sense that they changed our perceptions of distance in relation to time. Cities that once were six days apart became six hours apart; the idea, in the mind's eye, of "how far" it was from New York to Los Angeles changed, from four days to five hours, in less than a generation."[444] *Time Magazine* estimated the 707 shrunk the world by precisely 40 percent.[445] As a New York Times reporter explained, "Leaving Fifth Avenue at noon and pulling up a chair at a Parisian sidewalk café at mid-night is an experience that must change anyone's estimate of the size of his world."[446]

Until the 707 began flying to Europe, it was exceptional to travel across the Atlantic. A few wealthy businessmen and politicians made the trip, in steamships and low-flying, propeller-driven planes that bucked and kicked their way through storms and stopped in Newfoundland, Iceland and Ireland. The 707 transformed the experience of a transatlantic crossing. Instead of seeing the Atlantic as a barrier between the continents, travelers began to call the Atlantic "the pond," and to view a trip between America and Europe as routine.[447] Aboard the 707, millions could fly across the Atlantic each year, more than seven miles above the churning waters of the ocean, reading, sleeping, eating and watching movies, oblivious to the fact they were high above what had been considered a dangerous expanse of sea.[448]

PAT PARKER HAD to make an important decision in the summer of 1957 as the end of his naval career approached. He could return to Cleveland and begin to work his way up in the family business, or he could remain in Philadelphia and follow his own star. Pat and Peggy knew Helen had been counting the days until Pat could return home and begin to fulfill the dream she had harbored ever since he had been a little boy—to run the company his father founded in 1917.

Despite Pat's love for his mother and respect for all she had accomplished, he did not want her to plan out the rest of his life for him. His education at Harvard and his experience in the Navy had opened up the world to him. He yearned to experience more of it than he thought he could find in Cleveland. Pat and Peggy began to talk more and more about staying in Philadelphia, and Pat began to consider applying for a job at one of the city's investment banks. His plan was to learn corporate finance, and then start his own business.

Pat and Peggy decided Pat owed it to his mother to travel to Cleveland and learn what type of job Taylor and Cornell had in mind for him. From behind Art's old desk on Euclid Avenue, Taylor told Pat he needed to learn Parker's aircraft business. The best place to do that was in the manufacturing operations at the Parker Aircraft Co. on Century Boulevard, across from LAX airport. Pat was intrigued by the chance to live in Southern California, and to work on selling Parker's new products for jet planes. For the first time, he began to seriously consider working for his family's company, rather than starting his own business. He told Taylor and Cornell he would make a final decision after talking to his mother.

Pat and Peggy were staying with Helen at her Shaker Heights home. As soon as Pat walked in the front door after his meeting with Taylor, Helen asked when he and Peggy would be moving to Cleveland. Pat quietly told his mother to join him in the library. Sitting in his father's old chair, he told her he had abandoned his idea of starting his own business, but he had decided to move to California to work at the Parker Aircraft Co. Momentarily at a loss for words, Helen became red in the face, and then told Pat he could work his way up in the company just as well in Cleveland as in California. Helen could not appreciate Pat was trying to do the same thing she had done when she married Art—chart his own course in life, independently of his parents. Pat patiently explained that he needed to understand the company's aircraft business if he ever hoped to hold a high level executive position at Parker. After a long and difficult discussion, Helen finally gave in to the inevitable.

Pat and Peggy wasted little time in packing their bags for California. H. W. Brands has written that "since the days of the California Gold Rush, the West had long been the land of opportunity, the glittering destination of the American dream."[449] Pat and Peggy would find fulfillment of their own dreams in California during the next decade. They flew to LAX on a Douglas DC-7 propeller plane. As they landed in Los Angeles, they looked out the window and saw the words "Parker Aircraft Co." in large black lettering on the facade of Parker's plant on Century Boulevard. They purchased a home high on a hill in the Pacific Palisades area of Los Angeles, near Malibu. The house had a view of the Pacific Ocean on one side, and a deep canyon on the other.

Cornell assigned the 28-year-old Pat as a production line planner in the Check Valves and Fittings Division, which was making fittings and valves for the fuel systems of military and commercial aircraft. Cornell wanted Pat to learn how to run a plant. He was responsible for coordinating the delivery of raw materials, scheduling production runs, and making sure parts were getting out the door in time to meet the delivery deadlines of Boeing,

Parker Aircraft plant at LAX in the late 1950s.

Douglas, McDonnell, Martin, and Lockheed. Many of the aircraft manufacturers had locations near LAX, and Pat often put an expensive aircraft part in the backseat of his roadster and took off down the freeway to deliver it to a customer.

Taylor and Cornell expected Pat to prove to them he had what it would take to assume an executive position in an enterprise they were turning into a diversified American manufacturer. They soon realized that, despite Pat's privileged upbringing, he lacked any sense of entitlement and wanted to be judged solely by his own accomplishments. Pat possessed an inner confidence, derived from his mother's steadfast support. As Sigmund Freud wrote, "A man who has been the indisputable favorite of his mother keeps for life the feeling of a conqueror."[450]

Helen, Taylor and Cornell watched Pat master his production planning job in just a year. In 1958, they promoted him to the position of sales manager for the Check Valves and Fittings Division. Pat was now responsible for convincing Boeing, Douglas, McDonnell Aircraft, and the other aircraft manufacturers to continue to buy Parker's fittings and valves for the fuel systems of their planes.

In his new marketing position, Pat often made sales calls with 30-year-old Paul Schloemer, who had joined Parker just a year earlier, in 1957. Schloemer had graduated from the University of Cincinnati in 1950 with a degree in mechanical engineering. He had worked for seven years at Wright-Patterson Air Force Base in Dayton, testing the fuel systems of jet aircraft being purchased by the Air Force. During that time, he obtained his MBA from The Ohio State University. Schloemer was so highly respected by the Air Force that he was given responsibility for the final approval of the fuel systems installed on Republic Aviation's F-84 fighter, North American Aviation's F-86 and F-100 fighters, Boeing's B-52 bomber and its KC-135 military tanker, the four-engine jet plane derived from the Dash-80 prototype.

Schloemer had been working for Parker in Dayton, calling on aircraft customers east of the Mississippi, including Canadair, Bendix, TRW, North American Aviation, and McDonnell. Schloemer, one of the Air Force's foremost experts on the fuel systems of jet engines, had his choice of jobs with several larger companies than Parker, including TRW and Pratt & Whitney. He was sold on Parker after he met Bob Cornell. Schloemer told Cornell he could not leave Dayton because he had to help care for his elderly father. Seeing promise in Schloemer, Cornell created a sales job for him in Dayton, and promised that he could remain in the city for as long as he wished. That

Pat Parker and Bob Cornell at the Parker Aircraft plant.

commitment convinced Schloemer to leave the security of his government job for the sales position at Parker.

Pat and Schloemer had much in common. Schloemer was just one year older than Pat. Both were recently married young men working their way up through Parker's aircraft sales organization. Both were reporting to Al Zukas, the head of marketing for Parker Aircraft. Pat was impressed by Schloemer's air of quiet competence, and his intimate knowledge of jet aircraft. It was the beginning of a friendship between the two men that would last for decades.

Pat's office was on the second floor of the Parker Aircraft Co.'s plant on Century Boulevard. Directly across the street was the entrance to LAX airport. The terminal was little more than a Quonset hut, with a barbershop on the first floor and a sandwich shop on the second. Passengers walked over the tarmac to board four-engine propeller planes such as the Douglas DC-7 and Lockheed Constellation. By the late 1950s, Boeing's 707 and Douglas' DC-8 passenger jets began landing at the airport. The runways were surrounded by bean fields. The only other large structure in the neighborhood was the factory of McCullough Chain Saw, across the street from the Parker Aircraft plant. Just a block down the street sat the first Hyatt hotel, a simple two-story building called the "Hyatt House."[451]

One day, shortly after Pat began his new job as sales manager for the Check Valves and Fittings Division, he met a member of Boeing's purchasing department from Seattle, just as he was finishing a tour of the plant with one of Pat's marketing people.

The Boeing employee said, "Someone just told me you're the division sales manager. Aren't you kind of young for that job?"

Pat smiled and said, "My last name is Parker. Didn't you notice the name on the front door when you walked in?"[452]

THE ADVENT OF THE JET AGE presented Cornell, Pat, Zukas, Schloemer and their colleagues at Parker Aircraft with a once-in-a-lifetime opportunity to supply a large bill of materials for the new passenger jets being turned out by Boeing, Douglas and Lockheed. After the success of the 707, and Douglas' first passenger jet, the "DC-8," the aircraft companies began to build a series of new jet planes to serve various sectors of the travel market.

These new jetliners created a vast potential market for Parker aircraft components. Cornell, Pat, Zukas and Schloemer championed investments by Parker in an array of products that would fly on nearly every new commercial airplane. At the end of World War II, Parker's only aviation products were fittings, couplings, connectors and seals. Parker's executives envisioned a day when the company could supply a range of products that would control most of the engine, hydraulic, fuel, landing gear, and flight control systems aboard the new jet aircraft taking to the skies.

In 1953, Parker had formed the "Accessories Division" (later named the "Gas Turbine Fuel Systems Division") at the Euclid Avenue plant. It was tasked with producing one of the most complex products on a jet aircraft—fuel nozzles, which perform the delicate task of spraying fuel into a jet engine in exactly the right pattern to produce a controlled explosion. A typical jet engine includes 30 nozzles, located in the combustion chamber, the heart of the engine, where strong vibrations occur and temperatures routinely exceed 2,000 degrees Celsius.

In 1953, an Accessories Division employee named John F. Campbell obtained a patent for a jet engine fuel nozzle, the first of several he would obtain for Parker during the 1950s.[453] Campbell and his colleagues had been working for years to design a product strong enough to endure high vibrations and temperatures, and delicate enough to spray a fine mist of fuel within the combustion chamber of a jet engine. Pat Parker had seen one of Campbell's early designs for a fuel nozzle on a test stand in the summer of 1952, when he was working as a machinist on the night shift during his last summer vacation from college.

The potential customers for Parker's fuel nozzles were the three companies that made jet engines for military and commercial aircraft—Rolls Royce, Pratt & Whitney (a division of United Aircraft), and General Electric. In 1952, Parker sold fuel nozzles to General Electric for its J47 and J73 engines on North American Aviation's F-86 "Sabrejet."[454] The F-86 was the first fighter plane to break the sound barrier. The plane's ability to maneuver at high speeds made it a favorite of American fighter pilots engaging in "dogfights" with North Korea's Russian-made "MIGs" during the Korean War.

In 1960, Cornell, Zukas, Schloemer, and Bill Webster, the general manager of the Gas Turbine Fuel Systems Division, convinced General Electric to install Parker fuel nozzles on the J79 engine it was making for McDonnell Aircraft's F-4 "Phantom" naval fighter. Navy F-4's were selected as the "chase planes" for the rockets launched from Cape Canaveral in the early 1960s. The F-4's, with cameras mounted on their wings, flew close to the rockets at 35,000 feet, moving well past the speed of sound for 90 seconds to match the speed of the rockets. Jack Petry, one of the Air Force pilots, later said, "Those two J79 engines made all the difference.... Absolutely beautiful! To see that massive...[Titan II missile] in flight and be right there in the air with it—you can imagine the exhilaration."[455] The F-4 became the fastest, highest flying and longest range fighter for both the Air Force and Navy. It was used in the Vietnam and Desert Storm wars and by the militaries of 11 other countries.

Grumman's F-14 "Tomcat" became the best known of all the Navy supersonic fighters after it was featured as the plane used by Tom Cruise in the 1986 movie "Top Gun." Parker's fuel rod, called the "Ring of Fire," dumped large amounts of fuel into the Tomcat's engines through 20 spray bars that extended like fingers into the after-burner, giving the plane the power and thrust to double its speed in seconds, thereby out-maneuvering enemy aircraft.

Building on its initial success with America's early jet fighters, Parker went on to provide fuel nozzles to Rolls Royce General Electric and Pratt & Whitney for nearly every commercial and military aircraft in the world. Parker maintained that business by continually refining its fuel nozzles to produce an ever finer spray, which improved the combustion efficiency of jet engines and allowed for more fuel savings.

Parker used the technology developed for jet engine fuel nozzles to expand into the market for nozzles in the combustion chambers of other types of powerful engines. Naval destroyers operate with engines derived from those on jet aircraft, and Parker supplied the fuel nozzles that helped propel ships in the American fleet. General Electric equipped electric power generation plants the world over with engines that ramped up to supply peak power demand on hot summer days. Those engines included Parker fuel nozzles in their combustion chambers, providing a power source superior to that available from coal or gas powered plants. As Hank Tennekes has written, "The quick response of jet engines explains their popularity as auxiliary units in electric power generating plants. Just push a button and a few seconds later 20,000 kilowatts of emergency power can be delivered to a high-voltage grid. It takes hours to get up to full steam with a coal burning or gas-burning unit."[456]

JUST LIKE THE first passenger jet, the first wide-body aircraft might never have been built without a push from Juan Trippe, who was continuing to work toward his ultimate goal of allowing the masses of middle class people to travel the world. In the late 1950s, a travel agent described for *Holiday* magazine the new type of overseas traveler created by the 707, and the one he hoped would someday be served by larger jets: "Thirty years ago, I set up the grand tour [of Europe] for a wealthy widow and her elderly traveling companion. Fifteen years ago, I made arrangements for businessmen, Hollywood stars...and other members of high society.] Today, I deal with expense-account wanderers, solid suburban citizens and schoolteachers. Tomorrow, praise be, the office will be full of plumbers and their babies."[457]

In 1964, Juan Trippe approached Boeing's CEO, Bill Allen, about designing a plane that could carry 400 passengers, more than twice the number who could travel on the 707. Trippe joined Allen for a fishing vacation in Alaska aboard a yacht they leased from John Wayne. Trippe made a proposition in the form of a dare, saying "If you build it, I'll buy it." Allen replied, "If you buy it, I'll build it."[458] The result was the first jumbo jet, Boeing's 747, which was two and a half times larger than the 707.[459] The wingspan of the 747 was nearly twice the distance the Wright brothers covered in their maiden flight.[460] Joseph Sutter, Boeing's designer for the plane, called the 747 "a *place*, not a conveyance."[461] Fifty thousand Boeing construction workers, mechanics, engineers and administrators built the plane in less than 16 months in the late 1960s. Their efforts earned them the name "the Incredibles."

Boeing had to borrow $2 billion from banks to pay for designing and building the 747, the largest amount ever borrowed by a corporation up to that time. Boeing built the biggest building in the world in Everett, Washington to build the plane.[462] Allen later admitted, "It was really too large a project for us." Ultimately, however, his gamble succeeded, as Boeing enjoyed a monopoly in jumbo aircraft production for several years.

The 747 marked a breakthrough in Parker's relationship with Boeing. It occurred as a result of the Aerospace Group's relentless focus on customer service. Schloemer led a team that was determined to convince Boeing that Parker had the technology, design and service capabilities to provide an expanded bill of materials for the world's first jumbo jet.

Schloemer sent a group of Parker engineers to Seattle to work alongside Boeing's engineers in designing fluid power components for the 747. Parker bore the up-front costs during the design phase. Schloemer also agreed to hold in inventory replacements for several of the critical Parker parts on the 747. Schloemer's commitments to Boeing gave birth to Parker's "Customer Support" Division. Historically, the airlines had to keep their planes grounded for long periods of time as they waited for the delivery of spare parts. With the expensive 747, any delays would be costly. As Henk Tennekes has written, "An idle airplane is expensive, especially when it costs more than $20 million a year in interest and depreciation alone. (That's $2,500 an hour, 70 cents a second.)"[463]

Cornell, Pat, Zukas and Schloemer came up with a way to minimize the time a 747 would remain on the ground. Parker's Customer Support Division established locations in Brazil, China, Germany, Japan, Mexico, Malaysia, and Singapore, from which it could deliver spares, and perform repair services, within 24 hours, and get a grounded airplane, anywhere in the world, flying again. The airlines were so pleased with Parker's service that they began to ask the suppliers of other parts, "Why don't you do it like Parker does it?"[464] The airlines were willing to pay Parker handsomely for keeping their planes in the air, and the Customer Support Division became the most profitable of all Parker's divisions.

After months of effort, Cornell, Pat, Zukas and Schloemer convinced Boeing to purchase valves for the 747's fuel system, pumps, valves and flow regulators for the hydraulic power systems, pneumatic anti-icing valves, and nose wheel steering valves and actuators. One of the most impressive Parker products on the 747 was the landing gear actuation system. Parker's actuators raised and lowered the 6,500-pound main landing gear on four struts beneath the 747, which had to withstand 155,000 pounds of force whenever the million-pound plane touched down. If Parker's actuators failed to deploy the landing gear, 450 passengers would die the minute the plane impacted the runway. Boeing soon discovered that Parker's actuators were able to move the landing gear up and down, for thousands of takeoffs and landings, at the "flick of a cockpit switch."[465] Parker's mastery of this critical product helped build Boeing's lasting trust in the quality of its engineering.

For Parker, its bill of material on the 747 was as significant an entry to a new aviation market as Art Parker's sale of valves and fittings to Glenn Martin for the fuel system of his MB-2 bombers. In January, 1970, Pan American flew its first 747 from New York to London. Juan Trippe, Boeing and suppliers such as Parker had shrunk the world yet again, achieving the dream, harbored ever since Lindbergh's flight, that millions of people could cross the oceans quickly, comfortably, and at a reasonable cost. In 1960, a round trip on a Pan American 707 from London to Sydney cost 30 weeks of a passenger's average salary; by 2015, the same trip on a 747 cost only one week of a passenger's average salary.[466] As Mark Vanhoenacker, a 747 pilot for British Airways, has written, "Flying is a very old dream of our species, and when we look out at a 747 waiting to take us half way around the world, we're looking at a dream come true."[467]

The freighter version of the 747 dramatically reduced the cost of Pan-Pacific airfreight, facilitating trade between the U.S. and Asia. In a virtuous cycle, the revolution in the speed of international transportation of goods, made possible by the Boeing/Parker partnership on the 747, also helped accelerate the demand in Asia for Parker's industrial products.[468]

Parker's success in supplying critical parts for the 747, and making replacement parts and repair services available on a moment's notice around the world, cemented its reputation with Boeing, which became one of the company's largest customers. Parker had earned a reputation throughout the aircraft industry as a reliable supplier of fluid power products. By the mid-1970s, Parker would have a substantial bill of materials on nearly every commercial and military aircraft, prompting Pat Parker to say, "If it flies and doesn't have feathers, we're on it."[469]

Industrial sales kept pace with the increasing amount of parts Parker was selling to the manufacturers of the new passenger jets. In 1964, Parker had total sales of $76 million. Aerospace sales were $24 million, declining to 32 percent of Parker's total sales, from 36 percent in 1955, completing the vision of Taylor, Cornell, Sigmier and Helen that the company become a truly diversified manufacturer, no longer overly dependent upon aircraft business alone.

By 2015, 57 years after the first flight of the 707, 3.5 billion people were flying on passenger aircraft every year.[470] Developing jets for the airlines and military was one of the greatest technological successes of the 20th century. It was, however, about to be eclipsed by the race between the two superpowers to be the first to send men to the moon and return them safely to the earth.

# CHAPTER 15

# The Space Race

Robert Goddard began to dream of space travel as a child, when he read the novels of Jules Verne and H.G. Wells. In 1919, he wrote an article describing how a rocket could go to the moon, using gasoline and liquid oxygen as fuel. In a January 13, 1920 editorial, the New York Times ridiculed Goddard's idea, saying it would be impossible for a rocket to perform in the vacuum of space. Other newspapers began to refer to Goddard as the "Moon Rocket Man."[471] The adverse publicity bothered him so much that he conducted many of his rocket experiments in secret.[472]

In November 1929, Lindbergh called Goddard, who was then the Chair of the Physics Department at Clark University, to arrange a meeting where the two could discuss Goddard's rocket research. At dinner that night, Goddard told his wife about Lindbergh's call. She dead panned, "Of course, Bob, and I had tea with Marie, the Queen of Romania."[473] On November 23, Lindbergh met Goddard at his home in Worcester, Massachusetts. They talked on the porch for hours. Lindbergh asked Goddard if it would be possible to build a rocket that could reach the moon. Goddard replied that, yes, he already held a patent on such a vehicle. Goddard added, "But, it might cost a million dollars" to reach the moon.[474]

Lindbergh convinced the philanthropist Daniel Guggenheim to finance Goddard's rocket research. In the summer of 1930, Goddard set up a laboratory in Roswell, New Mexico. He eventually launched 34 rockets, some ascending as high as one and a half miles and traveling at more than 550 miles an hour.[475] Shortly before he died in August 1945, Goddard told a reporter from the Worcester Telegram: "I feel we are going to enter a new era.... It is just a matter of imagination how far we can go with rockets. I think it is fair to say you haven't seen anything yet."[476]

Like Goddard, Wernher von Braun grew up in Germany reading the novels of Jules Verne and H.G. Wells, and dreaming of space travel. He never tired of recounting the first time he looked through a telescope at the moon:

> *"It filled me with a romantic urge. Interplanetary travel! Here was a task worth dedicating one's life to. Not just to stare through a telescope at the moon and the planets, but to soar through the heavens and actually explore the mysterious universe. I knew how Columbus felt."[477]*

During World War II, von Brauns' group of German Army rocket scientists designed the "V-2" (short for "Vengence Weapon 2"), the first ballistic missile, the first man-made object to enter space, and the predecessor of all modern rockets. The V-2 stood nearly five stories tall. It used liquid oxygen as fuel, traveled 3,600 miles-per-hour, and flew to a height of 70 miles, with a six-ton warhead. The V-2 was built by slave laborers at an underground factory in the Hartz Mountains. Von Braun launched the first experimental V-2 from Peenemunde in October 1942. Walter Dornberger, von Braun's military commander, turned to him and said, "Do you realize what we accomplished today? Today the space ship is born!" Hitler, however, directed von Braun to aim his V-2's at London. When the first V-2 landed in a London neighborhood, von Braun thought, "The rocket worked perfectly except for landing on the wrong planet." He later described that moment as "his darkest day."[478]

A few weeks after Germany surrendered, a U.S. Army Private found Magnus von Braun, Werhner's brother, walking down a road near a ski resort in the Bavarian Alps. The Americans had agreed to turn the resort over to the Russians in two days. Magnus told the American Private, "My name is Magnus von Braun. My brother invented the V-2. We want to surrender."[479] A few days later, Wernher von Braun led the Americans to a mine shaft in the Hartz Mountains where his colleagues were hiding, along with documents detailing the results of their rocket and jet engine research. The Americans removed von Braun, his team and their research documents from Germany just hours before the Russian Army arrived to take control of the area.[480]

The U.S. government assigned the German rocket scientists to work on improvements to the V-2 missile at the White Sands testing facility in southern New Mexico, not far from where Robert Goddard had carried out his rocket tests.[481] In the fall of 1949, after Russia detonated its first atomic bomb, the U.S. Army concluded it would need long-range intercontinental ballistic missiles ("ICBM's") to counter Russia's nuclear arsenal. The Army transferred von Braun and the rest of his team to a rocket research center at the Redstone Arsenal in Huntsville, Alabama. Von Braun's team named their new rocket the "Redstone," after the Arsenal.[482]

Russia shocked the world on October 4, 1957, when it put the first satellite, called "Sputnik," (meaning "traveling companion") into orbit around the earth. The silver sphere was the size of a beach ball. All around the world, people looked up to the night sky to watch its blinking light arc through the heavens.

Americans had many reasons to feel confident in 1957. They were building an interstate highway system; many families were wealthy enough to afford two cars; and Dr. Jonas Salk had just discovered a vaccine against polio.[483] After the Sputnik launch, however, many Americans feared their country was weaker than the Soviet Union.

Thirty days after surprising the world with Sputnik, the Russians launched Sputnik II. It carried a small black-and-white, female terrier named "Laika" (Russian for "barker"), the first living being to leave the earth's atmosphere. Early signals from the satellite indicated Laika was agitated but eating her food. The capsule overheated, killing Laika on the fourth day of her trip into space.[484]

On December 6, 1957, the Navy attempted to launch America's first satellite, called "Vanguard." The rocket rose a few feet from the launch pad, burst into flames, and collapsed upon itself.[485] The Vanguard satellite fell from the top of the missile and landed in nearby scrub brush. One of the Navy's engineers noted with horror, "The fire died down and we saw America's supposed response to the 200-pound Soviet satellite—our 4-pound grapefruit lying amid the scattered, glowing debris, still beeping away, unharmed."[486] The New York Times called the disaster "Sputternik," and the Herald Tribune labeled it "Goofnik." Soviet Premier Nikita Khrushchev referred to the American satellite as an "orange."[487] The day after the explosion, the Soviet delegation to the United Nations facetiously offered financial aid to the U.S. as part of an assistance program for Third World countries.[488]

The Pentagon turned to von Braun to rectify the Navy's disaster. On January 31, 1958, von Braun's "Jupiter C" missile, a modified version of the Red-stone, launched America's first satellite, "Explorer." The missile contained Parker fuel control valves used on America's ICBMs.[489] Among those watching the launch was John F. Kennedy, a young Senator from Massachusetts. In the coming days, he noted the American people's excitement about their country's first step into space. An astute politician, he realized how popular the U.S. space program could become. Kennedy had already decided to run for President in 1960. He decided to make America's journey into space a cornerstone of his campaign.

Politicians from both parties, panicked by the Russians' pre-emptive move into space, demanded President Eisenhower accelerate the American space research. Eisenhower convinced Congress to create a new agency to supervise America's space program: the National Aeronautical and Space Administration (NASA). The Redstone Arsenal in Huntsville became part of NASA, and was called the "George C. Marshall Space Center." Von Braun became the Center's first director. His mission was to take former weapons of terror, such as the V-2, and transform them into vehicles for the peaceful exploration of space. At last, von Braun would be able to turn his efforts to advancing humankind rather than destroying it.

NASA designed the Mercury program to send "astronauts" (meaning "star voyagers") into space. Twenty-six astronauts would come from Ohio; six were from the Cleveland area. Most of them received a portion of their astronaut training at the Lewis Research Center at the Cleveland airport. It did not take long for the early astronauts to realize the odds they were facing. On July 29, 1960, a Mercury Redstone missile exploded in flight. On November 21, 1960, 13 days after Kennedy beat Richard Nixon for the Presidency, von Braun and his team watched as another Mercury Redstone lifted off from the Cape. Michael Neufeld called what then unfolded "a comic fiasco."[490] The rocket rose a few inches, fell back on the launch pad, and tottered there. Von Braun called the failed launch "a little mishap," but reporters began to refer to it as the "infamous four-inch flight."[491]

PAT PARKER turned 30 in 1960. His parents' company was selling $51 million of fluid power products a year. In a reflection of his growing importance to the company, Taylor and Cornell promoted him from division sales manager to be the general manager of the Check Valves and Fittings Division at LAX, replacing Walt Loeman, who had taken Cornell's place as the president of the

Parker Aircraft Co. Helen told Pat that Taylor was willing to continue as president of the company until 1962, when he intended to retire. She also confided that she and Taylor had asked Cornell to assume the Presidency of the company in 1963. She did not, however, tell Pat her fondest hope—that by the end of the decade he would have enough experience to run the company. Helen, Taylor and Cornell regularly discussed how Pat was learning the ropes at Parker Aircraft. Helen told Taylor and Cornell that they should continue to "hold Pat's feet to the fire." If he wanted to lead the company someday, he would have to earn it by continuing to work his way up through the ranks.[492]

Pat learned how to run a business during his years as the general manager of the Check Valves and Fittings Division, which was supplying valves and fittings for the fuel systems of most civilian and military aircraft. Just like his father, Pat established personal relationships with his employees, and his customers, including Boeing, Douglas, McDonnell, North American Aviation, Lockheed and Martin.

Pat and Peggy felt confident enough in their future in California to buy a home in Bel-Air, the Los Angeles suburb favored by movie stars. In the 1960s, Bel-Air was an elegant village, a refuge from the hustle and bustle of Los Angeles, with large homes sitting among palm trees and other dense tropical foliage, along narrow roads that wound through the Los Angeles foothills. Frank Sinatra and Mia Farrow lived across the street from the Parkers, and Dean Martin, Jack Kent Cooke (the owner of the Los Angeles Lakers), and Carroll Rosenblum (the owner of the Los Angeles Rams) were right down the block. The Santa Monica beach and pier were a 12-minute drive away, and the Sunset Strip was within walking distance. Pat had a sailboat at a yacht club on the Pacific, and on weekends he took his family on sailing trips to Catalina Island. While in California, the Parkers added two more children to their family, Susan, born in 1960, and their son Streeter, in 1962.

In April 1961, three months after Kennedy was inaugurated as president, the Russian cosmonaut Yuri Gagarin became the first human to orbit the earth. Five days after Gagarin returned to earth, CIA-trained Cuban exiles landed at the Bay of Pigs; all were either killed or captured. Kennedy believed that, after those two defeats, he needed a success to revive his presidency. He was also convinced Americans needed a tangible goal that would engage them in winning the Cold War, just as they had rallied to win World War II.

Three weeks after the Bay of Pigs debacle, on May 5, Kennedy, along with 45 million other Americans, watched on television, as NASA counted down the final seconds to Alan Shepard's lift-off atop a Redstone missile for a 15-minute flight into space. Shepard's Redstone rocket contained Parker valves that controlled the movement of propellants in its fuel system. Shepard had to endure several holds in the countdown for minor glitches. Finally, he yelled to the Cape's control room: "I've been here more than three hours. Why don't you fix your little problem and light this candle?" The countdown resumed, and just before lift-off Shepard thought, "The man upstairs will watch over me. So don't screw up, Shepard, don't screw up. Your ass is hauling what's left of your country's man-in-space program."[493] Later, when reporters asked Shepard about his thoughts as he waited for his rocket to lift off, he replied, "I wasn't scared, but I was up there looking around, and suddenly I realized I was sitting on top of a rocket built by the lowest bidder."[494]

Shepard's "Freedom 7" space capsule, built by McDonnell Aircraft, contained Parker seals protecting the windows, entrance hatch, and escape hatch from giving way to the vacuum of space.[495] The American people's enthusiasm over Shepard's flight gave Kennedy the confidence to reach for the moon. Twenty days after Shepard's flight, on May 25, 1961, he proposed the Apollo program to Congress, saying:

> *"I believe this nation should commit itself to achieving the goal, before this decade is out, of landing a man on the moon and returning him safely to the earth.... In a very real sense, it will not be one man going to the moon... It will be an entire nation. For all of us must work to put him there."*

Kennedy's challenge set in motion the greatest engineering feat in history, a collaborative effort between the government and private industry not seen on such a scale since World War II. A total of 34,000 NASA employees and 375,000 employees of private contractors would work on the space program by the time Neil Armstrong landed on the moon.

At the end of 1961, Cornell decided to invest in a new plant in Huntsville, Alabama, close to the Redstone Arsenal, where Parker could build valves for the propulsion systems of von Braun's manned rockets. Cornell assigned Schloemer as the marketing manager in Huntsville. He and Parker's engineers in Huntsville spent considerable time conferring with von Braun and his rocket scientists. At his first meeting with von Braun, Schloemer noted how he dominated the meeting room from the moment he walked in the door. With the upright pose of a general, he spoke with a sharp German ac-

Wernher von Braun, far right, meets with Parker executives at the Parker Aircraft plant, circa 1960s.

cent, and projected an air of unquestioned authority.

NASA's Lewis Research Center at the Cleveland airport had conducted tests demonstrating that only a rocket with liquid hydrogen in its upper stage could generate enough thrust to propel the heavy Apollo spacecraft beyond the earth's atmosphere. Von Braun initially resisted using liquid hydrogen for the propulsion system of the upper stage of the moon rocket. He remembered how 35 passengers and crew on Germany's Hindenburg airship died in 1937 when liquid hydrogen within the ship burst into flames as it was landing in New Jersey after a three-day trip from Frankfurt.[496]

Eventually, von Braun capitulated to the rocket scientists at the Lewis Research Center and agreed to use liquid hydrogen in the upper stages of the Saturn V. Von Braun's choice of liquid hydrogen complicated the design decisions of the Parker engineers working on valves for the propulsion systems of the moon rocket. Parker's engineers had to design valves that were light, yet robust enough to survive the vacuum of space, the extreme temperatures under which the liquid hydrogen would be stored, and the vibrations caused by the explosion of propellant at lift-off and during in-flight maneuvers.

Von Braun knew Parker had experience in sealing conveyance systems for dangerous fluids, starting with the fuel system of the Spirit of St. Louis. His scientists were designing a moon rocket that would include the most dangerous fluid system ever built, with volatile helium, kerosene, liquid hydrogen, and liquid oxygen flowing to its engines. After spending time with Parker's engineers at Huntsville, von Braun became comfortable in using Parker's fuel system valves and assemblies for his moon rocket.

In order to save weight, von Braun's scientists were designing the moon rocket with thin walls for its fuel tanks. Parker's valves would have to prevent those delicate tanks from bursting when they received their large loads of pressurized fuel.[497] A Parker engineer named Dick Kenyon devised a way to simulate the performance of the fuel valves in space. He came up with a method of using pressurized water to mimic the effects of rocket fuel. After the first unmanned test flights of the Saturn V moon rocket, Kenyon and his Parker colleagues at LAX were relieved to find that the actual parameters of the valves' performance in space corresponded precisely to the parameters Kenyon had achieved in Parker's laboratory.

Starting in the mid-1960s, Parker's aerospace engineers began to spend much of their time at the plants of the prime contractors for the Apollo program. The first stage of the Saturn V moon rocket was being assembled by Boeing at a plant near New Orleans. Boeing contracted with Parker to supply valves that would control the pressure of the liquid oxygen fuel in the first stage of the moon rocket. North American Aviation was building the second stage in Seal Beach, California, and it agreed to purchase Parker reservoirs and valves that controlled the flow of liquid hydrogen and oxygen to the propellant tanks of the second stage, and positioned the second stage engines to assure a proper trajectory for earth orbit. Douglas Aircraft's upper stage, being built in Huntington Beach, California, would contain Parker check valves designed to prevent back flow of liquid hydrogen and oxygen within the upper stage engines that would take the Apollo spacecraft from Earth orbit to the moon.

The command and service module that would take the astronauts from earth to moon orbit was being built by North American Aviation in Seal Beach. Parker's engineers convinced North American to use Parker valves to control the flow of hydrogen and oxygen to the fuel cells in the service module that would produce electricity and oxygen for the command module and lunar module.

Grumman Aircraft Co. was making the lunar module (called the "LEM") at Bethpage, New York, on Long Island. The spacecraft would take two astronauts from the command and service module to the surface of the moon. Grumann contracted with Parker to supply 26 valves to perform critical functions on the LEM. Parker's reaction control valves controlled the helium that pressurized the fuel tanks for the LEM's reaction control system, composed of 16 thrust chambers that would be used to turn the LEM and control the spacecraft's steering and attitude during its descent to the moon, and return from the lunar surface to the command module.

The LEM was separated into two stages: the "Descent Stage," containing the propulsion system that would guide the LEM to a moon landing, and the "Ascent Stage," which contained the engines that would lift the LEM from the moon, leaving the Descent Stage behind as a permanent memorial of the moon landings. The descent engine would have to be controlled with a throttle, so the astronauts could change their rate of descent and hover over the moon as they searched for a safe landing spot. The engine would have to achieve degrees of power varying from 9,870 pounds of thrust to just 1,050 pounds for the most delicate maneuvers.[498]

A NASA study published after the moon landings determined that "The lunar module descent engine probably was the biggest challenge and the most outstanding technical development of Apollo."[499] Very little research had been done on variable-thrust rocket engines before the Apollo program. Such engines would be a major advance in the state of the art. The leaders of NASA realized that a throttleable engine was completely new to manned spacecraft. The engine design was so novel that NASA required Grumman to run a design competition with two contractors—Rocketdyne and TRW.

NASA preferred the TRW design because of its lightweight and greater reliability. Instead of using turbo pumps, which added weight and were more likely to malfunction, the TRW design relied on light helium gas to move fuel to the descent engine. TRW touted its descent engine in an advertisement released shortly before the Apollo 11 flight to the moon, stating "The last ten miles [to the moon] are on us."

Pat, Cornell and Taylor knew TRW well. Its corporate headquarters were just a mile east of Parker's headquarters on Euclid Avenue in Cleveland, and its campus-like Space Technology Laboratories in Redondo Beach were 10 minutes south on the 405 Freeway from the Parker Aircraft Co. at LAX.

Grumman decided to use Parker's valves to pressurize the two fuel and two oxidizer tanks in the descent engine. The fuel was a volatile 50/50 mixture of two types of hydrazine, and the oxidizer was an unsymmetrical dimethyl hydrazine.[500] Since the LEM would be flying in the nearly gravity-free environment of the moon, with one-sixth the force of earth's gravity, it would require an activating force for its fuel and oxidizer tanks. Parker's helium pressure reducing valve, quad check valve, burst disc, and relief valve pressurized what Grumman called the "Supercritical" helium tanks,[501] forcing the proper mixture of fuel and oxidizer to the descent engine, in the precise amounts the astronauts needed to vary the engine's throttling power during their descent to the moon. As the NASA study explained, "The engine's mechanical throttling system used [Parker] flow control valves...in much the same way as does a shower head, to regulate pressure, rate of propellant flow, and the pattern of fuel mixture in the combustion chamber."[502]

Parker valves also prevented any back flow that might allow the volatile nitrogen tetroxide and nitrogen hydrazine fuel compounds in the descent engine to mix in an improper way. If they did not mix properly, the LEM would explode as it attempted to take off from the moon. In 1963, TRW tested the descent engine at its facility in San Juan Capistrano, California, and the Parker valves performed perfectly.

NINETEEN SIXTY-THREE was a year of transition in Parker's executive ranks. Klamm retired in October 1963, at the age of 75. Taylor retired as president, and became the Chairman of the Board. Cornell took Taylor's place as president, and would serve in that role until 1968. Pat became the general manager of the Aerospace Division at LAX, formed by a consolidation of the Fuel, Air and Gas, Hydraulics, and Check Valves and Fittings divisions.

In 1964, the astronauts chosen to fly the Apollo moon missions began to visit Parker's Aerospace Division at LAX in groups of three. Pat escorted them through the manufacturing and engineering operations. As Pat remembered, "The astronauts came to familiarize themselves with the hundreds of critical components Parker was making for their missions, but also to remind our team that those who were going to risk their lives on the lunar voyages depended upon the machinists, engineers and assemblers of these super complicated controls that had never been built before. These were shop visits, not front office courtesy calls."[503]

The astronauts need not have worried about Parker. All of Parker's men and women were inspired to do their utmost to insure their safety, just as a previous generation of Parker employees had been inspired to produce the valves and fittings that protected the young men flying the bombers and fighter planes in World War II. In fact, many of the veterans of Parker's war plants were still active, working in the operations designing, building and assembling the products that would help take astronauts to the moon.

In 1964, Parker recorded $76 million in sales. More than 4,000 Parker employees were at work in 14 divisions scattered across America. Flush with a strong balance sheet, the company was building new plants in Otsego, Michigan; in Plymouth, Michigan; in Cologne, West Germany; and in Grimsby, Ontario.

Ever since 1940, when Art issued 100,000 Parker shares to the public to help pay for the war effort, the Parker family had continued to dilute its ownership interest through additional public stock offerings. Helen and Pat did not regret their decision. Even though the Parker family owned just 46 percent of Parker's outstanding stock, the family's name was synonymous with a company soon to become a $100 million force in the fluid power industry. Now, Pat told his mother, it was time for the family to take the final step in going public and list the company's stock on the New York Stock Exchange. Pat explained to Helen this would give Parker access to funding from investors all over the world. Parker's stock had been popular in the over-the-counter market, because of the company's recent successes, and Pat anticipated it would begin trading at around $25 a share on the NYSE, a 67 percent increase from the price of $15 a share in 1960.

Since 1960, Parker's sales had increased by 50 percent, from $51 million in 1960 to $76 million in 1964, and earnings gained by the same percentage, from $6 million in 1960 to $9 million in 1964. The company had been paying its shareholders dividends every year since 1949, and it had increased its dividend nine times since that date. The Parker family's shares were now worth more than $31 million, an extraordinary return on the $1 million Helen had invested 20 years earlier when the company was on the verge of bankruptcy at the end of World War II.

At first, Helen resisted the NYSE listing, fearing the final step in the transition of her family's company to a publicly owned enterprise. Pat tried to console her by pointing out their family's name soon would be known throughout the world. He said there could be no better time for Parker to become a New York Stock Exchange company. Captivated by the "go-go" market of the mid-1960s, millions of Americans were buying stocks for the first time. Instead of putting their money into "pass book" savings accounts that earned less than 4 percent, they were, as David Halberstam explained, "doubling or tripling their money every year "through a magical device called a mutual fund..."[504]

Helen finally relented, and on December 9, 1964, Parker was listed on the New York Stock Exchange. With 2.7 million shares outstanding, the company had a market capitalization of $75 million. Parker's listing as a NYSE company, the most visible confirmation of the company's transition from a family to a public company, did nothing to lessen the attachment of Pat and his mother to the company. As Pat often told visitors to his office, "Your attitude toward the business is different when your name is on the front door."

In order to give Pat more exposure to the industrial side of Parker's business, which now accounted for more than half the company's sales, Cornell made him president of Parker's Seal Group in early 1965. Helen was disappointed that Pat agreed to take on the presidency of the Seal Group. She told him that she would prefer he return to Cleveland for his final training before assuming the presidency of the company. Once again, Pat found it difficult to disappoint his mother, but he told her it was important for him to continue to work where he could be closer to the company's customers than he would be at the Euclid Avenue headquarters.

Pat ran the Seal Group from its headquarters in Culver City, a southern suburb of Los Angeles. The group's offices were located across the street from the MGM Studios. The group sold rubber seals used to protect fluid power systems in automobiles, aircraft and in-plant machinery. Its products also were sealing the windows and hatches of America's manned space capsules. The Seal Group had been born in the basement of the luncheonette on Euclid Avenue before World War II, when Art began experimenting with methods of "cooking" synthetic rubber into O-Rings. Soon after he became president of the Seal Group, Pat opened a seals sales office in Argentina. His foray into Latin America began what would become a decades-long initiative to expand Parker's sales in that region.

In early 1965, Schloemer moved to California to run the Aerospace Group's sales operations. A few months later, he succeeded Pat as the general manager of the Aerospace Division, reporting to Al Zukas, who had both the Seal Group and the newly named "Parker Aerospace Group" reporting to him. Walt Loeman and Scott Rogers (who had been the president of the Seal Group) moved to Cleveland to take on high-level executive positions at the Cleveland headquarters. Rogers became the general manager of the Jet Division, which was developing jet fuel nozzles. It was clear to Parker's executives that Cornell was creating a "horse race" among Pat, Loeman and Rogers, which would determine who would succeed him as Parker's president in 1968.

Pat was visiting his mother at home on August 17, 1965, a few days prior to the company's next board meeting. Pat had been seeing Helen at least once every month, as he commuted from Parker Seal in Los Angeles to executive and board meetings in Cleveland. At age 62, Helen showed little sign of declining health, other than a chronic cough from her constant cigarette smoking. Augie, the Parkers' nanny, had died years earlier, but Anna, the cook, had continued to live with Helen, acting as her housekeeper. Pat had dinner with Helen and Jim Weeks in the dining room, where they discussed the agenda for the next day's board meeting. Shortly after dinner, Helen excused herself to go upstairs and prepare for bed. Pat told her to call down to him, so that he could come up and kiss her goodnight. Weeks excused himself and headed home.

Thirty minutes later, Pat heard Anna screaming for him to come up to Helen's bedroom. Pat found Anna bending over Helen, who was lying silently on the floor of her dressing room. For the second time in Pat's life, an ordinary evening at home had ended with the death of one of his parents from a heart attack.[505]

Helen did not live to see her company's products take American astronauts to the moon. During her last years, however, she was secure in the knowledge of something much more important to her—that her son would soon be running the company her husband began nearly 50 years earlier, and that she had saved from bankruptcy.

TRAGEDY STRUCK the Apollo program in 1967, when Edward White, Gus Grissom and Roger Chafee died in a fire while testing the Apollo 1 command module on the launch pad at Cape Canaveral. The event prompted a reassessment of America's space program. Many began to ask why the country should be spending $24 billion to send men to the moon when it was facing the problems of Vietnam, civil rights, and the pollution of America's lakes and streams. Von Braun argued Apollo was not just a project to land men on the moon, but to open the new frontier of space: "When Charles Lindbergh made his famous flight to Paris, I do not think that anyone believed that his sole purpose was simply to get to Paris. His purpose was to demonstrate the feasibility of transoceanic air travel. He had the foresightedness to realize that the best way to demonstrate his point was to pick a target familiar to everyone. In the Apollo program, the moon is our Paris."[506]

The Apollo 1 accident forced a long pause in the moon program, as NASA re-examined all its systems and procedures, and every component of the Apollo spacecraft As Alan Shepard recalled, "In the astronaut corps we marveled at the new Apollo spacecraft taking shape. We were gaining confidence all the while that, yes, they're creating something that will be safe for us to fly. After what happened to Gus, Ed, and Roger, that was saying a lot."[507]

Astronauts traveled to every contractor working on the Apollo program, including Parker, to check and double-check all design and production processes. The astronauts' understanding of every component aboard the Apollo spacecraft became just as intimate as Lindbergh's knowledge of the parts on the Spirit of St. Louis. Pat accompanied the astronauts as they walked Parker's plant floor at Century Boulevard. The workers treated them like rock stars, erecting banners in their honor and asking for their autographs. The astronauts asked the workers searching questions about the inspection procedures for the valves and fittings they were making for the Apollo spacecraft. Already accustomed to making critical parts for planes carrying millions of passengers every year, Parker's workers reassured the astronauts no unsafe part would ever go out the door.

In September 1968, Taylor and Cornell told Pat they were going to recommend that the Directors elect him Parker's president at the Annual Shareholders' Meeting in October. Even with the prospect of leading his family's company, Pat remained reluctant to give up his Southern California lifestyle and move to Cleveland. Peggy told him that, if he did not accept the presidency of Parker, he should look for another aerospace job in Southern California.

Pat mulled over his decision for several days. The more he thought about it, the more he came to believe he could put his own stamp on his parents' company, taking it places even they had not imagined. He knew the company was still primarily a North American operation. If he accepted the presidency, he would have the chance to expand his family's company beyond the borders of North America, to nearly every corner of the world. It was a challenge he could not refuse. He finally came to terms with giving up the Pacific Ocean and accepting Lake Erie in return. He and Peggy packed up the children and moved to an apartment overlooking the lake in the Cleveland suburb of Bratenahl, a short drive from Parker's Euclid Avenue headquarters.

At the October Shareholders' Meeting, Pat was elected president, and Cornell became the Chairman of the Board, replacing Taylor, who was retiring. At age 39, Pat stood in his father's place as the leader of the company, which now had total annual sales of $160 million, and more than 8,000 employees.

For the first time in 23 years, a member of the Parker family was once again running the company. In preparing her son to lead the company, Helen had achieved a goal that has escaped most family-owned enterprises. Amy Haimerl has written that "only 30 percent of family-owned businesses make it through the second generation."[508] Pat only wished his mother could have lived long enough to see her dream for him come true.

Parker's board was fully aware that their selection of Pat as the company's next president might be opposed by Parker's public shareholders, who knew how unusual it was to find qualified executives among the second generation of a family company. Parker's directors knew Pat so well that they were confident they could not find an outsider as qualified as him. Phillip Rauch, who would become Parker's chairman of the board in the early 1970s, would say, "Pat's only weakness is that his last name is Parker."

Pat moved into his father's old office on the second floor of the Euclid Avenue plant the day after Cornell vacated it. The office contained a lot of memories. Pat had first set foot there as a 6-year-old in 1935, shortly after his father bought the building from Hupmobile. He had spent many summer days riding his bicycle up and down the same hallways he now strode as the company president. He remembered his father sitting at the same desk, worrying about whether he would be able to make enough valves and fittings for America's warplanes.

Pat appointed Bud Aiman to run the industrial side of Parker's business. He made a formidable figure, with his shock of gray hair, piercing blue eyes, and the tough, confident demeanor of a man completely in charge. His colleagues at Parker, in a show of respect, called him "the Gray Eagle."[509] Pat chose Aiman because of his unrelenting focus on perfecting customer service. He had experienced firsthand how the quality of Parker's products could mean the difference between life and death. During World War II, Aiman had flown bombing missions over Europe in Boeing's B-17. He entrusted his life to the hundreds of Parker fittings and valves on the plane, and not once had he been let down. He expected nothing less from the products Parker was selling to its industrial customers.

The Aerospace Group continued to report to Pat, giving him a reason to return regularly to his beloved Southern California, where he could join Parker's engineers in monitoring the performance of Parker's products on the first moon missions. NASA sent the first men to circle the moon on the Apollo 8 mission in December 1968, two months after Pat was elected Parker's president. The Saturn V rocket launched perfectly on December 21, and on Christmas Eve, Jim Lovell, Frank Borman, and William Anders narrated a television broadcast to Earth as they orbited the moon.

Anders took a photograph of the earth, a colorful sphere in a dark void, rising over the lunar surface. Some believe the photograph began the environmental movement. John Platt said the image may have been "worth the cost of the whole Apollo project," as it revealed the uniqueness of earth in the solar system, and the need to conserve its precious resources.[510]

A Parker engineer in Los Angeles was watching the Apollo 8 broadcast from moon orbit on a television set in his living room. He looked out his window at a full moon in the night sky, thinking it looked closer than it ever had before.

# CHAPTER 16

# Tranquility Base

O n the evening of July 15, 1969, a million people converged on Cape Canaveral. Visitors camped on every green space and stretch of beach for miles in every direction from the Apollo 11 launch site.[511] After the sun set, spectators could see, from as far as 10 miles away, von Braun's gleaming white Saturn V rocket on Launch Pad 39A, lit by dozens of spotlights. Barely visible was the vapor from kerosene, liquid hydrogen, and liquid oxygen being loaded into the first two stages of the rocket, directed by Parker's ground support shutoff valves and six-inch ball valves.

The Saturn V had been sitting on the launch pad for 57 days, undergoing rigorous tests of each of its systems. Topping off at 363 feet, 60 feet higher than the Statue of Liberty, the rocket was 36 stories tall, longer than a football field, with the two Apollo spacecraft—the service and command module and the LEM—at its top. Nearly 80 percent of the rocket was taken up by the three fuel system stages required to boost the spacecraft into orbit. The first stage of the Saturn V would be delivering 7.7 million pounds of thrust to lift the 6.5 million pound Saturn V and Apollo spacecraft off the ground, and Parker's valves would have to direct that enormous power to send the spacecraft on a precisely calibrated path.[512]

The first stage of the Saturn V, filled with 200,000 gallons of kerosene and 300,000 gallons of liquid oxygen, was powered by five F-1 engines. Each mighty F-1, the most powerful rocket engine ever built, stood 19 feet tall and 12 feet wide. When Boeing fired the F-1s in a Huntsville test stand for the first time, the blast had shattered windows all over the city. The second stage, powered by five J-2 engines, held 80,000 gallons of liquid oxygen and 260,000 pounds of liquid hydrogen. On board the upper stage, powered by a single J-2 engine, were 20,000 gallons of liquid oxygen and 67,000 gallons of liquid hydrogen.

On the evening before the launch, NASA held a press conference attended by von Braun and the three Apollo 11 astronauts—Michael Collins, Edwin ("Buzz") Aldrin, and Neil Armstrong. The reporters noticed that, on their spacesuits, the astronauts would be wearing an insignia Collins had designed for the Apollo 11 mission: an eagle clenching an olive branch, with the lunar surface below and earth in the background, symbolizing America was coming to the moon with all its might, but coming in peace.

A reporter asked Armstrong, "You had mentioned that your flight, like all others, contains very many risks. What, in view of that, will be your plan in the extremely unlikely event that the lunar module does not come up from the lunar surface?"

Armstrong knew there was no back-up ascent engine on the "Eagle" lunar module. If the Eagle's propulsion system did not perform as planned, he and Aldrin would die on the moon. Armstrong also knew President Nixon's speech writer, William Safire, had prepared a speech for Nixon to give if Armstrong and Aldrin were marooned on the moon. At the end of Nixon's speech, NASA planned to end communications with the astronauts. A clergyman then would adopt the same procedure as in a burial at sea, commending their souls to "the deepest of the deep," and concluding with the Lords' Prayer.

Armstrong had no intention of dying on the moon. He coolly replied to the reporter, "We've chosen not to think about...[being marooned on the moon] up to the present time. We don't think that's at all a likely situation. It's simply a possible one."[513]

Another reporter asked Armstrong, "Will you take personal mementos?" He replied, "If I had a choice, I guess I'd take more fuel."[514] Armstrong's response reminded a few of the reporters of what Lindbergh said to Donald Hall, the designer of the Spirit of St. Louis, when he asked Lindbergh why he was flying alone to Paris. Lindbergh replied, "I'd rather have extra gasoline than an extra man."[515]

In every way possible, Armstrong did his best to present a positive face to the public. Privately, however, he believed that "the chances of a successful touchdown on the lunar surface were about even money—fifty-fifty."[516] Armstrong thought he was just as likely to abort the mission for lack of a flat landing spot, or to land on an uneven slope that would topple the lunar module over onto the rock-hard surface of the moon. He could only hope that he might be lucky enough to find a place in the lunar sand flat enough to support all four landing struts on the lunar module, and to arrive there before he ran out of fuel.[517]

Lindbergh had a chance to meet the astronauts after the press conference, and to wish them "God speed." At his side was B.F. Mahoney, who owned the small aircraft company that built the Spirit of St. Louis. David Brinkley, a journalist for NBC television, commented that the astronauts "stood in the utmost respect, even awe, of a man who had flown to Paris."[518] Armstrong later explained that "Lindbergh had flown solo with only a small team of technical backers," while the astronauts had been "a part of a three-man crew backed by a team of hundreds of thousands." Armstrong added that Lindbergh "flew through miserable weather and stretched the science and art of navigation to find Le Bourget. We could see our destination throughout our entire voyage."[519]

Pat Parker decided to leave his office in Cleveland and return to Los Angeles to watch the lift-off of Apollo 11 with Peggy and a group of their friends in the living room of their home in Bel-Air. Pat had a lot to worry about as he watched the CBS anchorman Walter Cronkite narrate the countdown to lift off. He remembered the early Redstone rockets that had blown up on the launch pad or crashed shortly after lift-off. He knew the Saturn V rocket and spacecraft contained 120 Parker components for critical operations such as the mixing of liquid hydrogen and oxygen fuel.[520] Those components would have to operate exactly as planned for a successful launch, and flight to the moon and back.

Six hundred million people around the world were watching the final seconds of the countdown.[521] In the cafeteria at Parker's plant at LAX Airport, hundreds of Parker engineers who had designed the valves for the propulsion systems of the Saturn V rocket, command and service module, and LEM were anxiously watching six small black and white televisions. In front of his television at his home on the west side of Cleveland, Carl Klamm, now 81 years old and retired from Parker for six years, was thinking about the days he spent in San Diego installing the fuel system on the Spirit of St. Louis. That system had to accommodate 450 gallons of fuel, which had seemed like a lot to Klamm at the time. Now Parker valves would be controlling the flow of 6 million gallons of fuel that had been loaded onto the Saturn V.

Collins, Aldrin and Armstrong were lying three abreast in the "Columbia" command and service module, named after the "Columbiad" spacecraft fired from Florida to the moon in Jules Verne's 1865 novel From the Earth to the Moon. The astronauts' living space was not much wider than a king-sized bed. Directly in front of the astronauts was a 180-degree instrument panel with 500 toggle switches that controlled the firing of rockets that would position Columbia throughout the voyage. The service module, connected to Columbia at the astronauts' backs, would provide them with heat, cabin pressure, oxygen and water during their flight to the moon and back. Fuel cells in the service module, supplied with hydrogen and oxygen regulated by Parker valves, generated the electricity and oxygen supply for the command and service module.

At "T-minus 9 seconds," the five F-1 engines in the first stage ignited. Four enormous metal arms held the Saturn V down on the launch pad for nine seconds, allowing it to gain the 7.7 million pounds of thrust necessary to lift the rocket from the launch pad. When the countdown reached "0", the arms gave way, and Parker switches sent signals for compressed gas to run up a pneumatic system on the launch pad, undoing the five service bridges connected to the rocket. A preprogrammed yaw maneuver turned the nose of the rocket a few degrees from vertical, pointing the nose away from the tower.

Most astronauts believed the seconds before a rocket clears the tower to be the most dangerous part of any space flight. If the rocket hit the tower, they would never be able to escape the explosion from 6 million gallons of rocket fuel. Armstrong, Collins and Aldrin felt a series of lurches and bumps just after lift-off. Collins said afterward, "Very rough. The rocket was steering like crazy. It was like...driving a car down a very narrow alleyway... [and the driver] keeps jerking the wheel back and forth... I was glad when they called 'Tower Clear,' because it was nice to know there was no structure around when the thing was going through its little hiccups and jerks."[522] As soon as the rocket cleared the tower, control of the moon mission transferred from the Cape to Mission Control in Houston.

After Lindbergh watched the lift-off, he said "I have never experienced such a sense of power." Later, he wrote a NASA director to explain he had calculated that, in the Saturn V's first second after lift-off, it burned more than 10 times the fuel he had used flying from New York to Paris.[523]

NASA/Scan by Kipp Teague

Apollo 11 Saturn V liftoff on July 16, 1969.

Parker's engineers at LAX watched carefully as the Saturn V rose into the sky atop a plume of fire. The burn looked perfect to them, and they breathed a sigh of relief as the rocket disappeared into the upper atmosphere. Mission Control kept saying the rocket was flying exactly as planned. Parker engineers assumed their ball valves and flow control valves were circulating liquid oxygen and kerosene to the engines and maintaining constant pressures in the fuel tanks of the first stage of the Saturn V in the precise quantities needed to maintain a constant acceleration into space. Parker propellant shut-off valves were standing by to shut off fuel in the event an engine malfunctioned.

As the rocket accelerated, the astronauts, lying next to each other on their couches, could hear the rumble of the first stage rocket engines and feel the pressure of up to four times the weight of gravity (4 "Gs"). Out their windows, they looked down upon the Atlantic coast, receding quickly beneath them. Sixty-six years earlier, a period shorter than the life span of millions of those watching on television, Orville Wright had flown 852 feet, at a spot a few hundred miles up the Atlantic coast. Now Collins, Aldrin and Armstrong were starting a 436,000-mile trip to the moon and back. Like the Wrights, Armstrong had been born and raised in southwestern Ohio. In his pocket, he was carrying a piece of fabric from a wing of the Wrights' 1903 Flyer.[524]

Almost 50 miles high, two minutes and 42 seconds after lift-off, the rocket jettisoned its first stage. Three minutes and 12 seconds after lift-off, the second stage engines ignited, and the Saturn V accelerated to 6,000 miles-per-hour. A Parker accumulator reservoir manifold assembly provided the hydraulic energy to position the second stage engines to the proper trajectory toward outer space,[525] and Parker hydrogen and oxygen control valves directed 260,000 gallons of liquid hydrogen and 80,000 gallons of liquid oxygen to the second stage engines. Nine minutes and nine seconds after lift-off, at an altitude of 108 miles, the second stage separated, and the upper stage ignited 10 seconds later. Parker check valves prevented the back flow of 67,000 gallons of liquid hydrogen and 20,000 gallons of liquid oxygen into their respective storage tanks, as the upper stage sent the astronauts into orbit around the earth. Eleven minutes and 39 seconds after lift-off, 118 miles above the earth, the third stage engines cut off.

Mid-way through the second orbit, two hours and 44 minutes after leaving Launch Pad 39A, the astronauts ignited their upper stage rocket engines once again, another testing time for Parker's products. Parker hydraulic check valves protected the hydraulic systems of the third stage during the five-minute "trans-lunar insertion" burn that pointed the spacecraft away from earth, beginning a journey across 218,000 miles of space to the moon. Just as Lindbergh, 40 years earlier, had gazed back wistfully at the comforting harbor of St. John's, Newfoundland as he set out over the Atlantic, Armstrong, Aldrin and Collins looked down upon an earth they were leaving behind for the unknown perils of space.

Four hours and 17 minutes after lift-off, Collins separated the command and service modules from the upper stage of the Saturn V rocket, to which the "Eagle" lunar module was still attached. Turning the command and service module around to face the rocket, Collins docked with Eagle and separated it from the upper stage, which flew toward the moon, whose gravity sent it three days later into an orbit around the sun.

On July 17, the day after Apollo 11 lifted off, the New York Times issued a retraction of its 1920 editorial criticizing Robert Goddard for claiming a rocket could fly to the moon. The Times said, "Further investigation and experimentation have confirmed the findings of Isaac Newton in the 17th century, and it is now definitely established that a rocket can function in a vacuum as well as in an atmosphere. The Times regrets its error."[526] The Washington Post called the editorial "one of the great retractions of our time."[527]

During the astronauts' three-day trip to the moon, the fuel systems of the command and service module were protected by Parker seals and fittings. The company's seals also ensured that no leakage would occur in the areas surrounding the observation windows and hatches in the command and service module and the LEM. Parker fuel and oxidizer valves regulated the flow of fuel to the auxiliary power unit on the command module. Parker fuel cell reactant supply modules controlled the flow of hydrogen and oxygen to the fuel cells, which provided oxygen and electrical power for the mission. Parker's oxygen and hydrogen modules regulated the temperature and pressure in the oxygen and hydrogen storage tanks, as well as the oxygen used to pressurize the command module.

A diagram of Parker products used on the voyage from Earth to the moon.

On July 19, the astronauts orbited the moon eight times, looking down on their planned landing site in the Sea of Tranquility, which they called the "Footprint." They were awed at the rugged terrain passing beneath them, and they were reminded how few places on the moon were suited to land a spacecraft. They hoped a meteor like those that had formed the craters on the moon would not land while they sat on the lunar surface.[528]

On July 20, Aldrin and Armstrong awoke for an early breakfast, and moved through a tunnel to the Eagle lunar module. They were sitting in a space smaller than the cage on a Ferris wheel. It was nearly as claustrophobic as the cockpit of the Spirit of St. Louis. Like Lindbergh's plane, the Eagle was designed to carry the greatest possible amount of fuel and the least possible amount of weight. As John Noble Wilford wrote for the New York Times, "Nearly three-fourths of the vehicle's weight was in propellants."[529]

Aldrin explained in his memoirs how it felt to sit in the LEM that day:

*"A technological wonder, it had to be as light as possible, so it was far from luxurious inside. Everything in the interior had been sprayed with a dull navy-gray coating. To further reduce weight...all the wiring bundles and plumbing...[were uncovered].... There were no seats...or sleeping couches.... We would fly the lunar lander while standing up, almost shoulder to shoulder, in our pressurized suits and helmets. We would be tethered to the deck...by elastic cords. Two small upside-down triangular windows provided our only sight of the surface. It was going to be an interesting ride."[530]*

Aldrin and Armstrong checked on the Parker oxygen control assembly, which controlled the oxygen used to pressurize the Eagle, and the astronauts' suits during their walk on the moon. Eight and a half miles above the lunar surface, they disconnected from the command and service module. Aldrin turned the Eagle around to face Collins in the command and service module, so he could inspect the LEM as it pirouetted in front of him. Parker's reaction control valves were turning Eagle to the proper attitude for descent. A hush came over the controllers in Houston as they realized the astronauts had taken the first step toward the moon landing.

Early in Grumann's design process, its engineers had decided the LEM need not be streamlined or aerodynamic. Unlike any other manned spacecraft yet made, it would never fly in the earth's gravity. In the vacuum of space, or the minimal gravity of the moon, there would be no need to worry about wind resistance. The Eagle, covered in a sheath of golden and black foil, was shaped awkwardly, with antennae, landing legs, a docking window, and a hatch pointing out in all directions.

Mission Control asked Collins how the spacecraft looked, and he replied, "The Eagle has wings."[531]

Collins said a soft goodbye to Armstrong and Aldrin: "You guys take care." In a reference to the main north-south highway next to the Cape, where

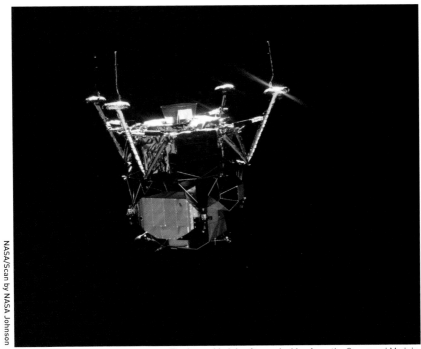

NASA/Scan by NASA Johnson

The Lunar Module after undocking from the Command Module, just before Aldrin and Armstrong began their descent to the moon.

the astronauts liked to race their sports cars, Armstrong replied, "See you later. Going right down U.S. 1, Mike."[532]

As Aldrin and Armstrong flew on the backside of the moon, they activated the Eagle's descent engine for the first time, to begin their approach to the lunar surface. The "descent orbit insertion burn" began the braking action that would take the spacecraft down from 64 miles in altitude to the planned landing spot in the Sea of Tranquility. Parker valves pressurized the propellant tanks of the descent engine and regulated the pressure of the helium that was forcing fuel and oxidizer to the engine, which was pointed toward the spacecraft's line of descent.

The auditorium at Mission Control was starting to fill up, as von Braun and several other dignitaries arrived. The controllers were waiting to reacquire communications with Eagle after it emerged from the backside of the moon. Gene Kranz, the flight director of Apollo 11, was sitting in the last row of seats. A no-nonsense man with a short crew cut, he had flown combat missions during the Korean War in an F-86 Sabrejet equipped with Parker fuel valves. Later, he had been an assistant flight director for the manned Mercury flights. Kranz had picked Charlie Duke, a young astronaut, as his "Capsule Communicator, or "CapCom," the only person in the room authorized to speak directly to the astronauts. Kranz believed that Duke, with his astronaut training and air of quiet confidence, was uniquely qualified for the job. He was sitting in the first row of Mission Control, in front of the video monitor that covered the wall at the front of the auditorium.

After receiving reports from other controllers that the burn on the backside of the moon had gone perfectly, Duke told Aldrin and Armstrong, "Eagle, Houston... You are Go for powered descent." The spacecraft was now 21 miles above the moon. What Kranz later called "the exquisite ballet of flight crew and ground controllers" was about to begin.[533] In 12 minutes, if all went well, the Eagle would be on the surface of the moon.

Kranz told his team: "Today is our day, and the hopes and dreams of the entire world are with us. This is our time and place, and we will remember this day, and what we will do here always.... [Today] we will land an American on the moon... You are a hell of a good team. I will stand behind every call that you will make. Good luck and God bless us today!"[534]

At 50,000 feet above the moon, Parker's valves began to play a starring role. Parker's reaction control valves controlled the operation of four banks of attitude thrusters on the outside surface of the Eagle, which positioned its angle and controlled its movement from side to side. A Parker pressurization system, composed of four different types of Parker valves, regulated the pressure of helium in the descent engine, which forced fuel and oxidizer to the engine, and determined the rate of Eagle's descent to the surface of the moon. The astronauts were still flying on their backs, controlling the Eagle by varying the thrust of the descent engine and using their attitude thrusters to maintain a level flight.

Armstrong and Aldrin had been lying face down, looking out backward from the Eagle ever since they began their descent. At 7,000 feet, with the landing site five miles ahead, Armstrong activated the Parker reaction control valves, and the Eagle pitched over to a vertical position. The astronauts came upright, looking directly down at the moon's surface through the Eagle's small triangular windows. Armstrong was flying the spacecraft and Aldrin was calling out their descending altitude from readouts on Eagle's computer. The motors in the descent engine, with propellant tanks pressurized by a system of five interconnected Parker valves, were burning in front of them as they passed through 10,000 feet. As the Eagle descended, Aldrin thought of his father, who had been a friend of Lindbergh and Robert Goddard, and who had told him of hearing them talk of their dream of landing on the moon.

Back in Mission Control, Kranz thought to himself, "As I look around, it becomes real for me; in the next 40 minutes this team will try to take two Americans to the surface of the moon. It will all be on the line. We will land, crash, or abort. In 40 minutes, we will know which."[535]

At 700 feet, Armstrong used Parker's reaction control valves to hover above the moon, as he looked for a flat landing spot. The Footprint was a 10-mile-long and three-mile-wide flat oval area on the western edge of the Sea of Tranquility. Suddenly, Aldrin and Armstrong realized the computer was guiding them toward what could be a fatal touchdown. They had overshot their planned landing spot on the Footprint by four miles. Eagle was heading straight for a group of large boulders surrounding a crater larger than a football field. "OK," Armstrong said quietly, "Pretty rocky area." The on-board computer, which had been controlling the descent, was sending out alarm signals, indicating it was overloaded with data. The computer had less memory than today's cell phones.[536]

In the living room of their home in Bel-Air, Pat and Peggy Parker were watching and listening, as Cronkite described the descent. A 30-minute drive south from the Parkers' home, on Century Boulevard at the entrance to LAX Airport, 100 Parker engineers were gathered in the cafeteria of the Parker Aircraft Co. to watch the moon landing. The room was quiet, except for the sound from several television sets sitting on tables in front of the room. For more than five years, the men and women in the room had been designing and re-designing, testing and re-testing, Parker's valves in the Eagle's descent engine. Parker's engineers were keenly aware that none of those tests had duplicated the near "Zero G" environment in which the Eagle was operating.

Very few of the billion other people watching around the world were aware of what the Parker engineers had realized—that Aldrin and Armstrong were in danger of crash-landing on the moon. Over the last several years, the engineers had watched hundreds of simulations of the moon landing, and none of them bore any resemblance to what was unfolding before them. Armstrong decided to take over manual control of the Eagle. At his right hand was a red pistol grip, similar to a joystick, which sent signals to Parker's reaction control valves to change the pitch, roll, and yaw of Eagle. At his left was a control which signaled the Parker valves in the descent engine to alter Eagle's rate of descent. Right in front of him was a big red "Alert Stage" button. If either astronaut hit the button, the Eagle would blast back up to Columbia, aborting the mission.

Armstrong was flying past crater holes and boulders the size of trucks.[537] He made a split-second decision to fly farther than Mission Control had planned, in search of a safe landing site.[538] Using a lever at his right hand, he directed the Parker valves maneuvering the jets to tilt the lunar module forward and shift its hovering position. He deactivated the autopilot and took over control of the spacecraft from the computer. Armstrong was disregarding his instrument panel and flying by sight, looking out his window for a place to land. He thought, "The rocks seemed to be coming up at us awfully fast."[539]

The Eagle had only 90 seconds of fuel left. Kranz told Duke to instruct Armstrong and Aldrin to continue their approach. Speaking into his microphone, Duke told the astronauts, "We're go, Eagle. Hang tight, we're go."

After a brief pause, Aldrin responded, "Roger, understand. Go for landing."

Kranz, realizing the courage it took for his team to continue the descent with hardly any fuel left in Eagle's tanks, thought to himself, "I am about to bust my gut with pride for my people."[540]

As the astronauts descended below 500 feet, Aldrin said, "Light's on," referring to a blinking amber light on Eagle's instrument panel, indicating the astronauts were about to run out of fuel.

Duke tersely responded "Sixty seconds," alerting Aldrin and Armstrong they only had a minute of fuel left.

Armstrong was gliding sideways, trying to conserve as much of his fuel as possible. The historian Joseph J. Corn has written, "Pilots have always closely monitored their fuel supplies—Lindbergh did so over the Atlantic...but the cost of miscalculation had never been higher than that faced by Armstrong and Aldrin."[541]

Carl Klamm, watching from the rocking chair in his living room in Cleveland, realized the implications of Duke's 60-second warning. He knew the astronauts had to find a safe place to land, and soon, or they would perish on the moon. He sat quietly, thinking about how Armstrong was using Parker's reaction control valves to control his steering and attitude. He kept waiting to hear confirmation the astronauts had reached the surface. He thought about that day in May 1927, when he pushed the Spirit of St. Louis down the runway at Roosevelt Field. He marveled that, just as Lindbergh had depended upon Parker to protect his fuel system, Aldrin and Armstrong were relying on Parker's valves to bring them to a safe landing on the moon. Klamm crossed his fingers and hoped the Eagle's flight to the moon would be just as successful as Lindbergh's trip to Paris.

Kranz thought, "You can almost feel the crew in Eagle reaching for the surface. I look at my displays. The descent rate is almost zero. They are hovering now, and I try some body English in my chair to help them find a place to land."[542]

Kranz knew that, at the current descent rate, the astronauts would have, at most, 30 seconds of fuel remaining at touchdown. He got "the feeling the astronauts are going for broke." No one, he believed, was better prepared to fly out of danger than Aldrin and Armstrong. Aldrin had grown up hearing his father, a military pilot, tell stories about flying test flights with Lindbergh. Armstrong had faced down death before, in a damaged fighter plane in Korea, the crash landing of his "X-15" rocket plane, and during his Gemini orbital mission, when he courageously brought a tumbling spacecraft back under control.

Kranz was thinking, "They are the right ones for the job. I cross myself and say, 'Please, God.'"[543]

Mission Control was quiet, as everyone in the room strained to hear the astronauts.

Kranz told Duke, "You better remind them there ain't no damn gas stations on the moon." In a calm voice, Duke simply said to the astronauts, "Thirty seconds."

After several long seconds, Armstrong finally had something positive to report. Slightly to his left, he could see the rocks were thinning out into a smooth, flat area. He said, "OK...looks like a good area here... Gonna be right over that crater.... I've got a good spot."

Aldrin later remembered that "I pretty much used my body 'English,' as best I could in a spacesuit, as if to say, 'Neil, get this thing on the ground.'"[544]

Using his last precious drops of fuel, Armstrong activated Parker's reaction control valves and fired his right bank of maneuvering jets to move Eagle to the left. The spacecraft swayed gently from side to side as Armstrong headed for the flat area.

Aldrin, calmer now, began to count down the last few seconds of their flight: "Forty feet, picking up some dust, 30 feet, seeing a shadow." The shadow was being cast by one of Eagle's landing pads on the surface of the moon. Now there was no margin for error. There was not enough time for the Parker valves and explosive charges to separate the upper ascent stage of Eagle from its descent stage. Aldrin and Armstrong had only one alternative—they had to land Eagle on the moon.

The dust being kicked up by the descent engine made it feel like the Eagle was landing in a ground fog.[545] As the Eagle descended below 40 feet, Kranz felt the enormity of what was about to happen strike him like a thunderclap. He thought, "They are going to make it! It is like watching Christopher Columbus wade ashore in the New World."

Aldrin looked out his window and saw one of the Eagle's four footpads touch the surface.

"Contact light," he said to Mission Control, referring to a blue light on his instrument panel indicating all of the Eagle's four footpads were now resting on the moon. Aldrin looked over at Armstrong with a glance of relief, grabbed Armstrong's hand and whispered, "We made it."

Armstrong was concentrating so hard on flying the Eagle that he had not noticed they had touched the moon, nor had he heard Aldrin call out the contact light.[546] Aldrin would later recall, "The lunar module settled gently, and we stopped moving. After flying for more than four days, it was a strange sensation to be suddenly stationary. I heard Neil say, 'Shutdown, OK, engine stopped.' We had less than 20 seconds of fuel left, but we were on the moon."[547]

From Houston, Duke said, "We copy you down, Eagle."

The next few seconds seemed like forever to the controllers in Houston, as they waited for confirmation from the astronauts that they had indeed landed on the moon. The astronauts were too busy to contact Mission Control. They turned to the checklist of tasks needed to ready the lunar module for a liftoff from the moon in the event of an emergency. Nixon's "burial-at sea" speech was on their minds. They never wanted him to have to use it. They had just a few minutes to make a "stay/no stay" decision. They quickly completed one of their most critical tasks, by opening the Parker pressurization valves in the descent engine and venting the remaining helium, oxidizer and fuel from the lunar module. Then, a billion people in every corner of the globe, holding their breath, finally heard Armstrong say, "Houston, Tranquility Base here. The Eagle has landed."

Duke replied, the relief evident in his voice, "Roger, Tranquility, you got a bunch of guys here about to turn blue. We're breathing again. Thanks a lot. Be advised there's lots of smiling faces in this room, and all over the world."[548]

Kranz remembers that "Spectators in the viewing room were drumming their feet on the floor and cheering." At LAX, the Parker engineers stood in the company cafeteria, cheering and congratulating each other as they heard Armstrong's words from Tranquility Base; in his Cleveland living room, Klamm broke into one of his widest smiles; and in Bel-Air, Pat and Peggy Parker lifted a glass of wine in celebration. Pat wished his mother and father could have lived to see the day Parker helped two men land on the moon. Now, for the first time, he could appreciate how his parents felt on that afternoon in 1927 when they heard a radio announcer confirm Lindbergh's landing at Le Bourget. Like Art and Helen, Pat felt an enormous sense of pride in his team; they had served their customers well, meeting their commitment to NASA, the astronauts, and the American people.

Collins, circling the moon in the command and service module, radioed his congratulations to Armstrong and Aldrin, saying "I heard the whole thing." Armstrong replied, "Thank you. Just keep that orbiting base ready for us up there."[549]

Six hours after landing, Armstrong and Aldrin donned the spacesuits designed for their walk on the moon, and depressurized the Eagle. They used the Parker oxygen control assembly to fill the backpacks in their spacesuits, transferring high-pressure oxygen from tanks in the Eagle. The Parker oxygen control assembly reduced the high-pressure oxygen in the storage tanks to a usable pressure for their suits.

As Aldrin and Armstrong waited for permission from Mission Control to exit the lunar module, they were connected by an umbilical cord to the oxygen stored in Eagle. A suit loop pressure switch, designed and manufactured by Parker, would activate if one of the astronauts suffered a tear in his spacesuit while the two of them were tethered to the umbilical cord. NASA understood no astronaut could survive such a mishap. If the oxygen continued to flow to the damaged suit, the other astronaut would quickly run out of breathable air. In order to save the life of the second astronaut, the switch was designed to automatically cut off the flow of oxygen to the man in the damaged suit. In a bit of gallows humor, a few astronauts started calling the pressure control the "Good-bye Charlie" switch.

Neil Armstrong's photograph of Buzz Aldrin in front of the lunar module.

Six-and-a-half hours after landing, Aldrin and Armstrong detached their umbilical cord and began to use the oxygen from their backpacks. They squeezed out through Eagle's hatch and walked down a ladder to the surface of the moon. As they descended the ladder, monitors in their suits recorded their highest heart rates during the entire mission.

Armstrong noticed the lowest rung of the ladder was high above the lunar surface, and he tested the last step gingerly to make sure he could get back up into the Eagle. As he stepped off the ladder and touched the surface of the moon, Armstrong uttered the immortal words: "That's one small step for man, one giant leap for mankind."

The astronauts described the lunar surface as "very fine grained, almost like powder." Norman Mailer wrote that "They were looking at a terrain unlike anything they had ever seen on earth. There was no air, of course, and so no wind, nor clouds, nor dust... nothing visible or invisible moved in the vacuum before them. All light was pure... Objects did not go out of focus as they receded in the distance."[550]

President Nixon, relieved he did not have to deliver his burial-at-sea speech, congratulated the astronauts on a telephone hook-up, saying "Because of what you have done the heavens have become a part of man's world, and as you talk to us from the Sea of Tranquility, it inspires us to redouble our efforts to bring peace and tranquility to earth. For one priceless moment in the history of man, all the people of earth are truly one."

Aldrin and Armstrong walked for two hours and 21 minutes, collecting 48 pounds of moon rock, photographing the lunar surface, and performing seismic and solar wind experiments. Back in the Eagle, they slept fitfully for a few hours, bathed in reflected light from the earth pouring through a window. Twenty-one hours after the Eagle landed, as the time for lift-off from the moon approached, they could not help thinking about the risks that still lay before them. Eagle's ascent stage had only one engine; there was no back-up system. The engine had never been tested in the near vacuum of the moon. If the engine did not flame up to 90 percent of its thrust in the first three-tenths of a second after it was activated, the astronauts would die on the moon.

Shortly before the time scheduled for lift-off, Aldrin inadvertently broke a circuit breaker that armed the ascent engine. For several long minutes, Mission Control believed Aldrin and Armstrong might be marooned on the moon. Just before Kranz made a call to the White House to alert the President, Aldrin was able to activate the switch for the engine with a felt tip pen he found in Eagle.

At 12:53 a.m. on Monday morning, July 21, Aldrin counted down to the firing of the ascent engine, telling Mission Control "We're No. 1 on the runway."

Aldrin and Armstrong donned their pressurized helmets and gloves, completed their check of the propulsion system, and engaged the ascent engine. The detonator cartridges exploded as planned, separating the ascent stage from the descent stage of Eagle. A Parker quad check valve acted as a seal, preventing any back-flow that might allow the improper mixing of the propellants or over-pressurization of the system. The ascent engine, activated by Parker valves, roared to life, and with a great jerk and wobbling climb, the astronauts lifted off from the moon. The Eagle accelerated and flew smoother as it consumed fuel and became lighter.

Aldrin said, with a palpable sense of relief, "That was beautiful. Twenty-six feet, 36 feet per second up.... Very smooth."[551]

Armstrong and Aldrin looked down at the Eagle's descent stage and an American flag they had planted in the rocky surface. A plaque on the ladder of the descent stage contained two drawings of earth and an inscription that said, "Here men from the planet Earth first set foot upon the moon, July 1969 A.D. We came in peace for all mankind." Underneath the inscription were the signatures of the three crew members and President Nixon.

Armstrong's voice rose as he counted down Eagle's ascending altitude from the moon, and watched the blue ball of the earth rise over the moon's desolate horizon. Parker's reaction control valves controlled pressurized helium that forced propellant to the thrusters in the Eagle's ascent stage, stabilizing the craft as it rose from the moon. Armstrong and Aldrin sailed toward their rendezvous with Columbia, and their place alongside Marco Polo, Columbus, Magellan, Lindbergh and the other great explorers of human history.

After the astronauts returned to earth, Lindbergh sent Armstrong a note of congratulation, adding in a postscript: "I wonder if you felt on the moon's surface as I did after landing at Paris in 1927—that I would like to have had more chance to look around."[552]

Collins was relieved to have Aldrin and Armstrong safely back on board Columbia. For months, he had been worrying that if he failed to dock properly with the Eagle, he would be forced to return to earth alone, as the mission's only survivor. He feared that, in such an event, he would be regarded as "a marked man for life."[553] Having spent the entire mission in the command and service module, Collins felt compelled to leave some lasting record of his role in Apollo 11. In the middle of the second night of the return trip to earth, he awoke and floated down to the lower equipment bay and wrote on the wall: "Spacecraft 107—alias Apollo 11—alias Columbia. The best ship to come down the line. God Bless Her. Michael Collins. Command Module Pilot."[554]

The Apollo 11 command module now sits on the floor of the atrium at the Smithsonian Air and Space Museum on the Mall in Washington D.C. Hovering above Columbia, near the roof of the atrium, looking as if it is still in flight, hangs Charles Lindbergh's Spirit of St. Louis, with Art and Klamm's fuel system still inside.

In 2009, a NASA satellite orbited the moon, taking pictures of each Apollo landing site. A New York Times editorial stated: "There's something terribly wistful about these photographs of the Apollo landing sites. The detail is such that if Neil Armstrong were walking there now, we could make him out, make out his footsteps even.... Perhaps the wistfulness is caused by the sense of simple grandeur of those Apollo missions. Perhaps, too, it's a reminder of the risk we all felt after the Eagle had landed—the possibility that it might be unable to lift off again and the astronauts would be stranded on the moon. But it may also be that a photograph like this is as close as we're able to come to looking directly into the human past."[555]

Neil Armstrong's and Buzz Aldrin's footprints are still visible on the moon; they could remain in the lunar sand for another million years, a reminder of humankind's first venture toward other planets.[556]

NASA

Buzz Aldrin's bootprint on the moon.

# CHAPTER 17

# Apollo 13

The Apollo 12 mission landed on the moon in November 1969. Television coverage was limited; it seemed the public was already beginning to view flights to the moon as routine. The Parker engineers who worked on the Apollo program, however, took no space flight for granted. They knew the complex fuel, propulsion and oxygen control systems within the Saturn V rocket, the lunar module, and the command and service module, which were regulated by Parker valves, had only been tested a few times in the harsh environment of space. They could not help worrying that an unanticipated problem might occur during a moon mission.

Several of Parker's engineers in Irvine were watching on television, as Commander Charles ("Pete") Conrad and Alan Bean landed the Apollo 12 lunar module on the moon's Ocean of Storms. The landing was much less dramatic than Neil Armstrong's frantic search for a safe landing spot. The astronauts landed on a flat surface within walking distance of their intended target, the unmanned "Surveyor 3" probe, which had landed on the moon in April 1967.

Mission Control had to remind Armstrong and Aldrin to cycle the Parker shut-off valves on the ascent stage of the Eagle immediately after the Apollo 11 landing on the moon. Those valves could close due to the vibration experienced during a landing. If they remained closed, helium might have remained in the descent engine propellant tanks, causing an over pressurization of the system that could rupture the propellant tanks and damage the ascent stage engine, marooning the astronauts on the moon. Realizing how critical the Parker valves were, NASA had added a requirement that the astronauts close, and then open, those valves after each landing. With the valves open, they would vent any remaining helium in the descent engine, insuring the propellant tanks would not remain pressurized and threaten the integrity of the ascent engine.

A Parker engineer in Irvine who was listening to Bean's transmissions from the moon sat up in his chair when he heard him tell Mission Control right after landing, "I ...recycled the Parker valve."

A controller in Houston responded, "What's a Parker valve?"

Bean replied, "That's one of those shut-off valves for the helium pressure."

The controller inquired, "And recycle?"

Bean said, "We recycled them—turned them back on and off—to make sure they were off."

Pat Parker was proud his family's name figured so prominently in Apollo 12's first transmissions from the moon. He enjoyed referring to the back and forth between the Apollo 12 astronauts and Mission Control as "the first advertisement from the moon."

Apollo 13 lifted off from the Cape at 1:13 p.m. Eastern Time on April 11, 1970. Very few Americans interrupted their workday to watch the launch. The flight was normal for the next 55 hours, 55 minutes, and four seconds. Unbeknownst to the three astronauts, their spacecraft contained a ticking time bomb. Two days before the launch, NASA engineers at the Cape had noticed that the No. 2 oxygen storage tank in the service module was not emptying completely. The tank (made by Beech Aircraft) provided liquid oxygen that mixed with liquid hydrogen in three fuel cells in the service module, to produce oxygen and power for the spacecraft during its flight to and from the moon. The NASA engineers decided to use a heater in the service module to "boil off" the excess oxygen remaining in oxygen tank No. 2. Since the spacecraft was still connected to the high-voltage electrical systems on the launch gantry at the Cape, the engineers were able to use a relatively high 65-volt charge to power the heater, in order to insure that all the excess oxygen was removed from storage tank No. 2.

The engineers, however, did not realize that a thermostatic switch in the heater was not designed to carry such a high voltage. Beech Aircraft had designed the switch only to operate with the relatively low 28-volt charge that would be available within the service module after launch. The 65-volt charge from the gantry at the Cape caused a switch on the thermostat to shut, rendering the instrument incapable of controlling or monitoring the heat within oxygen tank No. 2.

At 9:07 p.m. on April 13, the three astronauts, Commander Jim Lovell, lunar module pilot Fred Haise and command module pilot Jack Swigert, had just finished a televised report to Earth from the lunar module, which they called "Aquarius." Nearly 240,000 miles from Earth, almost to the moon, they returned to the "Odyssey" command and service module and settled down on their couches for a good night's sleep before beginning their preparations to land on the moon the next day.

The heat in oxygen tank No. 2 had been building up during the 56 hours since the launch. By the time the astronauts reached their couches in the command module, the excess heat had caused serious damage to the Teflon insulation on the electrical wires that provided power to the fans in oxygen tank No. 2. Since the thermostat for the tank had been ruined by the high voltage prior to launch, it had failed to provide any readings that would have alerted the astronauts to the heat build-up in the tank.

Unaware of the developing problem, Jack Swigert continued to follow the instructions in the flight plan, which called for stirring the liquid oxygen in the tank. The electric current that traveled into the tank to activate the stirring fans caused a short circuit in the tank's electrical system. The Teflon insulation on the electrical wires, damaged by the excess heat in the tank, caught fire in the pure oxygen environment. The fire increased the pressure of the oxygen in the tank, causing the No. 2 oxygen tank to explode, damaging the No. 1 oxygen tank, fuel cell No. 3, and other parts of the interior of the service module.[557]

Suddenly Odyssey shuddered, and the astronauts heard a sharp bang. Their first thought was they had suffered a hit from a meteorite, one of the worst accidents that can befall a space mission. Swigert saw, above his head, an amber warning light indicating a loss of power in one of two main power distribution panels.

"Hey," Swigert shouted down to Houston, we've got a problem."

Mission Control responded, "This is Houston, say again please."

"Houston, we have a problem," Lovell repeated.[558]

Gene Kranz, the flight director for Apollo 13, was sitting in the same spot in the back of the Mission Control auditorium that he had occupied during the Apollo 11 mission. One of his controllers reported he had lost all readouts from oxygen tank No. 2 in the service module. Another said fuel cell No. 3 in the service module had lost its pressure. The fuel cells were one of the most important pieces of equipment in the spacecraft. They generated all the electric power and oxygen needed for the mission.

Lovell was having trouble controlling the spacecraft. It felt like some great force outside the ship was forcing it this way and that. After several tense minutes, Lovell was able to right the spacecraft. He looked out his window and saw a gas cloud surrounding Odyssey. He told Houston, "It looks to me like we are venting something. We are venting something into space. It looks like a gas!"[559]

Fifteen minutes later, Kranz had worked out what he believed had happened to the spacecraft. Only one explanation fit the controllers' reports of a loss in readouts in oxygen tank No. 2, loss in pressure in fuel cell three, difficulty controlling the spacecraft, and Lovell's sighting of escaping gas. Oxygen tank No. 2, Kranz concluded, must have exploded. The explosion seemed to have damaged fuel cell three, which was apparently leaking its contents into space. Knowing the astronauts could not complete their mission without electricity from the other fuel cells and oxygen from the other storage tank, Kranz thought, "Our objective from here on was survival. The crew's only hope was Mission Control. My team had to start the turnaround."[560]

Kranz tried to steady his controllers, saying, "OK, let's everybody keep cool. Let's make sure we don't do anything that's going to blow our electrical power.... Let's solve the problem, but let's not make it any worse by guessing."[561]

Kranz and his controllers had to decide quickly whether to abort the mission immediately by firing the main engines on the service and command module, turning the spacecraft around, and heading back to Earth. This direct abort would require the astronauts to jettison the Aquarius lunar module. Although many of the controllers supported this approach, Kranz disagreed. He told them, "I don't want to jettison the lunar module... We need more time to work out the procedures for the return. We should hold onto the lunar module and go around the moon and take our chances with the lunar module power. I believe we will come up with a plan that gets us home."[562]

Kranz soon heard more discouraging news from his controllers. The Odyssey command module was continuing to lose oxygen and power. The controllers believed the spacecraft could only support the crew for a few more hours. Parker made the fuel cell reactant valves that controlled the flow of hydrogen and oxygen to the three fuel cells from the oxygen and hydrogen storage tanks in the service module. Kranz decided Mission Control should tell the crew to close the Parker reactant valves supplying fuel cell three in order to prevent it from leaking any more oxygen into space. That would mean the crew would not be able to access power from that fuel cell for the rest of the mission, making a moon landing impossible

Mission Control said to the astronauts, "OK, 13, this is Houston. It appears to us we're losing oxygen flow through fuel cell three, so we want you to close the react valve in fuel cell three. You copy?"

The three astronauts paused for a moment, stunned by the enormity of what they were about to do. As Lovell recalled later, "The problem was shutting the [Parker] reactant valves was a decision from which there was no turning back. The valves were such delicate, precisely calibrated bits of equipment that once shut, they could not be reopened without a team of technicians to adjust them and tweak them and certify them fit to fly. Since no such technicians were available 200,000 miles from Earth,... [the shutdown of the Parker valves] would, in effect, be a formal acknowledgment the mission was aborted."[563]

Haise replied to Mission Control, "Did I hear you right? You want me to shut the react valve to fuel cell three?"

Mission Control said, "That's affirmative."

Haise turned to Lovell and nodded sadly. "It's official," he said, accepting that he would not be the sixth man to walk on the moon.

"It's over," said Lovell, who would have been the fifth, "we've just lost the moon."[564]

Kranz realized there was only one way to save the astronauts. They would have to power down the command and service module, leaving just enough capacity in the batteries of Odyssey to power the spacecraft back up prior to reentry to the Earth's atmosphere. Then the astronauts would have to retreat into the LEM, which would act as their lifeboat for the four-day, 100-hour journey around the moon and back to Earth. Lovell was independently coming to the same conclusion. He said to his crewmen, "If we're going to get home, we're going to have to use Aquarius."[565]

The astronauts powered down each of the systems in the Odyssey command and service module carefully, realizing they would only survive if they could re-power Odyssey and use it as their re-entry vehicle to Earth. Then they swam through the lower equipment bay of Odyssey and into Aquarius, from which they had televised their report to Earth just two hours earlier. Haise said, "I didn't think I'd be back here this soon," and Lovell replied, "Just be happy it's here to come back to."[566]

The astronauts knew the trip back home would hold many perils. They would have to make at least two mid-course corrections, one to change their trajectory so they would orbit the moon in a way that would sling-shot them back to Earth, and another that would speed up their return, giving them a chance to make it home before they ran out of oxygen and electricity. With the command and service module powered down, they could not use its large and powerful engines for their mid-course corrections; their only resort was to use the smaller engine in the descent stage of the LEM. Grumman's engineers reminded Mission Control they had designed the LEM to land on the moon, not to carry the astronauts all the way back to Earth. The descent engine could generate less than half the thrust of the engine in the command and service module (9,870 pounds, versus 20,500 pounds from the command and service module engine).[567] No one could assure the astronauts the LEM's descent engine could achieve a burn strong enough to send them on the proper course back to Earth.

Mission Control and the astronauts had another, no less serious concern. Aquarius had enough oxygen and electricity to support two astronauts for the 45 hours it would have taken to land on the moon, explore the surface, and return to the command module. Lovell, Swigert and Haise, however, needed enough oxygen and power for all three of them to survive for another 100 hours in space.

Kranz led 15 of his best engineers into a small, windowless conference room located down the hall from Mission Control. It was like an operating room, with plain white walls, a tile floor, and bright artificial lights. Kranz's group of engineers would be called the "White Team" for the duration of the flight.

Kranz laid out his bleak calculations to the White Team. Aquarius had been designed to support the astronauts for less than half the time it would take them to return to earth. Kranz told his team his quick estimate had revealed that, even by using the minimum amount of oxygen available, the flight around the moon and back to Earth would leave the astronauts at least 36 hours short on their supply of breathable air. Unless the White Team came up with a solution, Lovell, Haise and Swigert would perish long before they came close to Earth.

Kranz ordered his men to figure out a way for Aquarius to sustain the as-tronauts until the final moments of the flight, when they would return to Odyssey and power up for the descent into Earth's atmosphere. He tried to rally his White Team by saying, "When you leave this room, you must leave believing this crew is coming home. I don't give a damn about the odds and I don't give a damn that we've never done anything like this before. Flight control will never lose an American in space. Now get to work!"[568]

Kranz told his engineers they had to include, as a part of their team, the employees of the NASA contractors who built the command module, the lunar module and their components. Kranz later recalled, "At this moment the battle for the return of Apollo 13 shifted to the back rooms and factories where the components were assembled and tested. We needed their data and we needed it fast."[569]

Parker made a complex part called the "oxygen control assembly," de-signed to pressurize the LEM cabin throughout the mission, as well as the astronauts' suits while they explored the lunar surface. The assembly also was designed to fill the astronauts' backpacks before they exited the LEM to the lunar surface. For all these functions, the assembly took high-pressure oxy-gen from storage tanks in the LEM and regulated it to the lower pressures nec-essary for the environment in the LEM cabin and the astronauts' space suits.

The original flight plan had called for Lovell and Haise to spend parts of two days on the lunar surface. The oxygen for those walks was stored in the high-pressure supply tanks in the LEM. Hoping the oxygen in the sup-ply tanks could be used to extend the astronauts' oxygen supply within the spacecraft, the members of the White Team in Houston contacted the gen-eral manager of Parker's Air and Space Division at LAX. They asked him to assemble a team of Parker engineers to determine how to transfer the oxygen from the high-pressure environment of the supply tanks in the LEM to the lower pressure environment of the command and service module and the LEM.

Parker's engineers realized the transfer of oxygen would be a delicate matter. They would have to fill the spacecraft with just the right amount of oxygen to sustain the astronauts. Earth's atmosphere is composed of 21 per-cent oxygen. If the spacecraft filled with a greater percentage of oxygen, the astronauts would die of oxygen toxicity, as their nervous systems, lungs and eyes would literally burn up; if the spacecraft did not have enough oxygen, the astronauts would suffocate.

Thirteen Parker engineers from the Air and Space Division assembled at a Parker testing facility in Newhall, California, northeast of Los Angeles. It was a remote, unpopulated area, chosen as a test site because a rocket fuel explosion would result in a minimum number of casualties. For the next several days, the Parker engineers would be testing highly explosive oxygen. One of the engineers, Bill Swift, had designed the oxygen control assembly. It was a complex product, including a primary and secondary regulator of oxygen flow, upstream and downstream relief valves, and a disc to reduce pressure in order to prevent a burst of the part.

Swift had been working on space products for Parker since 1963. He had become an expert on the control of oxygen on space flights. He and the rest of the Parker team spent their first day getting organized, setting up an oxygen control assembly on a test stand and putting it through a series of tests requested by NASA. The White Team was asking for proof that the oxygen control assembly could safely move oxygen from the high pressure, 1,000-pound-per-square-inch environment of the storage tanks to the five-pound-per-square-inch environment of the LEM and command and service module.

As Swift recalls, "We couldn't duplicate the environment of space in our lab. We were able to test our assembly under varying scenarios of pressure, temperature, and flow rate, as NASA asked us, but we couldn't predict exactly how it would perform. All we knew for certain was that it wasn't designed to do what we were going to ask it to do. A lot of unexpected things could happen up there, and most of them were bad—a fire, an explosion, or the loss of the remaining oxygen supply."[570]

The engineers tried to concentrate on the work at hand, not daring to think of the consequences if they failed to come up with a way safely to move the oxygen from the LEM storage tanks into the spacecraft. Their first test indicated, just as Kranz's had, that without the extra oxygen supply from the tanks, the astronauts would be 36 hours short of the oxygen they would need for the return trip to earth. As Maer Walter, a Parker laboratory director, later recalled, "Our first test indicated that, under normal conditions and assuming anticipated crew oxygen requirements, it was highly unlikely the astronauts would survive. That's when we really got to work to change the outcome. I don't think anyone on the team closed their eyes for more than 15 minutes over the next two days."

Swift would later say, "We were all very concerned about the lives of those astronauts. When we realized that our equipment was one of the most crucial factors in the return of Apollo 13, we became even more determined that we would do whatever it took to bring them back safely."[571]

As the Parker engineers began to work on ways to conserve oxygen, the controllers in Houston worried about the upcoming burn of the LEM's descent engine. Lovell later explained that the controllers knew the lunar module "was not made for flying this way. It was possible to nose the...spacecraft around by firing the...[descent engine] in tweaks and bursts, but a full-throttle, full-borne burn for something as crucial as returning to Earth? It wasn't something the engineers even wanted to consider. Unless somebody could come up with a way to bring the wounded service module's engine back to life, however, firing the lunar module engine to propel both ships was going to be the only route home."[572]

Five-and-a-half hours after the explosion in the service module, Lovell, Swigert, and Haise prepared for the first burn of the Aquarius descent engine. The maneuver, called the "free-return burn," was designed to move the spacecraft from its current trajectory, which would cause it to sail past the Earth, 40,000 miles above the cloud tops. Lovell realized the burn had to be perfectly executed. Too little thrust, and the spacecraft would miss the Earth; too much, and it would crash into the moon. As Lovell later recalled, "Even a tiny miscalculation in orientation during the free-return burn could cause the...[spacecraft] to augur into the far side...[of the moon], plowing a long, permanent trench in the lunar surface."[573]

Haise carefully typed into the computer the instructions for the burn of four of Aquarius' reaction control jets, pressurized by a group of Parker valves. The jets fired initially for 7.5 seconds, jolting the spacecraft slightly forward and forcing the descent engine fuel and oxidizers to the bottom of its tanks, eliminating bubbles and air pockets. Then TRW's descent engine ignited, firing at 10 percent thrust for five seconds to get the spacecraft moving. Parker valves regulated the high-pressure helium that was forcing fuel and oxidizers to the descent engine, and prevented any back flow that might allow the unsafe mixing of propellants, or over-pressurization of the descent engine's fuel system. The engine performed perfectly, revving up to 40 percent of full thrust for 25 seconds. TRW's variable thrust descent engine, originally designed so the astronauts could control their rate of descent to the moon, was now providing a lifeline home for Lovell, Haise, and Swigert.

As Lovell would later recall, he and the controllers in Houston "glanced instantly and simultaneously at their trajectory...and smiled at what they saw. The speed of the ship had increased almost exactly as much as it had been designed to increase, and the...[height of the spacecraft above the moon] had risen from the 60 miles that would have helped the spacecraft ease into lunar orbit, to a loftier 130 miles that would help swing it home."[574]

Eighteen hours after completing the free-return burn, the astronauts were rounding the backside of the moon, preparing an additional burn that would be performed two hours after they reached the "pericynthion," their closest approach to the moon. The burn was thus called the "PC+2 burn." It was intended to increase the astronauts' speed enough to arrive back on Earth 10 hours earlier, and move their landing spot from the Indian Ocean to the Pacific, where an American aircraft carrier, the Iwo Jima, was awaiting their splashdown.

It was 8:40 p.m. Eastern Time in the U.S. It had been 24 hours since the oxygen tank in Odyssey had exploded, and the entire world now knew of the astronauts' perilous situation. Walter Cronkite and television commentators from a hundred countries were on the air, narrating the progress of the flight of Apollo 13. The audience rivaled that for Apollo 11's landing on the moon.

Pat Parker watched the PC+2 burn on television at his apartment high above the shores of Lake Erie on the north side of Cleveland. He knew that Parker's valves were pressurizing the helium that was directing fuel and oxidizer to the descent engine during the burn, and he waited nervously for it to end. Peter Staudhammer, TRW's chief engineer for the descent engine, was watching from the auditorium in Mission Control in Houston. He and the controllers in Houston would be able to tell whether the burn had worked, based upon the split second Aquarius emerged from behind the moon. If the astronauts were only two seconds later than planned, they would nick the Earth's atmosphere and bounce away from the planet, passing into unchartered space for eternity. If the spacecraft was a second earlier than planned, the astronauts would fall to Earth too steeply and burn up in the atmosphere. When the astronauts came around at the precise fraction of a second planned by NASA, Staudhammer joined the others at Mission Control in applauding, as they realized the astronauts were now on a trajectory that would take them straight to the Pacific Ocean.

TRW's descent engine, designed for a spacecraft less than half the size of the command and service module, had worked perfectly, with a critical assist from Parker's valves. Two Cleveland companies that had brought Lindbergh safely across the Atlantic were now bringing the Apollo 13 astronauts home.

In the California desert, the Parker engineers had the television on in the background, but they paid it little attention, as they were still trying to figure out a way to stretch the astronauts' oxygen supply for the two-and-a-half remaining days of the flight. They were relieved to hear how perfectly their valves had worked for the free-return and PC+2 burns. They knew, however, the mid-course corrections would have been in vain if they could not determine how to stretch the astronauts' oxygen supply long enough to reach Earth. If the spacecraft's current path held steady, the astronauts would not re-enter the earth's atmosphere for another 75 hours. That period was twice as long as the oxygen in the lunar module had been designed to last.

On Aquarius, Lovell fully realized the seriousness of the situation. He told Swigert and Haise, "We're going to have to figure out some other way to operate this ship."[575]

The Parker engineers redoubled their efforts, working around the clock to devise a series of steps the astronauts could take to conserve their oxygen. They considered a number of variables, including inducing sleep to reduce the astronauts' oxygen intake. Each time a test parameter resulted in oxygen saved, the Parker engineers forwarded the results to the White Team, which relayed them to the Apollo 13 crew for implementation. Twenty-four hours after the problem with the fuel cells began, with the Eagle heading out from its orbit of the moon and still 240,000 miles from Earth, the Parker team had reduced the "oxygen gap" from 36 hours to a seemingly insurmountable 20 hours. Refusing to become discouraged, the Parker engineers went back to work on ways to move oxygen from the lunar module storage tanks into the spacecraft.

The Parker engineers feverishly tested, over and over, transferring highly pressurized oxygen from the LEM storage tanks through Parker's oxygen control assembly. Their calculations revealed that the assembly should be capable of slowly drawing oxygen from the storage tanks into the atmosphere of the spacecraft. The Parker engineers were jubilant when they completed their calculations. With the additional oxygen from the storage tanks and the conservation measures recommended by Parker's engineers, the three astronauts would have enough oxygen to last more than a week.

Forty-four hours after the oxygen tank on the service module exploded, the general manager of Parker's Air and Space Division informed the White Team of the results of the Parker engineers' tests in the desert. Finally satisfied they had found a way to bring the astronauts home, Mission Control told Jim Lovell that he could begin releasing oxygen from the storage tanks in the lunar module into the spacecraft.[576] The Parker engineers had rented rooms in a small motel just down the road from their laboratory. After making their call to Mission Control, they went over to the motel, collapsed on their beds, and slept soundly for the first time in two days.

It was now two-and-a-half days until the scheduled splashdown. The White Team's calculations were showing the astronauts might not have enough electrical power on the spacecraft to last the entire trip. They would have to power down the lunar module, which normally ran on 55 amps, to only 12 amps of power. The entire cabin would be plunged into darkness, and the already chilly temperatures in Aquarius would plunge even lower. Kranz tried not to think of how cold the crew was about to get.

Now that the astronauts were on the right trajectory for a splashdown in the Pacific, they no longer had any need to activate the LEM descent engine. They opened a Parker valve and vented the remaining helium in the engine's propellant tanks into space, thereby preventing any possible damage to the LEM's systems that could result from over-pressurization of the tanks.

On Thursday, April 16, the day before the astronauts were scheduled to splash down in the Pacific, an engineer at Grumman's Bethpage, New York plant tried to break the tension among his colleagues. One of the Grumman engineers who had helped design the Aquarius lunar module filled out a hypothetical bill for "towing services" and showed it to his fellow employees. The bill was made out to North American Rockwell, which had manufactured the Odyssey command module, and it was for the costs incurred by Aquarius in towing Odyssey back to Earth. Grumann calculated the towing charge at $400,001.00, based upon $4 for the first mile and $1 for each additional mile. There was a $4.05 battery charge for road service, and oxygen was charged at $10 a pound. The bill included "Sleeping accommodations for two, no TV, air conditioned, with radio. Modified American plan with view. Additional guest in room at $8 per night." There were incidental charges for water, baggage handling, and gratuities, all of which, after a 20 percent government discount, came to $312,421.24. Reflecting the hopes and fears of millions, a line near the bottom of the page read, "Lunar module checkout no later than noon, Friday. Accommodations not guaranteed beyond that time."[577]

By the evening of Thursday, April 16, conditions in Aquarius had become even worse. As Lovell remembered, "The crew noticed with alarm that every window, wall and instrument panel in the clammy cockpit had become covered with pearl-sized beads of water."[578] Lovell was worried the moisture would cause an electrical short in the command module when they tried to power up the spacecraft for re-entry.

Early on the morning of Friday, April 17, the sleep-deprived crew floated back into the command module. They knew their lives were riding on whether the crippled command module, soaked with condensation for the last several days, could repower its electrical systems. Lovell remembered, "As the first switch was thrown, sending a surge of power through the long-cold wires, Lovell braced for the sickening pop and sizzle indicating that the instrument panel had indeed found an unprotected switch or junction and shorted the ship right back out.... But as the power-up in the cockpit proceeded, as Swigert threw his first breaker, and his second, and his third, and so on, all the crewmen heard was the reassuring hum and gurgle indicating that their spacecraft was coming back to life."[579]

The astronauts jettisoned Aquarius, the ship that had been their lifeboat for nearly four days. Lovell looked back at the forward hatch from which he and Haise would have emerged on the moon, and the ladder on which they would have climbed down to the surface. Aquarius rolled over and started its long, fiery plunge into the Earth's atmosphere.

Swigert announced, "Houston, LEM jettison complete," and a controller replied softly, "OK, copy that. Farewell, Aquarius, and we thank you."[580]

Lovell added, "She was a good ship."

At Parker's Euclid Avenue plant and its aerospace facility at LAX, hundreds of Parker's employees gathered to watch the astronauts' return on television sets. Pat Parker was sitting in the front row in the Euclid Avenue cafeteria. The 13 Parker engineers who had assembled in the desert were pacing in the back of the cafeteria at LAX, too excited to remain seated. Many of them were worrying that, after all their efforts, and the efforts of thousands of others at NASA and its contractors, the spacecraft might simply be too damaged to survive its descent to Earth.

On CBS, Cronkite explained Odyssey was about to enter a four-minute period when the friction from the atmosphere would black out all communications. He went quiet so his audience could listen to Joe Kerwin, a young astronaut who had been assigned as the CapCom communicator in Houston for the re-entry stage of the flight. The emotion in Swigert's voice was obvious as he told Kerwin, "I know all of us here want to thank you guys down there for the very fine job you did."

Lovell chimed in saying "That's affirmative, Joe."

Kerwin responded, "I'll tell you we had a good time doing it."

A few moments later, the blackout started.

As the four-minute black-out period ended, Kranz told Joe Kerwin, "Joe, give them a call."

Kerwin kept saying, "Odyssey, Houston, standing by, over."

For one long minute, there was no answer, only static. No astronauts re-entering the Earth's atmosphere had ever been blacked out from communicating with Mission Control for more than four minutes. The Parker employees feared that, after surviving for several days in space, the astronauts might have died just as they were in the final stage of their return home. Television viewers heard the concern in Cronkite's voice as he counted off the time that had elapsed since the astronauts should have called Mission Control. He began to prepare his audience for the worst, saying softly that perhaps the astronauts might not have survived re-entry.

Kranz later remembered: "Seconds turned into minutes and minutes into

Jim Lovell (center) gestures in the recovery raft while a Navy diver positions the lift cage. Fred Haise is on the left side of the raft with Jack Swigert partly hidden beyond him on April 17, 1970.

NASA/Scan by Ed Hengeveld

infinity. A sinking feeling, almost a dread, filled the room. We wondered what the hell had gone wrong. I wanted to smash something.... Was there some screw up in the communications setup or relay? I told myself: they are there; we just are not hearing them."[581]

Suddenly there was a slight change in the static. Then a voice rang out with the words "OK, Joe." It was Jack Swigert, calling from Odyssey.

On the deck of the Iwo Jima, sailors were scanning the sky, looking for the astronauts' parachutes. Suddenly someone shouted, "There it is." A tiny black pod, suspended under three red-and-white parachutes, was dropping toward the water just four miles from the aircraft carrier.

At Mission Control, Joe Kerwin shouted, "Odyssey, Houston. We show you on the mains. It really looks great. Got you on television, babe!"[582]

Watching the television feed from the deck of the Iwo Jima, Parker's employees in Cleveland and LAX could see Odyssey's parachutes deploy, as the command module coasted toward its splash down in the Pacific. They could also see Kranz and several of the other controllers crying in Mission Control. In the Parker cafeterias in Cleveland and LAX, Parker's employees stood up and cheered, proud of their company's role in bringing the three astronauts safely back to Earth.

Rear Admiral Donald C. Davis (USN), Recovery Task Force Commander, welcomes Fred Haise (left), Jack Swigert and Jim Lovell aboard the U.S. Iwo Jima after their safe return to Earth, April 17, 1970.

The astronauts felt the command module slide smoothly into the water. They looked out the portholes and saw water running down the side of the five panes of glass. "Fellows," Lovell said, "We're home."[583]

A few weeks after the landing in the Pacific, Haise, Swigert, and Lovell visited Parker's aerospace plant at LAX. Beneath a large banner of welcome in the factory, they thanked hundreds of cheering Parker employees for bringing them safely back to Earth. Several years later, Pat Parker met Jim Lovell at the Paris Air Show.

After Pat introduced himself, Lovell said, "Thank you for the part you played in saving our lives."

In his typical self-deprecating way, Pat replied, "Well, I'm just glad to hear we have another satisfied customer."

Pat Parker and Paul Schloemer.

PART 5

# COMPETING IN A GLOBAL MARKETPLACE

## 1971 TO 2000

---

*"We are poised to enter the '80s as a billion-dollar company. A company with assets, facilities, people and products around the world. An almost unimaginable achievement for a corporation which saw its total assets go over a Pennsylvania hillside but a few decades ago."*

Pat Parker, in a speech to the Newcomen Society at the Union Club in Cleveland, on October 4, 1979

# CHAPTER 18

# Another Parker at the Helm

For Pat, his election as Parker's President marked the end of the period of relative freedom he had enjoyed in California. He was assuming responsibility for protecting everything his parents had accomplished in the half century since his father founded the company. Pat realized many at Parker believed he had been promoted because he was the son of the founder. That realization spurred him to work even harder to prove himself. As Lindsay Ueberroth, the CEO of her family's company, the Preferred Hotel Group, told the New York Times: "Family businesses are hard because you have to work three times as hard to prove yourself, because everybody thinks you are overpaid and that everything is handed to you. People always have a lot of preconceived notions about you, and it just takes a lot more time and more work to prove yourself."[584]

Sons (especially oldest ones) often measure themselves against their fathers, striving to outdo them in their chosen fields. Holding the future of the family business in his hands was a heavy burden, but outwardly, Pat showed few signs of the strain. The more formal the occasion, the more likely he was to puncture it with self-deprecating humor, almost like he was winking at his audience and reminding them the occasion was not really as important as it seemed. Perhaps he was also trying to convince himself, as much as his audience, of that fact. During one shareholders' meeting, Pat poked fun at the company's board of directors (of which he was the Chairman), saying "As usual, the company's accountants have received more votes from the share-

Pictured clockwise from top: Pat Parker, Phillip Rauch, Bob Cornell
and Ghost Taylor, circa 1970s.

holders than the board of directors." At another shareholders' meeting, he
gave a presentation on the prospects of the variety of applications for the
company's new valves, fittings and connectors. At the end of the presentation, he surprised the audience when he said, "Just remember, the world will
always need a plumber."

Pat found relief from his responsibilities by rebelling against convention in certain small ways. He loved to flout the dress code at his Cleveland country club, often showing up in a Scottish kilt and hat, which he knew irritated the club's managers. At Parker's headquarters, Pat often wore loud ties and the rope belt he used to tie himself to the mast while sailing his boat. For Pat, sailing was another means of escaping the tensions of his job. Out on the water, he could forget about the burdens of his job, if only for a few hours.

Though he was warm and friendly with his colleagues at Parker, Pat never let anyone with whom he worked get too close to him. He was an extrovert, thriving in the limelight and the company of others, but he also had an inner reserve—a part of himself he rarely revealed, even to those with whom he worked most closely. On one occasion, however, Pat did display his deepest emotions: In the mid-1970s, Jim Wood, a Parker consultant on shareholder relations, discovered a dust-covered reel of old film in the basement of the Shaker Heights home of Paul Kozak, who had been a communications consultant for Art Parker in the 1930s. Wood passed the film on to Bob Cornell, and he arranged to show the film to Pat and several Parker executives in the boardroom of the Euclid Avenue plant.

When the lights went down, Pat saw, in flickering black and white, scenes taken at the Berea Road plant in 1933. Art had made the film to demonstrate to his employees and customers the quality of his manufacturing processes. He appeared on camera for a short time, smiling as he strode confidently through the plant, and for a few seconds, the camera swiveled to an attractive young woman with her hair in a bob, going through files at her desk. It was Pat's mother Helen.

As soon as Pat saw his parents on the screen, his eyes welled up with tears. Embarrassed by his show of emotion, he excused himself and left the room before the lights came back on.[585] For weeks after, Pat returned to the boardroom on his own, watching every frame of his father's movie, over and over.[586]

BY THE LATE 1960s, real estate prices had soared in the neighborhood around the Parker Aircraft facility at LAX. The property Parker had purchased for $1 million in 1948 had appreciated substantially in value. The airport had become a hub for the airlines' jet planes flying from Asia, Hawaii, and the East Coast. Jack Kent Cooke, one of Pat's neighbors in Bel Air, built a new arena for his Los Angeles Lakers basketball team and Los Angeles Kings hockey team two miles east of LAX, which he called "the Fabulous Forum." The airport's growing importance to travelers, together with the visitor traffic generated

Pat Parker, circa 1970s.

by Cooke's teams, made the area around LAX attractive for the national hotel chains, and they began to look for sites where they could build large, convention-size hotels. Parker's aircraft plant, fronting on Century Boulevard, the main road into the airport, had become one of the most sought-after locations for a large hotel.

Due to increasing demand for Parker parts from the jet aircraft manufacturers and NASA, Parker had run out of manufacturing room at LAX, and there was no space on the property to expand the plant. Cornell wanted to take advantage of the appreciation in the value of the plant, by replacing it with a larger facility at a less expensive location. He assembled a team of Parker Aircraft executives to find a new location for Parker's aerospace business. As the general manager of the Standard Components Division, Paul Schloemer was an important member of the team. Cornell told him, "I want you to find a place that has just as much public visibility as LAX."[587]

The Marriott Corp. offered to pay Parker $8 million for the LAX property. The relocation team found the ideal spot for Parker's new aerospace headquarters in the middle of Orange County, within a recently incorporated city called "Irvine." It was a 75-acre site, bounded by the San Diego (I-405) Freeway, Jamboree Road, Michelson Avenue, and Von Karman Avenue. The site was surrounded for miles by orange groves, and little else. Schloemer and the other members of his relocation team called the site the "Jamboree property," because of its location on Jamboree Boulevard, named for a Boy Scout Jamboree held in 1953 on a nearby hillside.

The Jamboree property had been owned for decades by the Irvine Co., the largest landowner in California, which controlled one-fifth of the acreage in Orange County. The company traced its origins back to the 1800s, when California was still a Spanish colony. Franciscan missionaries from Spain had built a string of 21 missions along the California coast in the late 1700s, linked by the "El Camino Real," or "The Royal Road." The mission at San Juan Capistrano was just a few miles south of the site where Parker planned to build its new aerospace headquarters. Richard Henry Dana Jr., who wrote about his sailing adventures aboard Spanish ships in the 1830s, called the area of hills around San Juan Capistrano leading down to the ocean, "the only romantic spot in California."

The King of Spain made several large land grants to Spanish settlers in Southern California. In 1864, James Irvine and three partners purchased, for 50 cents an acre, three ranches that had been included in the original land grants near San Juan Capistrano. From those three ranches, he and his partners assembled a 100,000-acre, 185-square-mile tract of land that extended from the Pacific Ocean to the foothills of the Santa Anna Mountains. When Irvine died in 1886, his son, James Jr., inherited his portion of the land, and eventually bought out his father's partners. After building reservoirs to irrigate the land, James Irvine Jr. planted thousands of acres of orange groves. By the end of the century, he incorporated his land holdings, and named his new company the Irvine Land Co.

By 1960, the outlying suburbs of Los Angeles were starting to encroach upon Orange County. The Irvine Land Co. commissioned a master development plan for its 100,000 acres. Over the next several decades, Irvine grew to become a city of 250,000, and it acquired a reputation for having one of the highest qualities of life in California, due to the requirements for setbacks, landscaping, building heights and open spaces strictly enforced by the Irvine Land Co.

The relocation team was anxious to accept the Marriott's $8 million offer for the LAX plant, and use the proceeds to purchase the Jamboree property in Irvine, but it faced a serious dilemma. The LAX plant had been depreciated to a carrying value of only $400,000. Parker would have to pay taxes at a rate of 52 percent on its $7.6 million gain, which would net the company only $4 million on the sale. The relocation team came up with a brilliant plan. They asked Marriott to buy the Jamboree property and construct a headquarters facility and plant for Parker on the site, for a total cost of $8 million. After building the facility, Marriott completed a "like-kind" property exchange that was tax-free for Parker.

In 1971, Parker moved its aerospace headquarters to the Irvine property. Parker retained nearly all its highly skilled machinists from LAX, who completed the move without any interruption in deliveries to the aircraft manufacturers. The company leased the western half of the property, a tract of 30 acres, to a farmer who grew strawberries and beans. The farm provided a buffer between Parker and one of its competitors, the Bertea Corp., located on the other side of the street. The relocation team had succeeded in replacing an outdated, inadequate plant at LAX with an expanded modern facility in Irvine, which, for the next 30 years, would provide a home for Parker's aerospace employees in one of the most attractive locations in Southern California.

The value of the Jamboree property appreciated substantially, as the nearby John Wayne airport expanded and Irvine became one of the most popular locations in California for hotels and office buildings. In 1981, Parker leased to a developer the 30 vacant acres of the Jamboree property that it had leased to the farmer, for an annual rental payment of $1 million. The developer built four office buildings and a Marriott hotel on the site. In 1999, Parker sold the property to the developer for $39 million, netting a total of $58 million from the transaction ($19 million in rental payments from 1981 to 1999 plus the $39 million purchase price in 1999). Parker was able to benefit its employees by donating the entire $58 million to the company's pension plans, in another tax-free transaction.

In 2003, Parker sold the remaining 45 acres of the Jamboree property for $65 million, and moved its aerospace headquarters a few miles south to another office complex in Irvine. Parker received approximately $1.6 million per acre for land it acquired in 1971 for only $25,000 per acre. With the completion of the pension plan and Jamboree transactions, Parker had leveraged its 1948 investment of $1 million at LAX into a gain of more than $122 million from its California real estate.[588] A Marriott executive later said that "Parker ought to build a statue along the Freeway to whoever negotiated that deal for Parker."[589]

DURING PAT PARKER'S first few years as CEO, he received numerous calls from investment bankers advocating that Parker become a "conglomerate," by acquiring a group of businesses unrelated to fluid power. Companies like ITT, Litton, Textron, Teledyne, Gulf and Western, AT&T and Transamerica were taking advantage of low interest rates and a bull market to buy companies in new lines of business in leveraged buyouts, often at deflated values. Pat resisted such financial engineering. He remembered that the diversification philosophy Cornell, Taylor and his mother followed after World War II had been tempered by their determination to stay within the confines of their fluid power charter. Like them, Pat intended to stick to businesses he knew, and in which Parker held a competitive advantage.

Pat was determined to continue expanding the reach of an enterprise his parents had grown from a small machine shop to a significant force in the U.S. fluid power industry. His determination to pass on Parker's culture to new generations of employees drove him to spend most of his time away from his family. As the company began to expand outside the U.S., the burden of that responsibility increased dramatically.

Having spent 20 of his 40 years outside his hometown of Cleveland, Pat had developed a broad perspective on the world. He had grown up hearing his father's stories of serving with French and English soldiers in World War I, and his parents' recounting of their trip to Nazi Germany before World War II. Pat had an active and restless mind, an avid curiosity, and an openness to new ideas. At Williams and Harvard, he had become friends with several students from abroad, and he began to develop an appreciation for the history and cultures of their countries.

Pat believed the time had come for Parker to venture abroad. His first priority was to enhance Parker's presence in Europe. Just as his father had formed friendships with the German aircraft manufacturers before World War II, Pat began to get to know the German industrialists responsible for the country's remarkable recovery from the war. Germany had become once again the largest manufacturer of industrial goods in Europe. Pat decided he should learn German, so he could develop closer relationships with his German customers. A Cleveland friend, George Hammer, owned a company that imported wine from Germany. The Hornickle family, which operated a German winery on the western bank of the Rhine, was one of Hammer's most important suppliers. In 1969, the Hornickles' oldest daughter Madeline had just turned 20, and the Hornickles decided to send her to live with the Hammer family in Cleveland for several months so she could improve her English skills.

Pat mentioned to Hammer that he was looking for someone to tutor him in German, and Hammer recommended Madeline. She met Pat twice a week in his office at Euclid Avenue for his German lessons. She was impressed with his charm and eagerness to learn new things. She enjoyed the twinkle in his eye and his sense of humor. She also noticed that he did not seem to take himself too seriously. As she spent more time with him in his office, she saw how quickly and easily he connected with others, from his fellow executives to the young man delivering his mail.

It was not long before Pat and Madeline began to form a platonic friendship. Pat had grown accustomed to their twice-weekly language lessons and was disappointed when, after four months, Madeline left to study at the University of California at Berkeley. At the end of 1969, she returned to her family in Germany, never expecting to see Pat again. By that time, it had become apparent to Pat and Peggy their marriage was failing, due to their different priorities. Pat was immersed in growing Parker's worldwide business. He spent most of his time away from home, planting the Parker flag in various countries, while Peggy remained in Cleveland with the children. Peggy missed having Pat at home, and she longed to see her friends in Southern California.

After much soul searching, Pat and Peggy agreed to divorce, and Peggy moved back to Bel-Air with the four children. Pat commuted to Southern California nearly every weekend to be with the children, but the visits were no substitute for a normal family life. Several years later, Peggy entered into a happy marriage with Walter Graumann, a World War II veteran who had flown B-17 bombing missions over Germany. Graumann, an intelligent and gentle man, was an accomplished television director, later known for long-running shows such as "Murder She Wrote," starring Angela Lansbury.

After the divorce, Pat began writing letters to Madeline, and she invited him to visit her and her family during his business trips to Europe. At first, Madeline's parents were not pleased their 21-year-old daughter was seeing a 41-year-old man. As they came to know Pat better, however, they began to respect him more and more, and they were pleased when Madeline married Pat in 1972 and moved to Cleveland.

Like Pat, Madeline had an adventurous spirit, and she began to accompany him on his business trips to Europe, Latin America, and Asia. Those trips were becoming more frequent as Parker expanded its operations overseas. During the first three years of the Parkers' marriage, they spent less than six weeks in Cleveland. With an outgoing personality, language skills, and love of different cultures, Madeline was the perfect companion as Pat met with customers, acquisition candidates and government officials around the world.

Pat could go anywhere in the world and find a friend. In 1975, he was traveling alone in Tasmania, prospecting for customers. Driving late one night, he spied the lights of a lone bar far out in an empty countryside. He walked inside, sat down at the bar, and noticed on his left a man wearing a John Deere cap. Pat struck up a conversation and discovered the man was a John Deere distributor, who was selling Parker couplings, seals, and fittings to local farmers for their tractors. The man almost fell off his chair when Pat told him he was Parker's president. The two spent the rest of the night drinking and talking like old friends. By the end of the evening, Pat had convinced his new friend to increase his purchases from Parker.

Pat's early days as Parker's president coincided with the last heady years of the American automobile industry. Since the end of World War II, the "Big 3"—General Motors, Ford and Chrysler—had been the mainstay of the U.S. industrial economy. They became a cozy shared monopoly, secure in their belief the domestic automobile market was impervious to entry by new competitors. David Halberstam believes the Big 3 did not need to fear disruptive innovations in car design because all three "played it safe and no... [company] tried something new unless it was reasonably sure the other two were going to try it as well."[590]

George Romney, the president of American Motors (considered to be "Detroit's upstart car company" because of its small, fuel efficient cars)[591] warned his colleagues in the American automobile industry that "there is nothing more vulnerable than entrenched success."[592] The executives of the Big 3, however, saw no reason to worry. In the late 1950s, only 8 percent of the automobiles sold in the U.S. were imported. In 1958, Toyota sold just 288 "Toyjet" sedans in America, while General Motors was producing 2.1 million cars.[593]

Lurking beneath the boom in the automobile business, and the rest of U.S. manufacturing, were two unperceived threats—a growing scarcity of oil in the U.S., and the arrival on American shores of high quality consumer goods from America's World War II enemies, Germany and Japan, who had rebuilt their industrial bases after the war.[594] It would not be long before Detroit, and American manufacturing as a whole, would be humbled by foreign competitors who were exceeding American quality standards, and undercutting U.S. companies' prices.

After the war, the Japanese initiated a program of exporting to the world, but they found it hard to shake their reputation for shoddy products. In 1953, Akio Morita, who would later become the Chairman of Sony, was at a restaurant in Dusseldorf, Germany. He ordered a dish of ice cream. Stuck into a scoop was a miniature paper parasol made in Japan. The waiter said to Morita, "This is from your country." Morita was humiliated by the thought that the Japanese "had a long way to go" before the world would admire the quality of what they produced.[595] Morita and other Japanese industrial leaders vowed to erase the gap in quality between goods produced in Japan and those made in America and Western Europe. Their goal was to mass produce high quality products, and sell them in the U.S. and Europe at lower prices than their competitors.

The Japanese turned to an American expert on quality control named W. Edwards Deming to help them turn around their reputation for making inferior goods.[596] Deming taught the Japanese a means of continually improving their manufacturing quality, by using statistical controls to establish ever finer tolerances. His methods required regular consultation and teamwork among the workers on the line and the managers at a plant. Deming told the Japanese, "Who can put a price on a satisfied customer, and who can figure out the cost of a dissatisfied customer?"[597] Deming's belief in the value of perfecting the efficiency of work struck a chord with the Japanese, who held similar cultural values, believing work should have a higher purpose and that quality products were a worthy end in themselves.

While Deming was a hero in Japan, the Big 3 gave him short shrift. There was little support at the top of the largest American automobile manufacturers for quality-driven programs. Since American consumers could not compare the quality of automobiles made in the U.S. with those made in other countries, the Big 3 saw little reason to waste time and money on a quality program, or on making their cars more fuel efficient. They gave only token support to better-made cars, appointing mid-level managers to promote quality within their companies. Without visible and sustained enthusiasm from the executive suite, workers in the plants paid little attention to the Big 3's quality programs. They were given few opportunities to suggest ways in which the manufacturing process could be improved. As a result, they felt little connection to the quality of the cars they were making. In the mid-1970s, disgruntled workers at Lordstown, Ohio, were accused of sabotaging the assembly line in a protest over how fast the line was moving. The workers joked that "there was no need to sabotage their plant because the cars were falling apart all by themselves."[598]

Instead of focusing on quality, the Big 3 concentrated on convincing the American people to constantly upgrade to a new car. As Patrick Cooke explained, "Planned obsolescence became a sales virtue. Studebaker designer Brooks Stevens decreed that buyers should be instilled with "the desire to own something a little newer, a little better, a little sooner than is necessary."[599]Comfortable with their market position, the executives at the Big 3 missed the social changes occurring in America in the late 1970s. Consumers were beginning to demand smaller, more fuel efficient, environmentally friendly cars; the executives at Ford, Chrysler and General Motors took little notice. They were isolated in their executive suites, unaware of their customers' changing tastes in automobiles. Lee Iacocca, the president of Ford, said, "We've got to pause and ask ourselves: How much clean air do we need?" When reporters asked Iacocca about the front-wheel drive cars just becoming popular in Europe, he said customers wanted something more tangible, that they could see and feel: "I say give 'em leather. They can smell it."[600]

Parker was fortunate that, due to the diversification strategy begun by Taylor, Cornell, and Helen after World War II, the company was not unduly dependent upon the U.S. automobile industry or any one other customer or product market. In 1974, General Motors was Parker's largest customer, but it accounted for only 6 percent of the company's sales.[601] In an interview with the Cleveland Plain Dealer, Pat said, "We're sort of the General Electric of the fluid systems industry, in that we offer a broad range of products to meet every growing need... I run a very large industrial supermarket, since we virtually offer something everyone needs."[602]

By 1980, the Japanese held 30 percent of the U.S. automobile market, led by Toyota, which had been building a culture of continuous manufacturing improvement for decades. In 1982, Honda opened the first Japanese automobile plant in America, in Marysville, Ohio.[603] In 1981, Japan's fuel-efficient cars made it the world's largest producer of automobiles. Roger Smith, GM's CEO, remained in denial, saying, "What did the Japanese invent in cars? The only thing I can think of is that little coin holder."[604]

UNLIKE MANY OF THE EXECUTIVES of the Big 3, who were captives of their executive suites, Pat Parker spent more than half his time away from his office, visiting Parker's customers and its employees on the factory floor. His visits opened his eyes to the challenges facing American manufacturers from high-quality imported goods flowing into America from Germany and Japan. When Pat went on the road, the executives at customers such as Deere, Caterpillar, and Boeing made it clear to him that they were competing in a global marketplace, where they faced aggressive competition from companies outside the U.S. Pat learned firsthand how his customers were fighting for survival. They had no choice but to demand higher quality and lower prices from suppliers such as Parker.

Pat understood that, in a global marketplace, he and his employees could never become complacent about serving their customers. Pat believed it was his responsibility to communicate to the men and women on the factory floor the importance of producing quality products. During his teenage years, he had watched his father walk past the machine operators at the Euclid Avenue plant, thanking them for turning out parts for the bombers of World War II. As he rose through Parker's ranks, Pat never forgot the importance of maintaining a personal relationship with his employees. Like his father, he felt it was important to communicate to his workers that they were all on the same team, working together to serve their customers.

Pat often arrived at a Parker plant dressed in a work shirt and overalls. On a typical visit, he bypassed the executives in their offices and headed straight for the factory floor. Often a security guard stopped him, wondering just what this odd-looking stranger was doing in the plant. Pat delighted in surprising the guards by sticking his hand out and saying, "Hi, I'm Pat Parker." He repeated his greeting as he walked among the workers in the factory. They were surprised to learn who he was, but he quickly put them at ease, asking them about their families, their history with the company, and any concerns they might have about Parker's future. Pat liked to call his plant visits "management by walking around." Just as during his dinners with the flight crews on the Forrestal, he learned how an operation was running by talking to those who were closest to its customers. The accountants at Parker's divisions often noticed a sharp increase in productivity after one of Pat's visits.

In the late 1970s, many of Parker's largest customers, including the Big 3 automobile makers, Caterpillar, and John Deere, began to open plants outside the U.S. Pat decided that Parker should follow its customers to the rest of the world. The U.S. contained only 6 percent of the world's population. Pat realized his company would be throwing away 94 percent of the potential market for its products if it did not expand outside America. The Asian market alone, where 59 percent of the people in the world lived, was 10 times larger in population than the U.S. market. Pat saw nearly unlimited potential for Parker's broad product lines to grow in untapped markets in Europe, Mexico, the Middle East, Latin America, and Asia. He realized billions of people outside America had aspirations to join the middle class. They would need to use Parker's fluid power products to build the infrastructure of a "first world" economy—highways, airports, rail lines, water purification plants, oil and chemical refineries, steel mills, office buildings, trucks, aircraft and automobiles.

Under Pat's leadership, Parker doubled its sales from 1970 to 1975, from $211 million to $411 million, despite two serious recessions. In the 1976 Annual Report to Shareholders, he explained how Parker had grown outside the U.S. during his seven years as CEO, and the consistency of its culture over the last 59 years. Pat, it was clear, had finally emerged from the long shadow cast by his parents, and was making Parker his own company. He wrote:

> "Parker Hannifin today is a worldwide corporation operating 71 manufacturing facilities around the globe, employing about 12,000 people, and selling about $400 million worth of components and parts and systems to its customers. The key fact that emerges in this performance is consistency of action and understanding by all the members...of the real purpose of its existence. In more than 50 years, the company has had only four chief executive officers. [Art Parker, Ghost Taylor, Bob Cornell, and Pat]. This led to policies which have been consistent..."

Pat made it clear the company's expansion had not diluted the culture of empowerment initiated by his father and implemented by Taylor and Cornell in their divisional structure:

> *"Management and decision-making responsibilities remain at the lowest possible level. Practically every daily operating decision is made somewhere far removed from the central management office. This flexibility undoubtedly has been significant for the story of this enterprise. Consistency of purpose and policy has been part of the company's success."*

Pat believed his primary responsibilities were to set the company's vision, to inspire his employees to live by the values that had made Parker prosper, and to act as the company's chief spokesperson with Wall Street, customers, suppliers, and prospective acquisition candidates. He expected his executives to supervise the day-to-day operations of the company, and he trusted them enough to grant them leeway in running the company.

Shortly after he became Parker's President, Pat told a reporter, "I'm not a detail guy. I'm seeing the big picture, and I allow the detail to be handled by a lot of folks that report to me."[605] As the general manager of the Check Valves and Fittings Division in California, Pat had appreciated how Taylor and Cornell empowered him to run his own business, and he was determined to continue to empower his own general managers. Jack Myslenski, who led Parker's Hose Division in the 1980s and later ran all Parker's sales operations, told a reporter in October, 2004 that "Pat nurtured the entrepreneurial spirit so that a person runs their individual business under the umbrella of Parker Hannifin. Division managers make a lot of decisions themselves instead of carrying out orders from the top."[606]

Pat, a superb judge of character, hired an extraordinary group of executives to run Parker's operations during the time he led the company. Parker's executive group in the 1970s was diversified by ethnic and religious background, unusual for multinational companies in the 1960s, most of which were filling their executive ranks with white, Anglo-Saxon Protestant men. Pat promoted executives only on the basis of talent, without regard to their ethnic, religious or socioeconomic background.

In the summer of 1975, a 25-year-old Parker engineer named Don Washkewicz was driving to a meeting in Washington D.C., where he hoped to convince a Navy Admiral to allow Parker to begin bidding on the sale of hose fittings for Navy ships. He was traveling on the Pennsylvania Turnpike with a Parker executive named Louis Zirhl. A heavy-set, formidable looking man, Zirhl had immigrated from the Balkans to the Cleveland area as a young man and still spoke with a strong Eastern European accent. Believing he had to "Americanize" his last name if he wanted to be promoted to an executive position, he shortened it from its original version to "Zirhl."

As Washkewicz and Zirhl were driving through Pennsylvania, not far from where Art Parker and Carl Klamm had suffered their accident on the Lincoln Highway, Zirhl suddenly turned to Washkewicz and said in a loud voice, "Lose it."

Washkewicz had no idea what he was talking about, and he asked, "What do you mean?"

Zirhl said, "Your last name, you have to change it like I did, so it will sound more American. You'll never go anywhere at Parker with a name like Washkewicz."

Washkewicz could not think of an appropriate reply. He was proud of what his family had accomplished in America since his grandparents emigrated from Europe in the early 1900s. He vowed to leave Parker if he found his ethnic background a disadvantage. He would soon learn he would be judged at Parker only by his accomplishments.

After World War II, many American manufacturing companies came to be dominated by men with financial backgrounds. At Ford, Robert McNamara led a group of former Pentagon statisticians, first derisively called the "Quiz Kids" because of all the questions they kept asking Ford's older employees. Soon, however, they came to be known as the "Whiz Kids," as they used their analytical techniques to modernize Ford's financial systems. Their success helped propel McNamara to the presidency of Ford in 1960. Soon thereafter, President Kennedy selected him as his Secretary of Defense.[607]

By the late 1960s, men like the Whiz Kids were elbowing out the traditional operations-oriented men who had run most American manufacturing companies. According to Halberstam, "The theory of management then asserting itself in American business was a new one: Managers should no longer be of the plant. They should come from the managerial class, as it arrived from the best colleges and business schools, and they should view management as a modern science. Their experience should not be practical, as it had been in previous generations, but abstract. Practical experience was, if anything, a handicap. They were not men who knew the factory floor, nor did the people on the boards of directors know it either."[608]

Parker was an exception to the trend toward the managerial class; it continued to be run by engineers who had experience managing a factory. In Parker's nearly 100-year history, Pat was the only non-engineer to lead the company, and during his time as CEO, he was content to let the engineers supervise Parker's day-to-day operations. He wanted his company to be guided by men with "elbow grease," who knew how to take a machine apart and put it back together again, and who were more comfortable on the factory floor than in the executive suite.

Pat allowed his general managers to run their divisions almost like separate companies. He gave them the freedom to succeed, or to fail, on their own terms. Many of Pat's general managers liked to say, even after they were promoted to higher executive level positions, that "Being a division general manager at Parker was the best job I ever had."[609] Parker's divisional structure created "bench strength" for promotions to executive level jobs. Whenever a position opened, Pat could reach into the general manager ranks and pick a promising executive from a large pool of candidates who had shown promise in running their own multi-million dollar operations. He explained:

> *"My legacy was to build the team—promoting from within and developing a team of young people... and finally, not managing the business but letting the upcoming people lead it. It was developing the talent, and then getting out of the way and letting the good players play."[610]*

Four engineers rose to high executive positions under Pat; three would lead the company after he retired. Pat promoted them because they had values compatible with the culture established by his parents. Each was driven by a passion to serve Parker's customers; each believed in empowering those closest to a customer to meet that customer's needs; each fostered a spirit of teamwork; and each possessed an implacable will to prevail over any obstacles that came their way.

# CHAPTER 19

# Passing the Torch

Paul Schloemer was elected the president of Parker's Aerospace Group in 1978, a challenging time for that business. The Apollo program had ended, and Parker was just starting to develop products for the fuel systems of the Space Shuttle. The market for new military planes had been in decline ever since the Vietnam War ended in 1975, and the passenger aircraft manufacturing business was entering an era of consolidation. Soon after Schloemer was promoted to lead the Aerospace Group, President Jimmy Carter deregulated the airline industry, freeing the carriers to make their own decisions on routes and fares, and ushering in an era of cutthroat competition that reduced the airlines' bottom lines. As a result, the carriers began to demand lower prices for planes from the aircraft manufacturers, who in turn pressured suppliers such as Parker to reduce their prices for aircraft components.

Few companies could access the amount of capital required to compete in the passenger aircraft market. The manufacturers had to develop entirely new planes every few years to meet the demands of the airlines for larger, faster, more comfortable, and more fuel-efficient aircraft. Designing and building a new passenger plane cost hundreds of millions, sometimes even billions, of dollars. Such an investment meant that the aircraft manufacturers were betting the future of their companies upon the success of each launch of a new aircraft.

By the mid-1960s, aircraft manufacturers such as Lockheed, Douglas and McDonnell were finding it difficult to keep up with the larger commercial aircraft makers. Douglas made its last commercial aircraft, the DC-9, in 1965. The plane was unable to compete with Boeing's 737, which began service in 1967. Facing imminent bankruptcy, Douglas was forced in 1967 to merge with McDonnell, a defense contractor headquartered at Lambert Field in St. Louis. The new company, called McDonnell Douglas, developed the DC-10, MD-80, MD-11 and MD-95 aircraft, but none of those aircraft ever rivaled Boeing's passenger aircraft in popularity. Steadily losing market share in the passenger aircraft market, McDonnell Douglas was on the verge of bankruptcy when it was acquired by Boeing in 1997.

Lockheed rolled out its last airliner, the L-1011, in 1972. Although the plane was technologically advanced, with the first "fly-by-wire" automatic flight control system, it was plagued with engine problems. Lockheed was finding it impossible to compete against Boeing and Airbus, the European aircraft consortium, in the passenger aircraft market. Lockheed exited the passenger aircraft business to concentrate on the defense market, and in 1995, merged with Martin Marietta (the successor to the Glenn L. Martin Co.), forming Lockheed Martin, which became the Pentagon's largest aircraft supplier,[611] and one of Parker's largest customers for fluid power components on military aircraft.

When Schloemer took the reins of Parker's Aerospace Group, the market for making passenger planes carrying more than 150 passengers, which in the mid-1960s had included five manufacturers, was left with just two viable worldwide competitors—Boeing and Airbus. As members of a duopoly in the international aircraft market, Boeing and Airbus had enormous leverage over suppliers such as Parker. Schloemer and his colleagues at Parker's Aerospace Group realized that if they were not selected as the supplier for a component on a Boeing or Airbus plane, they would lose the lucrative replacement business for that product for the future decades in which the plane remained in the air.

Schloemer decided that in order to survive in the new deregulated airline market the Aerospace Group would have to reduce its costs, enhance its quality, and upgrade its service—much as Art and his employees had to continually improve customer service to survive the Depression. Schloemer led initiatives to improve the Aerospace Group's Information Technology systems for the design and manufacture of products. He made sure his engineers were staying ahead of the technology curve, particularly in the area of electronic controls, which were replacing traditional mechanical flight controls on most aircraft.

Schloemer knew that in a marketplace dominated by two large customers with leverage over their suppliers, personal relationships and consistent
performance over an extended period were the key to success. As he said,
"The customer had to have confidence that, if trouble came along, Parker
could help find a way out of it." He placed a premium on delivering products
quickly to the airlines whenever they had a plane sitting on the ground anywhere in the world, awaiting a replacement part. Schloemer made sure his
engineers became partners with the engineers at Boeing and Airbus, traveling to their plants to help in the design of flight controls and other fluid
power systems for new aircraft.

Paul Schloemer, circa late 1970s.

As a way to counter the leverage of
Boeing and Airbus, Schloemer worked
to diversify Parker's aerospace product
lines, converting Parker from a maker
of components to a supplier of entire
integrated systems for aircraft. His goal
was to ensure that none of Parker's competitors could match the breadth of its
aerospace product lines.

Parker filled a gap in its aerospace
product line in 1978, when it acquired
America's pre-eminent manufacturer of
aircraft flight controls. For three years,
starting in 1975, Pat Parker courted Dick
Bertea, the principal owner of the Bertea Corp., located just steps away from
Parker's aerospace headquarters in Irvine. Pat and Bertea shared remarkably
similar backgrounds. Both men lost their fathers when they were teenagers;
both served on aircraft carriers in the 1950s; both felt the pressure to succeed
their fathers as the leaders of their companies; both agreed to dilute their
family's ownership in order to expand their operations; and both presided
over companies that placed a premium on customer service.

The Bertea Corp. opened for business in quarters every bit as humble
as Art's second-story loft. Dick Bertea's father, Alex, started the company
in 1939 in a group of adjoining storefronts in Pasadena, California. Just as
Glenn Martin helped Art Parker get his start, Douglas helped Bertea survive

its early years. Bertea's first product was a de-icing valve for the Douglas DC-3. During World War II, the company diversified into flight controls that moved the flaps, struts, ailerons, and elevators on military and commercial aircraft. Alex Bertea died of polio just before the war. Like Helen Parker, Bertea's mother brought in professional managers to run the company, hoping that someday her son, Dick, would take their place.

Dick Bertea served as a jet fighter pilot during the Korean War, flying combat missions from an aircraft carrier a few miles off the Korean peninsula, in a FJ-2 Fury equipped with Parker fuel nozzles. After the war, he returned to work his way up in his family's company. During the 1950s and 1960s, he oversaw Bertea's production of flight controls for Boeing's 707 and 747, Douglas' DC-10, Lockheed's L1011, and the C-5 military transport. Dick Bertea became president of the company in 1965, just three years before Pat became Parker's president. In 1966, Dick moved the company's headquarters to Irvine, just across the street from the Jamboree property, where five years later Parker would locate its new aerospace headquarters.

Like the Parkers, the Berteas agreed to dilute their ownership of the company in order to expand, taking the company public in 1968. Bertea, like Parker, was known for its engineering expertise and its large cadre of long-term employees. Many were sons and daughters of men and women who had first worked in the company's Pasadena storefronts.

Bertea was supplying flight controls for commercial and military planes and helicopters made by Boeing, Lockheed, McDonnell Douglas, Rockwell, Martin, Sikorksy, Bell, Hughes, and Northrop. Serving these customers required a substantial capital investment, one that Bertea could not afford on its own. The company's stock dropped to a price of $5 per share, lower than when it first went public. Faced with a lack of capital and the absence of any family successor who could run the company, Dick Bertea considered selling the company to several potential buyers. Bertea spent hours with Pat Parker, discussing the similarity in their backgrounds and their companies. Pat convinced Bertea that Parker was the most likely of all his suitors to continue to grow his family's business, retain its employees, and honor its culture of teamwork, empowerment, and customer service.

The Bertea acquisition, completed in July 1978, was the largest yet undertaken by Parker. The acquisition confirmed the company's strong financial position, as it was able to issue $40 million in stock to pay for the transaction. Dick Bertea was elected to Parker's board, and he became the largest individual owner of Parker stock, surpassing the Parker family. Schloemer concentrated on integrating Bertea's operations into Parker, while at the same time retaining the entrepreneurial spirit that had made the company so successful. Schloemer was able to persuade nearly all of Bertea's experienced engineers and other employees to stay with Parker, and he promoted many of Bertea's top executives to important positions in Parker's Aerospace Group.

Six months after the closing of the Bertea transaction, Parker sold 15 vacant acres of land behind the Bertea factory for $4 million. After the integration of Bertea into Parker Aerospace was completed in the late 1980s, Parker closed the Bertea plant in Irvine and leased the property to a developer for $2 million a year for 10 years. When the lease expired in 1995, Parker sold the developer the property for $23 million, netting a total of $53 million from the Bertea plant property. With the $4 million from Bertea's vacant land and the $53 million from its plant property, Parker received $17 million in excess of the $40 million purchase price it had paid for the entire company.

As president of the Aerospace Group, and later as Parker's CEO, Schloemer continued to acquire aerospace competitors and develop proprietary technologies that allowed Parker's aircraft business to expand to provide com-

Paul Schloemer beside a space shuttle under construction, circa 1970s.

plete systems that could move and control a broad range of critical aircraft components, including fuel nozzles for jet engines, pneumatic valves and pumps for anti-icing and cooling systems, fuel valves, pumps and electronic gauging systems, thrust reversers, fuel inerting systems to prevent explosions in large aircraft fuel tanks, and computerized flight deck displays. By the middle of the 1990s, Parker, a company that since its beginning had sold only a few narrow lines of aircraft fittings, valves and couplings was controlling nearly everything that moved on most commercial and military planes in the world.

PAT PICKED TWO MEN, Dennis Sullivan and Duane Collins, who would become leaders of Parker's industrial business for the last three decades of the 20th century. Both were engineers from large Midwestern colleges, and both were hired within a year of each other by the same person from the Human Resources Department at the Cylinder Division in Chicago. Together they would transform Parker's industrial business, as they made a series of bold decisions that put at risk a significant portion of Parker's profits. Pat put his trust in those men, placing an enormous bet on their ability to bring decades-long research and development projects to successful conclusions.

Dennis Sullivan grew up in Chicago in the 1940s and 1950s. His father owned a machine shop, where Sullivan worked during the summers. Sullivan wanted to join the family business, but his father told him he needed to become a "doctor, a lawyer or engineer." Sullivan obtained his engineering degree from Purdue in 1960. One of his fraternity brothers at Purdue was Roger Chafee, who would die in 1967 in the Apollo 1 fire at Cape Canaveral. After an interview with Bill Davis, the Human Resources Manager of the Hannifin Division, Sullivan accepted a position as a Hannifin sales trainee in Chicago. He attended training classes in fittings technology conducted by Carl Klamm. Like the other trainees, Sullivan referred admiringly to Klamm as "the Chief," in deference to his uncompromising commitment to designing quality products.

After Sullivan finished his training, Bud Aiman, the sales manager of the Connectors Division, asked Sullivan to help him develop a plan for Parker to enter an entirely new market, one that touched a wide range of fluid power applications, including air conditioning for automobiles, air brakes for trucks, mining equipment, in-plant machinery, manlifts, construction equipment, and refrigeration components. The product lines Aiman envisioned—rubber and thermoplastic hose—were considered by many as "low tech" commodities, with little potential for profitable growth. Aiman, however, had a more sophisticated perspective on the hose market. He had studied it carefully, and was convinced it could be profitable for Parker if the company was willing to make the necessary investment. Aiman's dream was to build a line of hoses that would convey and control air, water, oil and hydraulic fluid in thousands of different applications, with the ability to withstand pressures ranging from 150 to 8,000 pounds per square inch, and temperatures from 70 degrees below zero to 300 degrees Fahrenheit.

Dennis Sullivan, right, with Maurice Schwarz, a Parker director, circa 1978.

Aiman realized customers could not wait long to replace hoses that had worn out in service. He was convinced they would be willing to pay a premium to the company that could deliver replacement hoses quickly. Aiman knew Parker controlled a national network of distributors, close enough to most of its customers to meet the short deadlines in the hose replacement market.

Aiman believed the hose business was much like the razor business, where the real money was made, not in selling the razors themselves, but the disposable razor blades, which wear out quickly and must be replaced.

Aiman was convinced Parker's hoses could become the "razor blades" for machinery in a wide range of industries, commanding a premium price from customers willing to pay for quick delivery.

Aiman's strategy of targeting the replacement market for hoses was similar to the approach Art and Pat Parker had followed in the aircraft market—to capture the original equipment market in order to dominate the replacement market when a Parker product wore out in service. Aiman knew enough about the company's aviation history to realize Parker's competitive advantage. Once its products got on board original equipment, Parker was likely to retain the replacement business, as long as its products continued to perform to a customer's satisfaction. Parker's replacement strategy created a barrier to entry for its competitors, who found it difficult to secure their place on original equipment without already having a track record in the service and replacement business.

Parker was making steel fittings for rubber and thermoplastic hose, but it had no in-house capability to make the hose itself. Aiman was buying hose from the large rubber and plastic manufacturers such as Samuel Moore, Uniroyal, B.F. Goodrich, Electric Hose and Rubber, and Gates. Parker installed its fittings on the hose, and then sold the assembly to customers. Pat and Aiman believed Parker could not succeed in the hose market as long as it remained a captive buyer from the hose manufacturers. In order to compete effectively, the company would have to develop its own proprietary lines of hose.

Aiman asked Sullivan to head out into the field to confirm whether his assessment of the hose market had been accurate. He expected him to learn every aspect of the business firsthand, by traveling to every customer and competitor he could find. Sullivan began his investigation in Chicago, using the yellow pages to find every location from which hose was being sold. During the next six months, he visited 1,200 firms in the Chicago area alone. After Sullivan exhausted his list of Chicago locations, Aiman sent him first to Detroit, and then to the East Coast, to continue his investigation of the hose market. Sullivan discovered that, just as Aiman had suspected, the most profitable portion of the hose business was the aftermarket for replacement hoses.

Parker formed the Hose Products Division in September 1964, with four employees in a small conference room on Euclid Avenue. Aiman was the Division's general manager, and Sullivan was named the manager of sales and administration. Sullivan became the division's general manager in November 1967, at the age of 29. He would be the youngest general manager in

Dennis Sullivan, circa 1974.

Parker's 100-year history. Sullivan would soon be joined by a young engineer from Wisconsin named Duane Collins.

Collins was born in 1936 on a Wisconsin farm, the third child in a family of eight boys and one girl. He, his brothers and sister rose before dawn every morning to help attend to the livestock. Collins spent grades 1 through 8 in a one-room schoolhouse, with two other students in his class. He later liked to say he was ranked third in his class. When he began high school, his family moved to the nearby town of Jefferson, halfway between Madison and Milwaukee. His father bought a grocery store, and put Collins to work at the check-out counter. His customers found him to be polite, cheerful and helpful. It was his first experience of the satisfaction derived from treating customers well.

Collins married his childhood sweetheart, a fellow student in his high school class named Joyce Schiesl. He received a degree in mechanical engineering in 1961 from the University of Wisconsin. A few weeks after graduation, he appeared for an interview at the Cylinder Division with Bill Davis, the same man who had hired Dennis Sullivan one year earlier. Davis believed Collins would make a good salesman, and he sent him to Cleveland to attend a three-month training program in sales techniques conducted in part by Carl Klamm. Like Sullivan, Collins would henceforth refer to Klamm as "Chief."

At the end of 1961, Collins was assigned as a field salesman in Parker's Atlanta sales office. His first assignment was to convince NASA to buy Parker valves and fittings to control the fire suppression and fuel loading systems on the gantries for the rockets at Cape Canaveral that were taking American astronauts into space. Early in 1963, Collins moved to an apartment in Orlando, Florida, within a short driving distance of the Cape. Security at the Cape was tight, because NASA feared the Russians were attempting to obtain classified information on America's rocket technology. When Collins pulled up to the trailer at the entrance to the Cape, he had to telephone a security guard stationed 10 miles away. It took hours for the guard to meet him at the trailer and drive another 10 miles back to the offices of the Cape's maintenance contractor, Noble Engineering. Collins found he was spending more time being escorted by security than talking to his prospective customer.

Collins was a uniquely persistent man, and he was not about to let a security guard keep him from meeting the people he needed to see at the Cape. His boss, Jack McBride, Parker's regional sales manager in Charlotte, had told him that, in order to succeed in sales, he would have to get to know his competitors. Collins visited Denison Hydraulics, a company competing with Parker to sell hydraulic valves for the launch pads at the Cape. The Denison regional manager, Carl Sherman, took a liking to Collins, and did him a favor. Sherman arranged a lunch to introduce Collins to Sid Brown, an executive at Noble Engineering. Collins' enthusiasm for the quality of his products impressed Brown, who agreed to sponsor him for a security pass. With the pass in hand, Collins could drive through the security gate at the Cape on his own. On his next visit, he smiled to himself as he drove by a large group of contractors, waiting in line in the hot sun to be admitted to the grounds.

Carl Klamm traveled from Cleveland to join Collins on one of his first visits to the Cape. The man who had designed and installed the fittings for the fuel system of the Spirit of St. Louis was now helping put Parker products on the gantries that would launch men to the Moon. When Collins and Klamm met with Brown, he confided that NASA was concerned the salt air at the Cape might corrode the machinery on its launch pads. Seeing an opening, Klamm pointed out that Parker's fittings and valves were made of the highest quality brass and stainless steel, and would not corrode on the launch pads.

Brown was surprised when Klamm and Collins recommended that, if he purchased Parker's valves and fittings, he should install them with tools made by Parker's competitor, Imperial Eastman, which in their opinion, were of higher quality than Parker's tools. Brown realized Klamm and Collins were more interested in providing their customers with the best possible service than in winning a sale. He concluded Klamm and Collins were people he could trust, and he agreed to purchase Parker's fittings and valves for the fire suppression systems on the Cape's launch pads, and to control the flow of liquid hydrogen and oxygen to the rockets as they were fueled prior to launch.

It did not take long for Collins' superiors to recognize him as a rising star in Parker's sales force. In 1964, he was promoted to oversee a larger sales territory from Nashville, and in 1968 he became Parker's regional sales manager for industrial products in the entire southeastern U.S., working from Parker's sales office in Atlanta. Collins came to appreciate the importance of Parker's distribution system during his time in Nashville and Atlanta. In a country of such vast distances as America, Parker needed to have inventory available to its customers in every region of the country. Parker could not have afforded to build its own warehouses throughout the U.S. to serve its customers. Instead, the company appointed independently owned distributors to provide the necessary parts and service to its customers.

Collins spent most of his time traveling to meet Parker's distributors. He was impressed by their entrepreneurial orientation and their desire to help their customers. Collins learned that the distributors were so close to their customers that it was almost like having a Parker salesman right in a customer's plant. A distributor could anticipate a customer's needs much faster than an internal Parker salesperson, and take advantage of opportunities to substitute Parker's products for those of a competitor.

Dennis Sullivan was watching Collins' career closely from his office at the Hose Products Division in Cleveland. As the division increased its sales of fittings, he decided he needed to hire a sales manager, and Collins was at

the top of his list. He invited Collins to watch the Apollo 11 Moon landing in
his living room in Cleveland in July 1969, taking the opportunity to tout the
future prospects for growth at the Hose Products Division. Sullivan offered
Collins the job a few weeks later, and he and Joyce moved to Cleveland in
early 1970.

Over the next two decades, under the leadership of Sullivan and Collins,
the Hose Products Division grew from 13th place in the hose market to the
largest and most powerful hose manufacturer in the world. Sullivan and Collins had similar management styles. Both had grown up at Parker out in the
field, visiting customers. They both believed in empowering those closest
to a customer to solve that customer's problems. They realized the importance of staying ahead of the wave of technological change in industrial markets, by constantly improving their products. They were both approachable,
down-to-earth, and above all else, practical men, who relied upon common
sense to make their business decisions.

The Hose Products Division would become a proving ground, not only for
Sullivan and Collins, but also for a group of their colleagues, who learned to
adopt their values of premier customer service, and who would go on to lead
the company in the '80s and the first decades of the 21st century, including
a future CEO, two executive vice presidents, two vice presidents of Information Technology, and a vice president of
manufacturing.

Just before he received his engineering degree from Cleveland State in June
1972, Don Washkewicz noticed a posting on a university bulletin board for a
job in the research department at Parker's Hose Products Division. He applied
for the job, and a few days later, he was
interviewing with Sullivan at the division's plant in Wickliffe, an eastern suburb of Cleveland. Washkewicz bought a
$59 pinstriped suit for the occasion. He
arrived at the division in a '64 Chevy so
rusted out that he could see the road
through its floorboards. He had tied the
rear bumper to the body of the car with

Duane Collins, circa 1974.

a bungee cord to keep it from falling off. Washkewicz parked in back of the plant, at the farthest spot from the front door, so no one could see his broken-down car. Little did he know he was about to begin a career that would culminate in his election as Parker's CEO 29 years later.

During his interview with Sullivan, Washkewicz mentioned he was working his way through college, by working nights and weekends as an automobile mechanic. Sullivan sensed he was more comfortable diagnosing the problems with a car engine than sitting in an office. He seemed to be a true engineer, with a mission to fix things. Sullivan was intrigued by Washkewicz's senior research project, a study on how to reduce noise in the thermoplastic hose used in automobile air conditioning systems. Sullivan was planning to develop a proprietary brand of thermoplastic hose for the same purpose. He submitted Washkewicz to an exhausting series of 12 interviews, including one with Collins, before he decided to hire him.

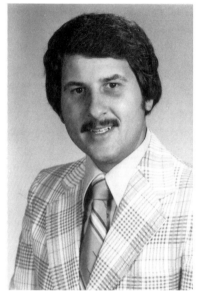

Don Washkewicz when he joined Parker in 1972.

Fighting, and winning, was in Washkewicz's blood. He learned from his family never to give up on a goal, no matter how difficult it might seem. His parents were first generation children of immigrants. Washkewicz's fraternal grandfather, Stanislaus Washkewicz, immigrated to Cleveland from Poland in 1908. For more than 25 years, Stanislaus walked more than five miles each way to work a 10-hour shift as a laborer at the Otis Steel Mill (later called "Jones and Laughlin") in the Flats. It was one of the mills supplying Art Parker with the steel for his first valves and fittings.

Stanislaus endured dirty and dangerous working conditions at the mill, where steel was being made in the "open hearth" process. The blast furnaces often shot out red-hot splashes of molten steel. Occasionally, they exploded, injuring or killing workers in the area. Most of the plant was badly lit and lacked any central heating. Stanislaus and his fellow workers had to crowd around the steel furnaces in the winter to keep their hands warm enough to work. Stanislaus was offered a promotion to the more comfortable—and safer—job of foreman. He turned the higher-paying job down, fearing he did not understand English well enough to manage others.

Washkewicz's parents met in the early 1940s, when, by sheer coincidence, they both were working at the Superior Die Casting Co., which was leasing a portion of the Euclid Avenue plant from Art Parker. Washkewicz's mother, Anne, trimmed metal in the shop, and his father, Stan, was a foreman there. Washkewicz was the third of six children. He grew up in the southeastern Cleveland suburb of Garfield Heights, a city filled with children being raised by hard-working descendants of European immigrants.

Stan owned a machine shop on the west side of Cleveland. With six children to support, he had to work night and day just to get by, and he expected his children to help shoulder the burden. Like Dennis Sullivan's father, Stan told Washkewicz he had three choices for a career: he could be a doctor, a lawyer, or an engineer. He also had three choices for the college he could attend: Cleveland State, Cleveland State, or Cleveland State. Stan chose the newly founded school in downtown Cleveland because it was the least expensive of all the state schools in Ohio.

The Hose Products Division was at a turning point when Washkewicz accepted Sullivan's job offer in 1972. It was making steel and brass fittings for thermoplastic and rubber hose. The division, however, was dependent upon buying thermoplastic and rubber hose from the large rubber and thermoplastic manufacturers. Several of those manufacturers were vertically integrating to make fittings as well as hose. If they succeeded, they would have an insurmountable competitive advantage over the Hose Products Division.

In 1973, Sullivan was promoted to be a vice president of Parker's industrial operations, and he moved into the executive wing at the Euclid Avenue plant. Collins was promoted to be the general manager of the Hose Products Division, reporting to Sullivan. Sullivan and Collins were convinced that, if Parker wanted to stay in the hose business, it would have to develop an in-house capability to manufacture its own rubber and thermoplastic hose, as well as its current line of fittings.

Collins made Washkewicz the junior member of a three-person research team assigned to develop a proprietary brand of thermoplastic hose that could be used to position dump trucks and aerial lifts, to conduct Freon in automotive air conditioning systems, and to activate the air brakes on large trucks. The division's research and development manager, Al Crow, a former employee of Samuel Moore, led the team, which operated in a 2,000-square-foot laboratory behind a Parker plant in Kent, Ohio.

Crow left Parker in 1973 to return to Samuel Moore. At about the same time, Parker's board approved building a 50,000-square-foot plant in Ravenna, Ohio, to make thermoplastic hose. Collins assigned Bill Currie to take Crow's place leading the thermoplastic hose research team. The team now faced the challenge of designing the new hose line without Crow, the only person at Parker who had understood how to make thermoplastic hose. The team was spending $1 million a month, about the same amount as the Hose Division was making each month, and it was operating under the watchful eye of the board, which fully expected the team to have its new product ready for production at the Ravenna plant within the year.

Shortly after Sullivan and Collins received the go-ahead to build the Ravenna plant, Currie came to Washkewicz with a new assignment. Knowing Washkewicz had worked as an automobile mechanic, Currie decided he was the perfect person to replace Parker hoses on three hundred trucks about to arrive at Jones Motor Freight in Richfield, Ohio, at an exit of the Ohio Turnpike. Currie expected Washkewicz to remove each hose within 60 minutes of a truck's arrival at the depot, so the driver could get back on the road quickly. Washkewicz later recalled, "I had to figure out how to get the hoses apart without melting my arm, and there was no way I could do it in 20 minutes." After several days, he devised a solution. He welded several wrenches together, soaked a bunch of rags in ice water, and wrapped them around his hands and arms. Even with the rags, he burned his hands and arms when he leaned over the steaming hot truck engines. With the combined wrenches, he was able to cut the removal time in half, beating Currie's 60-minute deadline.

By the end of each day, Washkewicz's clothes were so caked with oil and grease they stood straight up in his bedroom until he climbed back into them the next morning. After dutifully changing out the engine hoses for six months, he began to wonder why he had ever accepted the job at Parker. As Washkewicz recalled in a 2007 interview with the Wall Street Journal: "I kept thinking to myself, I didn't go to college to spend time doing this."[612] Six months went by, without any call from Currie. Just as Washkewicz was beginning to think about looking for another job, Sullivan summoned him to a conference room in a Holiday Inn on Euclid Avenue, near Parker's headquarters, to update him, Collins, Pat Parker, and several other executives on the hose research project.

In the men's room of the hotel lobby, Washkewicz tried to scrape as much of the truck engine grease from his hands as possible. As soon as he sat down at the conference table, Sullivan asked him for a progress report on the hose research project. Washkewicz replied, "Well, I've been busy changing hoses on trucks for the last five or six months."

Pat was amused by the whole thing, thinking to himself, "So this is the young engineer I've heard so much about. Here they asked him to work on the hose project and then Currie told him to be a truck mechanic instead. Well, at least he's persistent, and he sure doesn't take himself too seriously."

Sullivan yelled "What? You mean you've been changing out truck hoses instead of working on the research project? Who told you to do that? We're spending $1 million a month on this project, and you're changing out engine hoses!"

Washkewicz had to think quickly of a reply that would not embarrass Currie, who was sitting next to him. He ended up telling Sullivan he would be happy to forget about the trucks and get back to work on the research project right away.

During the next several months, Sullivan and Collins met nearly every week with the thermoplastic hose research team. They rolled a 54-inch wide reel of hose out into the middle of the Kent research lab and used it as an improvised desk, discussing how they could design a product that would not infringe a group of patents already filed by Parker's competitors. Thermoplastic hose was a deceptively complex product. It comprised an inner tube which held fluid, a nylon reinforcing layer that gave the tube strength to withstand high pressures, and an outer cover to protect the hose from abrasion, contamination and extreme temperatures. The challenge was to make a new hose with all of those characteristics, and to design it in a way that would be enough of an improvement over the competitors' products to qualify for a patent.

As the weeks went by, Collins and Sullivan became impressed not only by Washkewicz's engineering skills, but also by his ability to motivate a team to succeed at a difficult challenge. As Collins later explained, he was a "doer," someone he could rely on to bring a difficult project to a successful conclusion. Sullivan and Collins decided to promote Washkewicz to the position of research and development manager for the Hose Products Division, with the responsibility for leading the thermoplastic hose research team. Washkewicz's team would soon come to be known at the Hose Division as the "A Team."

Jim Collins (the author of *Good to Great*) and his colleague Morten Hansen have described the essential qualities of successful corporate leaders: "[Successful leaders] are utterly relentless, monomaniacal even, unbending in their focus on their quests... They're capable of immense perseverance... [They]...weren't just disciplined; they were fanatics."[613] Mandy Bendix, who teaches the importance of persistence, has said, "You look at anybody who has long-term success, and every one of them exhibited at some point this grit, this tenacity to keep going."[614] From the time Washkewicz first set foot in the Hose Division, to the day he retired as CEO, he kept a quote from Calvin Coolidge on his desk. Inscribed in raised letters on top of a wooden box, the quote was titled "Persistence," and it amounted to a summary of his creed for success: "Nothing in the world can take the place of persistence. .. Persistence and determination alone are omnipotent. The slogan 'press on' has solved and always will solve the problems of the human race."

Washkewicz would need all his persistence and all his will to produce the new thermoplastic hose line Pat, Sullivan, Collins and the Directors were expecting. If Washkewicz could not find a way around the competitors' patents, he would have failed in the defining moment of his career. Sullivan told

Don Washkewicz, far right, with the 'A Team,' circa 1970s.

Washkewicz not to become discouraged, saying "It's a long season. We're just at the beginning. Take the long view, Don. Don't look for quick answers. And don't ever give up."[615]

Every night, after working all day with the A Team at the Hose Division, discussing ways to make the new thermoplastic hose, Washkewicz took a pile of the competitors' patent applications home and spread them out on his bed. He awoke each morning with a stack of patent applications scattered around him. After months of study, Washkewicz came upon an elastomer made by DuPont. From his tests on the elastomer, Washkewicz learned it was just as durable as that being used by Samuel Moore for its thermoplastic hose. Washkewicz drafted several patent applications for a new brand of thermoplastic hose with an inner liner and outer jacket made from the DuPont compound. Seven of his applications were approved by the patent office, and shortly thereafter, Parker started making the new hose at the Ravenna plant.

After Washkewicz finished the thermoplastic hose project, Sullivan and Collins decided he needed a new challenge. They asked him to find a way of making a new type of rubber hose. The product had always been finished by curing it in a steam oven for two hours at 310 degrees. A lead covering was used as a mold to protect the hose during the curing process. Lead, however, had several drawbacks: it was expensive, toxic, and difficult to dispose of in landfills. Sullivan and Collins wanted Washkewicz to come up with a way of making rubber hose without the lead.

When Washkewicz started working on the project, Sullivan and Collins were already building a new 64,000-square-foot plant in Manhattan, Kansas that they planned to devote to making rubber hose in a lead-free process. Once again, Washkewicz faced the pressure of developing a new product for which Parker had already committed a substantial investment. And once again, he called upon the A Team to lead the project.

One night, while lying on a shag carpet in the living room of his home, reading Kent's engineering handbook, Washkewicz came up with an idea for a substitute for lead that could protect the hose during the curing process. He and his A Team conducted test runs in Ravenna, making rubber hose without the outer protective layer of lead. They called their new curing process the "white lead" approach. The senior engineers at the Ravenna plant told Washkewicz the new process would never work.

Persistence in the face of doubt was becoming one of Washkewicz's trademarks. On New Year's Eve, 1979, Washkewicz was celebrating with a group of friends at his home in the Cleveland suburb of Aurora. He was waiting to hear from one of his employees, Dennis Delbane, who was supervising the first run of rubber hose to come off the assembly line of Parker's new plant in Manhattan, Kansas. Several years earlier, Washkewicz had challenged his team to produce a commercially viable run of Parker's rubber hose, using the new process, before the decade ended. He had issued the challenge in a moment of bravado, knowing how difficult it would be to meet the deadline. Washkewicz, who grew up during Kennedy's Presidency, was echoing his challenge that America land a man on the Moon before the end of the '60s. Suddenly Washkewicz's phone rang. It was Delbane, calling from the floor of the Manhattan plant. He said, "Don, guess what, we did it! I'm watching the hose come out of the oven right now, and boy does it look beautiful."

In July 1982, Collins named Washkewicz the general manager of the newly formed Parflex Division in Ravenna, formed to manufacture and market the new line of thermoplastic hose that his team had developed. Armed with Washkewicz's new thermoplastic and rubber hose, the Hose Products and

Pat Parker proposing to the board of directors the construction
of an addition to the Ravenna, Ohio, plant, circa 1970s.

Parflex Divisions grew to sell hundreds of millions of dollars worth of hose every year. Parker had moved from last place to first in the worldwide hose market. When asked why Parker's Hose Products and Parflex Divisions had become so successful, Washkewicz replied, "It just shows what you can accomplish if you're dedicated and stick with it. You must have passion, persistence, and a killer instinct."

After he became CEO, Washkewicz kept locked in a cabinet in his corner office a memento of one of his proudest accomplishments at Parker. It was a dog-eared engineer's notebook, filled with his trigonometry calculations for the new hose brands many of his colleagues told him could never be made.

Don Washkewicz next to patent wall at Parker's headquarters. Washkewicz is the inventor or co-inventor of seven patents for Parker hose and fitting designs.

# CHAPTER 20

# First Steps to the World

On October 4, 1979, Pat Parker was the speaker at a dinner meeting at Cleveland's Union Club, in the same oak-paneled dining room where his father had met Bill Boeing more than 50 years earlier. Among the guests that evening was Jim Weeks, the lawyer who helped Art Parker buy the Euclid Avenue plant and counseled Helen Parker on how to keep the company alive after World War II. Weeks introduced Pat, who was scheduled to give a presentation on Parker's history. Both Ghost Taylor and Bob Cornell were in the audience. Weeks mentioned that Taylor would be retiring at the end of the month after 34 years of service at Parker, first as president, then as CEO, and finally as a director.

Weeks explained why Pat had been so successful in convincing business owners to sell their companies to Parker: "Pat's respect and regard for the individuals who built those companies, together with the fact that one never works for Pat—you work with him—serves to maintain in those individuals the same active interest and the same spirit of entrepreneurship in the joint enterprise."

Weeks said he "remembered quite well" when Taylor and Cornell decided to bring Pat into Parker's top management ranks, at the time Taylor retired as CEO in 1963. Weeks revealed it had been an easy decision, picking a man with Pat's talents and passion for the business. He pointed out that Pat had "a very substantial share of his worldly goods invested in Parker. To know that the man who's making the decisions has a real investment in the company, has always meant a great deal to me."[616] Weeks told the dinner guests that an investor who bought one hundred shares of Parker at $7 a share in May 1945, at a total cost of $700, would now own 1,296 shares, selling at $31.50 a share, and worth $130,000.

When Pat got up to speak, he sadly noted the absence of Carl Klamm, who had died three months earlier. He then recognized Taylor and Cornell as the "men who helped make Parker what it is today and set the course for what we think it will be tomorrow." Pat kidded Weeks about being the only one at his law firm on that Saturday morning in 1935 when Art Parker showed up looking for a lawyer, saying, "Well, it seems that back in those days lawyers hadn't discovered the benefits of working Saturdays."

With a catch in his voice, Pat described that New Year's afternoon of 1945, when his father died after shoveling snow. Pat remembered seeing "millions of partially completed pieces lying around the factory floor" after the government canceled its World War II aircraft orders. He proudly explained that his mother "was made of tough fiber also" and had "resisted any suggestion of sale or liquidation of the company her husband had so painstakingly built."

Pat recounted the obstacles he and his parents had overcome during the last 60 years to build a company that was expanding to the entire world:

> *"From an enterprise starting with two men, through the war years, to our first acquisition in the '50s when we became an "over the counter" company with sales of $30 million, today [in 1979] we employ over 20,000 talented people around the world in over 100 manufacturing facilities. For the fiscal year ended June 30, 1979, we reported sales of $846 million, and it is probable that the next nine months will see us pass the $1 billion mark. We are...serving the industrial, automotive, aviation, space and marine industries with over 90,000 off-the-shelf products.... We are... a company with assets, facilities, people and products around the world. An almost unimaginable achievement for a corporation which saw its total assets go over a Pennsylvania hillside but a few decades ago.'"*[617]

In 1980, Pat promoted Duane Collins to the presidency of the Fluid Connectors Group, the largest operating group in the company, and the one that traced its legacy back to Art Parker's 1925 patent for the two-piece flared tube fitting. Collins oversaw an aggressive acquisition strategy, fill-

ing in the missing pieces in the group's product lines. Always the consummate salesman, he concentrated on expanding the group's network of distributors in North America, so that nearly every customer could be served
within hours by a local engineer familiar with that customer's needs. By
the end of his eight-year tenure as group president, annual sales of connectors products would nearly double, from $215 million in 1980 to $389
million in 1987.

Parker's rapid growth in the 1970s and 1980s led to the formation of several new industrial divisions. Aiman, Sullivan and Collins were careful to
ensure that each new division contained no more than 500 employees, the
maximum number they believed any general manager could get to know on
a personal basis. They tried to establish new divisions in small towns, where
the general manager could become an important member of the community. They chose towns with special amenities, such as colleges and research
facilities that would attract talented employees and their families.

Paul Schloemer had succeeded Pat as the general manager of the Aerospace Division in 1965. In July 1982, he succeeded Pat as the company's CEO.
Pat retained the title of Chairman of the Board. During his 13 years as CEO,
Pat had overseen the completion of 33 acquisitions, an increase in Parker's
sales by more than five times, from $197 million in 1969 to $1.1 billion in
1982, and an increase in the company's market capitalization from $152
million to $444 million, creating nearly $300 million in additional wealth
for Parker's shareholders. Pat's notable acquisitions included Bertea, which
brought Parker into the aircraft flight control business; Rosaen Filter, the first
in a series of acquisitions that would make Parker a worldwide force in the
filtration business; Refrigerating Specialties, Parker's entree to the refrigeration valve market; and Ermeto, Germany's pre-eminent maker of tube fittings.

Pat believed he needed to spend an extended time away from the office, to
send a message to Parker's employees and shareholders that Schloemer was
now running the company. Pat and Madeline moved to a home at Presqu'ile
de Giens, on the Mediterranean Sea in Provence, France, returning to Cleveland only for the occasional board meeting. He and Madeline now had two
young children—Max, born in 1978, and Astrid in 1983.

In 1984, after living in Europe for a year and a half, Pat decided to move
back to Cleveland and resume a more active role at Parker. Schloemer and
Pat had a mutual respect, gained over the nearly thirty years they had worked

together. They developed a clear dividing line between their responsibilities. Schloemer made the important executive decisions, while Pat supervised the board, continued to solicit acquisition candidates, and traveled the world as a good will ambassador for the company.

Pat was content to let Schloemer operate the company, while he assumed the role of "senior statesman." It was the first time a member of the Parker family had not been actively involved in operating the company. Pat's diminished role signified the culmination of Parker's evolution from a family-run to a truly public company.

Schloemer had to deal with a challenging economy during his years as CEO. In the early 1980s, inflation in America was in double digits. The simultaneous rise of inflation and unemployment gave rise to a new term, "stagflation", to describe America's economic quandary. The Federal Reserve raised interest rates sharply to curb inflation. Thirty-year fixed mortgages topped out at 17.5 percent. The high interest rates pushed the economy into a recession. Six months after Schloemer was elected CEO, in December 1982, American unemployment peaked at 10.8 percent. Not since the Great Depression had so many Americans been out of work. A strong dollar made it easier for German and Japanese manufacturers to increase their market shares in America. One-third of American manufacturing plants were idled, most in the Middle West, and the demand for Parker's industrial goods declined sharply.

Parker was also facing a sharp decline in the market for farming equipment. Family farmers were finding it difficult to make payments on their high-interest loans, especially as a steep increase in the price of oil raised their costs. With so many farmers hurting, the market for Parker fittings, connectors, seals and cylinders in farm machinery crashed. One of the few bright spots was the aerospace market, where President Ronald Reagan's expanded military budget increased demand for Parker's products on the Armed Services' helicopters, fighters, and bombers.

The costs of complying with government regulation increased substantially during Schloemer's years as CEO. Parker's staff departments had traditionally been among the most lean in the manufacturing industry. In 1974, Pat Parker had told a reporter from the Cleveland Plain Dealer, "Our corporate staff is small compared to the size of the company. There are only seven of us staff people here at corporate headquarters."[618]

Schloemer realized he had to add experienced professionals to guide the company through increasingly complex rules on accounting, the environment, equal opportunity, and product liability. He was particularly worried that Parker lagged other multinational public companies in the rigor of its financial controls. Having grown up in Parker's aerospace business, where the government required stringent accounting, Schloemer was comfortable interacting with Parker's financial staff, and determined to implement the types of formal financial controls necessary for the multinational enterprise into which Parker was evolving.

Unlike the "Whiz Kids" at Ford, however, the staff departments at Parker remained focused on serving the needs of operations, rather than on trying to run the company themselves. Like Pat, Schloemer made sure the engineers remained in charge of operations.

As an Aerospace general manager and group president, Schloemer had already encountered several of the challenges Parker was beginning to face in its industrial businesses. Like the aircraft manufacturers, Parker's large industrial customers, such as General Motors, Deere, Caterpillar, and General Electric, were facing increased competition, at home and from products made abroad. In order to survive, they had to reduce their costs, and all of them looked to their suppliers to help in that effort. Parker's largest customers began cutting down the number of their suppliers, forcing the company to compete for business it had long taken for granted. Many of Parker's longest term customers were asking the company to commit to lower prices before even starting the bidding process. Schloemer facetiously called the process "being invited to the procurement party."

Schloemer asked each of Parker's industrial groups to become a supplier of entire fluid power systems to their customers. He remembered how he and his colleagues at Aerospace had won more business from Boeing and Airbus by becoming a supplier of entire systems for aircraft. He saw no reason why Parker's industrial divisions could not pursue a similar strategy with customers such as Deere, Caterpillar, and General Motors. In order to move Parker from a components to a systems supplier, Schloemer oversaw an aggressive initiative to acquire companies that would fill gaps in Parker's product lines. He was convinced Parker's evolution from a components to a systems supplier would give the company an insurmountable advantage over most of its competitors, most of whom sold only a limited number of fluid power products. As a systems supplier, Parker would only have to compete at the "procurement party" with two or three multi-line companies, rather than the large number of small "single-line" firms.

Schloemer's predecessors had concentrated on running Parker's business, rather than spending a lot of time with Wall Street analysts. For a company of its size, Parker had an unusually low profile. After Ghost Taylor retired as CEO and became Chairman of the Board, in 1963, he told a group of Parker executives, "I never paid much attention to Wall Street. I just wanted to be the best damn manufacturing man I could be, and let the chips fall where they may. Now I think we should pay more attention to telling our story."[619]

Schloemer realized that, in order to create the greatest value for shareholders, Parker had to have a higher profile on Wall Street. When he met with Wall Street analysts, he liked to emphasize the diversity of Parker's markets, and how it protected the company from a downturn in a particular industry, such as automotive and agriculture. The analysts on Wall Street started to pay attention, as Schloemer described Parker as "its own mutual fund of diversified industrial businesses."

Schloemer was an advocate for the decentralized strategy initiated by Helen, Taylor and Cornell after World War II. As he said, "The philosophy was of divisions as profit centers, and it was always to push that profit responsibility down as far in the corporation as possible. The idea was simple: put someone in charge of a division and give them the tools to succeed—the manufacturing facilities, the marketing support, whatever they needed to be successful."[620]

Schloemer believed in designing compensation plans that would incentivize all Parker's employees to increase the company's profitability. The most far-reaching of those programs was called the "Return on Net Assets," or "RONA" program. The program was based on the "Cost Goal" plan Helen Parker had advocated in the 1950s, which was later championed by Dennis Sullivan and Duane Collins for Parker's industrial divisions in the 1970s. It provided a quarterly bonus based upon the return on assets of the division at which an employee worked (corporate employees were paid based on the return on assets for the company as a whole). The program was designed to improve Parker's profitability through efficiencies in procurement, manufacturing, pricing and distribution practices.

Sullivan, Collins and Schloemer chose Washkewicz's Parflex Division as a pilot site to expand the RONA program to every employee at a division, from the general manager to the workers on the factory floor. Washkewicz had been holding quarterly meetings with his employees, encouraging them to run the plant more efficiently. As his employees gathered round in the division's conference room, he tried to explain the importance of holding less inventory and reducing costly scrap and production variances. As he later explained, "All I got was a bunch of blank stares. I could just imagine what they were thinking. All management wants us to do is to work harder."

Everything changed at the Parflex Division after the new RONA program was implemented. Washkewicz was finally able to make an exact connection between manufacturing efficiencies and his employees' paychecks. He explained:

> *"Now when I held my meetings I didn't get any more blank stares. They were actually paying attention, because I could explain what would happen to their paychecks if they reduced scrap or the amount of our inventory. Many of the folks in the plant began to send me ideas on how to operate more efficiently, and it wasn't long before we were able to achieve some real improvements in profitability. As soon as my people began to see larger RONA checks, they were sold on our new approach."*

After the success of the RONA program at Parflex, Schloemer began to expand the incentive plan to cover employees at most Parker locations in the world. To him, it was a way of demonstrating that all Parker's employees were on the same team, and that, if they worked together to achieve operating efficiencies, everyone would share in larger bonus checks.

In 1984, two years after he was elected CEO, Schloemer wrote an article for the *Iron Age* magazine in which he described the challenges and opportunities facing Parker. He explained "the increasing demands being placed upon manufacturers by their customers for better quality, price and 'just-in-time delivery.' These demands, he believed, presented an opportunity for Parker's fluid power products, which could increase the productivity of manufacturing processes. Technological change—in particular the integration of microprocessors and microcomputers with fluid power products—held the promise for historical breakthroughs in the efficiency of manufacturing. Schloemer called it "the marriage of brain and brawn."

Schloemer acknowledged in the *Iron Age* article that U.S. manufacturers such as Parker "must be prepared to compete on a worldwide basis. Customers heading for offshore manufacture will insist upon local sources of supply and service. Unless a company is prepared to step up to this challenge, it faces the prospect of shrinking market share. As the major...[vehicle and equipment manufacturers] place greater demands on the supplier base, only those with established offshore manufacturing and distribution backed by substantial financial and technical resources will be able to compete."[621]

Schloemer was concerned American manufacturing was declining from its historic rate of growth after World War II. He concluded the company would have to look to markets in Europe, Latin America, and Asia for growth. Many of the company's largest customers, such as Caterpillar, John Deere, and the automobile companies, were moving their operations to those regions. Schloemer intended to follow those customers, and keep their business, regardless of where they made their products.

IT HAD BEEN more than 20 years since Parker took its first step overseas. Entering the European market was another example of Parker's continuous quest for premier service, making sure it remained as close to its customers as possible. As Parker's long-time Director Jack Breen noted, "Parker people were less driven by the romance of globalization than simply by how to serve customers better."

Duane Collins described Parker's careful, step-by-step globalization process as follows: "The Parker path around the world is to follow the customer, use local nationals, make low risk, small bets, and build the business as demand for our products grows." Parker started by assigning a salesperson to prospect for customers in a new country. Once sales reached an adequate size, the company opened a local sales office. If business in the country continued to grow, Parker would begin to stock local inventory. The last step would be the beginning of a manufacturing operation, which was usually accomplished by acquiring a local manufacturer.

In 1961, Cornell and Taylor had established a warehouse in the duty-free zone at Amsterdam's Schiphol airport. For centuries, the Dutch had been a trading people, traveling the known world to sell their products. To Cornell and Taylor, Amsterdam seemed a natural location from which to export Parker products to the entire European community.

One of the first initiatives Pat had taken in 1965, when he took the reins of the Seal Group, was to expand Parker's sales of seal products outside America. He placed an inventory of seal products at the Schiphol warehouse, and soon thereafter, began eyeing the market for seals in Latin America. On one of his first trips to Argentina, he had the good fortune of meeting Maurice Castoriano, who was working in the purchasing department of a Peruvian shipyard that built and repaired fishing boats. Castoriano had bought Parker fittings and seals for the fuel system of one of those boats from a local Parker salesman. Impressed with the quality of the product, he asked Pat to appoint him as a Parker distributor. Sensing that Castoriano was a master salesman, Pat made him Parker's first distributor in Latin America.

When Pat became Parker's president in 1969, he announced a goal that seemed impossible to most of his executives—to make Parker's sales grow at a greater percentage outside America than inside the country. At the time Pat announced the goal in 1969, only $19 million, or 9.4 percent, of Parker's sales were in international markets. From 1969 on, Parker's sales outside the U.S. would accelerate at a much greater rate than sales within America. By 1985, Parker would sell $225 million of products outside the U.S., which amounted to 15 percent of Parker's total sales.

Parker's increased sales outside the U.S. were due in large part to the integration of the European economies in a "Common Market." The European Coal and Steel Community, created in 1952, was a first step toward an economic confederation of the European countries. In 1957, several countries signed the Treaty of Rome, creating the European Economic Community ("EEC"). The EEC's goal was to create a single European market by eliminating trade barriers and implementing a standard system of laws for all member states. It was the EEC's policy to insure the free movement of people, goods, services, and capital among European countries. The Maastricht Treaty of 1993 was designed to create a European monetary union. The "Euro" came into existence on January 1, 1999. Beginning with 12 countries, the "Euro Zone" eventually expanded to include 19 nations. With a common currency, the Euro members were able to establish a European Central Bank that could promote a centralized monetary policy, and ensure price stability.

Ever since 1964, when Parker acquired a cylinder manufacturer named Presswork Hydraulics, the company had been making products in Watford, England, 20 miles from downtown London. In 1976, Pat leased offices nearby, on Clarendon Road, to house Parker's first European headquarters. Pat called the new office "Star House." By 1975, Parker's European sales were nearly $60 million, most of which were to customers in the countries Parker's executives were beginning to call the "Big 4": Germany, the United Kingdom, France and Italy.

Pat wanted to ensure Parker's European operations would be infused with the same values that had made the company successful in America—premier customer service, teamwork, constant innovation, and the will never to give in to hard times. He decided the best way to pass along those values would be to send American executives steeped in Parker's culture to Europe for several years, to run the company's operations there. Pat understood the cultural chasm separating America and Europe. He hoped the American executives he sent to Europe would return home with a better understanding of the continent's culture, values and stringent regulation in areas such as environmental protection, the treatment of workers, and fair trade.

In 1976, Pat named Al Lindstrom Parker's first president of Europe, and sent him to work at Star House. He also sent a rising marketing executive named Jim Mockler to Star House to supervise Parker's European sales operations. Mockler had started his career in 1956, as a salesman with the Hannifin Corp., and had been promoted to increasing levels of marketing responsibility at Parker after it merged with Hannifin in 1957. He had been responsible for helping to establish Parker's network of independently owned distributors in North America. During his time in Europe, he worked to form a similar network of distributors on the continent.

Mockler was shocked by what he discovered when he arrived in Europe. As he later recalled, "The products were inferior and delivery was awful." Mockler soon found that Parker's European operations had not even developed a cost accounting system. The plant managers in each country had no idea whether or not they were making a profit, and if so, how much. Mockler gave the managers cost accounting books and told them to implement a system that would track costs and profits by product line. He also spearheaded quality control procedures to ensure no inferior products would be allowed to go out the door.

In the late 1970s, Parker's European divisions operated autonomously within each of the Big 4 countries. The plant managers for each product line reported to a country general manager in their home countries. The country general managers reported to Parker's president for Europe (who was located at Star House and reported to Pat). Each of the country general managers operated autonomously, focusing on their own countries. They had minimal interaction with their counterparts in other countries. There was little, if any, coordination across Europe on standard human resources, information technology, or accounting policies. The greatest challenge facing Lindstrom and Mockler was to convince the country general managers to adopt common approaches to their operations. They wanted the country general managers to think about their businesses, not just from the perspective of their own country, but in the context of the entire European Union. Lindstrom and Mockler envisioned that, just as the EEC evolved to promote economic cooperation across Europe, Parker's operations on the continent would mature from a country-centric culture to a pan-European orientation.

During his visits to Europe, Pat convened regular meetings of Lindstrom, Mockler and the country general managers, hoping to convince them to adopt pan-European approaches to operations. Pat, Lindstrom and Mockler found that, despite those meetings, the European country general managers continued to resist common operational, accounting and human resource initiatives.

In 1976, Lindstrom hired Mark Jarrad to become Parker's lead financial manager in Europe. Jarrad had risen through the financial ranks at Singer Corp. to become the company's European controller, working from London. Lindstrom arranged for Jarrad to meet Pat Parker and Phillip Rauch, the Chairman of Parker's Board, at La Guardia Airport in New York, while he was visiting the city on business for Singer. Jarrad was so impressed with the thoughtfulness of the two men, who had taken the time to come to New York to meet a potential new employee, that he decided after the interview that Parker was the company he wanted to join.

Jarrad had a tall, commanding presence and spoke with an accent so refined he could have been a BBC commentator. He was able to communicate his opinions forcefully, but in an unfailingly polite manner. He soon discovered the culture at Parker was markedly different from the competitive atmosphere that dominated his accounting firm. Jarrad found that his new colleagues got their satisfaction by helping each other succeed. As he looked back upon his career after his retirement, he recalled, "Everyone at Parker bent over backwards to make things easier for you. Everyone went out of their way to help you."[622]

In 1978, Pat appointed Barney Barnd to replace Lindstrom as European group president. Barnd once owned an Eaton, Ohio, company named Eaton Screw. In 1956, Cornell had come to visit Barnd in Eaton. He confided that Parker was having difficulty improving the efficiency of its manufacturing operations in Cleveland and Los Angeles. He offered to purchase Eaton Screw, believing the company could help Parker improve the quality of its in-plant operations. Impressed by Cornell, Barnd agreed to sell his company to Parker, and in the years following the acquisition, he was promoted to increasing levels of responsibility at Parker.

In the summer of 1957, Pat Parker was finishing a short stint in the accounting department on Euclid Avenue, as he waited to travel to California
to begin his job as a production planner at the Parker Aircraft Division. Pat
and a group of his colleagues in accounting arrived at Eaton Screw in early July, nearly a year to the day since the company was acquired by Parker.
Their job was to ensure Eaton's financial records were in compliance with all
accounting rules. The employees at Eaton knew Pat's last name was Parker,
but he was so low-key and easy-going they could not believe he was Art and
Helen Parker's son. One of Barnd's employees asked him "Who is this Parker
guy?"

Barnd replied, "Well, I'm not going to say a lot about him, but I think you
ought to treat him very nicely, because I think one day he's going to be your
boss."[623]

Barnd's appointment as Parker's European president in 1978 was a culmination of 21 years of promotions to greater levels of responsibility. He would
soon find his job in Europe to be the most challenging of his career. As Jarrad
explained the problems facing Parker's European business, Barnd began to
become just as discouraged as Lindstrom and Mockler had been about the
company's ability to succeed on the continent. Jarrad told Barnd that Parker's European divisions had no common accounting rules, no tax planning,
no common human resource or information technology policies, and no coordinated strategy for serving their customers. Just as Sullivan and Collins
had trusted Washkewicz to design the new products for the Hose Division,
Barnd empowered Jarrad—a brand new, untested Parker employee—to implement a new Pan-European organization.

Barnd asked Jarrad to help him establish common human resource, accounting, and information technology policies across all Parker's European
divisions. Jarrad drafted Parker's first European financial policies manual,
which set forth a common format for the European divisions to report their
financial results to Star House. Realizing how critical the manual would be to
Parker's success in Europe, he sent it for review to a respected senior partner
at Parker's outside accounting firm, Coopers & Lybrand. The partner would
later become the Lord Mayor of London.

At Jarrad's request, Barnd agreed to change the reporting relationships of
the division controllers, who had reported to the country general managers.
Under the new European structure, the division controllers reported directly
to Jarrad, making it easier for him to ensure that standard financial practices

were implemented across Parker's European operations. The country managers and plant managers feared Star House would take too much control from the local operations. It took four years of struggle, and a lot of help from Pat during several meetings at Star House, to convince the country general managers to envision their businesses in terms of the entire European market rather than their individual countries.

By 1980, Pat, Barnd and Jarrad had created a truly pan-European organization. For the first time, a Parker executive could look across all Parker's European operations at a glance, and pinpoint trends in sales and profitability in every country where Parker was doing business. Fueled by the new European organization, Parker's sales in Europe jumped from $54 million in 1976 to $141 million in 1980, an increase of nearly 300 percent over four years. In 1980, Parker moved its European headquarters to an office in Hemel Hempstead, England, less than an hour's drive from the middle of London. Pat called the new headquarters "Parker House," and he traveled there frequently to chair meetings of his European executives.

Pat's interest in European culture made him the perfect ambassador to the owners of companies outside the U.S. that were on Parker's list of prospective acquisition candidates. Flush with cash, Parker went on an acquisition binge in the 1980s, and in Europe, nearly all of those acquisitions were of companies headed by executives who had become friends of Pat.

In 1982, Pat decided to give Barney Barnd responsibility for all of Parker's international operations. Pat believed that with more than $100 million in annual sales outside the U.S., the company needed a senior executive to coordinate all its foreign operations.

During the late 1970s, Pat had traveled regularly to meet with Maurice Castoriano in Latin America. Like Pat, Maurice was an extrovert, and a natural salesman. A constant talker, he would strike up a conversation with nearly everyone he met. He was focused on constantly enhancing the quality of Parker's manufacturing processes in Latin America. The Parker executives from Cleveland who visited Maurice's plants found them to be among the most advanced in the entire company. Maurice focused initially on the markets for Parker's products in Brazil and Argentina. His biggest challenges were dealing with the corruption endemic in Latin America in the 1980s, and hyperinflation, as he constantly had to increase his employees' wages to cope with the skyrocketing cost of living.

In the early 1980s, Maurice reported to Mark Jarrad, who was running the company's Latin American operations from Parker's Cleveland headquarters. Jarrad brought his wife and three children to live in Cleveland for several years. His family was the first of many Europeans Parker would bring to the U.S. to familiarize themselves with American culture and business practices. Jarrad spent most of his time on planes, traveling from Cleveland to Brazil and Argentina.

During one of those visits, Maurice told Jarrad that, if Parker did not make a cash payment to a purchasing agent in Brazil, the company would lose at least half its business with one of its largest Brazilian customers. When Jarrad returned to Cleveland, he told Pat that Parker should refuse the bribe, no matter what the fall-out might be. Without hesitating, Pat replied, "Get it stopped, and do it now." A few weeks later, after it became known around Sao Paulo that Parker would not pay a bribe in order to get business, a local paper published an article touting Parker as the first foreign company to refuse to pay bribes in Brazil. As it turned out, despite refusing the bribe, Parker retained all its business with its Brazilian customer.[624]

In 1987, Pat gave a talk to a group of Brazilian executives in Sao Paulo, explaining how Parker had benefited from its replacement parts business in Latin America: "I emphasize to users of machinery—whether you're washing clothes, cooling this room, or flying down to Rio, you're wearing out Parker parts. Over 50 percent of our business comes from users—the so-called replacement market. It had been our dedication to this user market that has differentiated Parker from other components suppliers and has enabled us to become the worldwide leader in motion controls."[625]

Parker's sales outside North America grew steadily, increasing from $31 million in 1970 to $225 million in 1985. The company's profits in international markets, however, lagged behind its earnings in North America. By the mid-1980s, Parker's directors were beginning to become impatient with the company's results overseas, and some were starting to question whether Parker should continue to invest as aggressively outside the U.S. Schloemer remained committed to international expansion, but he realized the company could not continue to sustain under-performance in its overseas operations. He and Pat assigned one of their most talented executives to increase Parker's profitability overseas.

In July 1987, the board promoted Duane Collins from president of the Fluid Connectors Group to president of the International Sector, replacing Barney Barnd. Collins and his wife Joyce moved to London, so he could be more closely involved in Parker's international operations. For the next six years, Collins would spend 70 percent of his time on an airplane, flying to Parker's operations around the globe.

During his years as president of the International Sector, Collins built upon the efforts of Lindstrom, Mockler, Barnd and Jarrad to tie Parker's European divisions more closely together. His plan was to convince the European divisions to standardize their operational practices, just as Barnd and Jarrad had led them to coordinate their financial, human resources and information technology policies. It was an opportune time to implement best operating practices across the European Union, as most trade barriers between the members of the Common Market had been eliminated. Now a Parker plant could profitably ship products beyond the borders of its own country. Collins realized he could take advantage of economies of scale, and he encouraged his division general managers to invest in manufacturing operations that could ship products across all of Europe.

Collins was proud to explain to Wall Street analysts how Parker had redone its international operations to enhance its customer service. Where each division had previously adopted its own unique specifications for a particular product, customers could now take advantage of a "one-world" approach. They could purchase a product anywhere in the world, and be confident that the specifications to which that product was built would be the same in every country.

# CHAPTER 21

# Becoming a Multinational

I n the late 1980s, a confluence of unexpected events suddenly opened markets for Parker's products in Eastern Europe. Since the end of World War II, the region, dominated by the Soviet Union, had been closed to Western manufacturers. Having lost nine million soldiers in the war, Stalin felt entitled to retain the territories his troops conquered on their way to Berlin, including Poland, Czechoslovakia, Hungary, the Balkans, and East Germany. In order to prevent the people of those countries from escaping to the West, the Soviets erected an "Iron Curtain," a no-man's land guarded by soldiers, which extended from the North Sea to the Balkans.

The easiest path of escape from Soviet-occupied territory was through Berlin, where East Germans could cross into West Berlin, and from there to West Germany. From the end of World War II through 1961, 3.5 million East Germans managed to escape to the West. They had accounted for 20 percent of East Germany's population. In 1961, Russia took a desperate step to prevent further escapes. It assisted East Germany in erecting a concrete barricade that divided Berlin into two cities—in the East, a communist government, and in the West, a democratic one. Along the Berlin Wall, East Germany constructed guard towers and cleared a wide area (known as the "death trap"), in which its soldiers shot civilians on sight. The Berlin Wall became a potent symbol of the divide between the Soviet Union and the West.

In 1985, shortly after Mikhail Gorbachev became the leader of the Soviet Union, he implemented the new policies of "Perestroika" (restructuring) and "Glasnost" (openness), which allowed greater freedom of speech and of the press, and transparency from the government. Suddenly, the people of Russia and Eastern Europe could listen to Western music and learn of the freedoms and economic prosperity enjoyed by their neighbors in the West. Isolated protests in Eastern Europe against restrictive Communist rule soon grew into mass rallies, led first by students and later joined by millions yearning for better lives. It was not long before the protesters in Eastern Europe began to demand democracy, and the resignation of leaders appointed by the Soviet Union.

In June 1989, Hungary took down the barbed wire along its border with Austria. Thousands of Hungarians and East Germans began to take advantage of the first hole in the Iron Curtain to escape to the West. Most of the East Germans found their way from Austria to West Germany. Shortly after Hungary opened its borders, Duane Collins and his wife Joyce traveled to Stuttgart to meet a group of Parker executives concerned about the refugees streaming into West Germany. Collins and Parker's executives from West Germany decided they had a humane duty not to discourage their employees from giving refuge to families arriving from the East.

Freedom was on the march all across Eastern Europe, and there was little the Soviet-appointed rulers could do about it. Russia had dispatched troops to put down uprisings in East Germany in 1953, Hungary in 1956, and Czechoslovakia in 1968, but Gorbachev was not willing to take that step again.[626]

On November 9, 1989, Gunter Schabowski, the newly appointed Communist Party spokesman in East Berlin, had just returned from vacation to discover the East German Parliament had given its citizens the right to apply for visas to travel to West Berlin and West Germany. It was his job to explain the new visa requirements at an evening press conference. Without any fanfare, he disclosed the Parliament's decision as the fifth item on his list of otherwise routine announcements. A hush came over the reporters in the room as they heard Schabowski say that East Germans could travel to the West. One of the reporters asked "When does it take effect?"

Schabowski paused, and then looked up, seemingly confused. Several reporters repeated the same question as he sifted through his papers. No one had told him that the rules for obtaining visas would not take effect until the next day, nor what those rules would be. The East German Parliament had intended to require detailed documentation for visas that would have to be presented by travelers at designated exit points along the Berlin Wall. Schabowski, however, knew nothing of all that. Finally he shrugged and said that the right to travel would take effect "immediately, without delay." The room erupted, as the reporters realized the significance of what he had just said. Unwittingly, in an offhand way, he had brought down the Berlin Wall, the symbol of five decades of Cold War.[627]

That night, Schabowski's statement led the news on West German television stations, which were broadcasting live into East Germany. A news anchor said, "This is a historic day. East Germany has announced that, starting immediately, its borders are open to everyone.... The gates to the Berlin Wall stand open." Within a few months, Schabowski's mistake would, as the New York Times reporter Michael Meyer explained, "bring down not only Communist East Germany, but the entire Soviet empire."[628]

Collins and Joyce were watching on television from their flat in London, as thousands of East Germans began to gather at the Berlin Wall, demanding the border guards open the gates. The surprised guards made several calls to their superiors, asking for instructions on how to handle the crowd. What could have been a disaster soon turned into a celebration. No one among the East German authorities was willing to order the use of force against their own citizens. At 10:45 p.m., Harald Jager, the commander of the border guards, yielded, telling his men to open the checkpoints and allow the East Germans through. As they surged through the Wall, they were met by thousands of West Berliners with hugs and kisses. Soon a crowd of young West Berliners jumped on top of the Wall, where they were joined by other young people from East Berlin.

As he watched from London, Collins realized the fall of the Wall posed a once-in-a-lifetime opportunity for Parker. He believed the markets of Eastern Europe would soon open up to Western manufacturers. Collins expected it would not be long before the young people he was watching on television would begin to demand the same consumer goods their neighbors in the West had been enjoying for years. He was certain the opening of Eastern Europe would give Parker free rein to supply a broad range of fluid power products for the machinery in the new plants that would be built to meet the increasing demand for consumer goods. He also began to eye the market for construction equipment, which he expected to grow as Poland, East Germany, Czechoslovakia, Hungary and the Balkan countries began to build better highways, bridges, dams and other infrastructure.

COLLINS ALSO LOOKED to expand Parker's reach in Asia, where for years the company had only operated a few sales offices. In the 1980s, nearly all of Parker's growth outside the U.S. had been in Western Europe. But by the mid-1980s, some of the fastest growing economies in the world were in Asia. China had begun to open its markets to foreign investment, hoping to attract Western companies that would manufacture products, not just for the domestic Chinese market, but also for export to developed countries.[629] Collins realized Parker would not be a truly multinational company until it had manufacturing operations in every important market in Asia. He began to spend much of his time on long flights to Japan, Hong Kong, Singapore and Australia, overseeing Parker's expansion of its manufacturing footprint to the major countries on the Pacific Rim. Just as Collins had found in Don Washkewicz a young engineer who would transform the Hose Products Division, he was fortunate to find another young man perfectly suited to build Parker's operations in Asia.

Joe Vicic grew up on East 145th Street in Cleveland's Collinwood neighborhood. He later liked to say he was "born in the shadow of the Parker water tower" atop the Euclid Avenue plant. His parents were a first generation son and daughter of immigrants from Slovenia. Vicic began his career at Parker in 1967 as a sales trainee at the Cylinder Division in Des Plaines. In 1968, he joined the Navy and volunteered to serve in Vietnam. For 15 months, Vicic was assigned to a Navy Seal unit in Vietnam. He rose to the rank of lieutenant, ending his Navy career in 1972 as an intelligence officer in Taiwan. Vicic returned to Parker in 1972. Intelligent, focused, resilient, adaptable, unafraid of challenges, and comfortable in nearly any setting, he readily earned the respect of others. A natural salesman, he resumed his career in marketing at Parker, assigned to Parker's sales office in Cherry Hill, New Jersey.

Vicic had an adventurous spirit. He began looking for an opportunity to work in sales for Parker outside the U.S., and was intrigued by the excitement of planting the Parker flag in places that had never seen a Parker salesperson. In 1978, Dennis Sullivan named him the international sales manager for the Fluid Connectors Group. Vicic's office was in Cleveland, but he spent most of his time traveling to Australia, where Parker had established its first manufacturing plant in the eastern Pacific. When he was not on the way to and from Sydney, Vicic was on the road to Singapore, where Parker had opened its first Asian sales office, and Brazil and Argentina, where he met with Maurice Castoriano to help establish a foothold for Parker's products in Latin

America. Vicic quickly discovered that Parker's sales offices in Asia and Latin America were focused on just a few connectors' product lines favored by the local salesperson. Customers could order only a handful of Parker products; there was no opportunity for them to purchase an integrated system of several Parker components. Vicic vowed to diversify Parker's product offerings in Asia and Latin America.

In 1981, Sullivan appointed Vicic a regional sales manager for hydraulics products in Southern California. Like Pat Parker, Vicic loved the sea. He bought a home on the Pacific Coast near his office, where he could keep a boat. George Stephens, who was leading Parker's operations in Asia and Latin America from an office in Cleveland, had his eyes on Vicic. He was convinced that with his experience serving in the Navy in Asia, his sense of adventure, and his natural abilities as a salesman, he would be the perfect choice to run Parker's new sales office in Singapore.

Parker chose Singapore because it was transitioning from an English colony, viewed as "a small backward Third World outpost,"[630] to a regional economic power. Led for 31 years by the strong hand of Lee Kuan Yew,[631] who became the longest-serving prime minister in world history,[632] Singapore united its disparate ethnic groups into a cohesive society focused on economic growth. The country achieved an average growth rate of 7 percent from 1976 to 2000. Its per capita income grew to $50,000, making it the wealthiest country in Asia.[633]

Early one morning in mid-1981, Stephens showed up at Vicic's California sales office, pulled up a chair, looked across the desk at Vicic and asked him whether he could be willing to move to Singapore to become Parker's general manager for Southeast Asia. Vicic accepted Stephens' offer on the spot. He was happy to be returning to Asia, not as a warrior, but as a businessman helping the Asians build better lives. Vicic moved to Singapore just as several Asian countries were growing their economies at an astonishing pace, as they opened up their markets and adopted the rudiments of a capitalist system. The four "Asian Tigers"—Hong Kong, Singapore, South Korea and Taiwan—had been moving toward an export-led growth strategy since the 1960s. For three decades, each of those countries averaged 7.5 percent growth each year.

In the late 1970s, China had begun to transform itself from a socialistic to a market economy, and from an agrarian to an urban society focused on industrialization. In 1978, Mao Tse Tung's successor, Deng Xiaoping, allowed

Chinese citizens to own farms and start their own businesses. His mantra became "to get rich is glorious."[634] In early 1980, Deng sent a delegation of Chinese businessmen from Wuhan, in south-central China, to Ohio in an effort to encourage local companies to invest in the Wuhan area. Pat Parker met with the Chinese businessmen in Columbus, and agreed to send a group of Parker executives to Wuhan to discuss a possible joint venture to manufacture seals.

The Parker delegation was one of the earliest forays by an American company into mainland China. It had been less than 10 years since President Nixon shocked the world with his trip to China to meet with Mao.

Jim Baker, a member of Parker's legal department, joined three Parker executives on the trip. Baker and his colleagues were overwhelmed by the poor conditions in China. The country lacked even the most rudimentary means of transportation. They encountered lengthy delays waiting for their turbo prop flight from Guang Zhou to Wuhan. The flight times were written in chalk on a blackboard, so the gate attendants could erase them every time there was a delay. Whenever Baker asked if the flight would be on time, the attendants cleaned the blackboard, posted a new time, and replied that of course the flight was right on schedule.

Upon their arrival in Wuhan, the Parker executives were surprised to see that not a single motorized vehicle was operating on the unpaved streets, which were filled with pedestrians and workers pulling carts of merchandise. Baker watched in amazement as he passed by downtown buildings where workers were lifting steel and cement to higher floors by hand. Along the Yangtze River, thousands of workers were building a dam, bit by bit, climbing to the top of a hill, filling their barrels with stones, and dumping the stones into the river. Baker and his colleagues traveled by van to visit factories in nearby towns. Working conditions in the plants looked more like those during the early Industrial Revolution than the 20th century.

At the end of their 10-day trip, the Parker executives gathered in Hong Kong to decide whether to recommend to Pat that the company invest in a joint venture to manufacture seals in Wuhan. The executives recognized there was a tremendous demand in China for seals, as nearly every fluid conveyance system in the country was plagued by leaks. The executives concluded, however, that the Chinese lacked an infrastructure sufficient to support a manufacturing operation. There was no legal system in place for private companies, no effective transportation system, no means of obtaining qual-ity raw materials, no workforce capable of operating modern machinery, and no "front-office" talent that could oversee financial systems and controls.

The executives returned to Euclid Avenue, prepared to tell Pat that now was not the time to start a new venture in China. Pat, however, was deter-mined that Parker become one of the first American companies to invest in the country, and he told the executives to proceed with the seal joint venture in Wuhan. He appreciated how primitive business conditions were in Chi-na, but he saw the potential for the country to become an industrial power, once its politicians freed their people to operate under a freer market sys-tem. Pat was certain that, eventually, Parker's investment would be repaid many times over.

During the 1980s and '90s, in China's second stage of economic liberaliza-tion, Deng privatized many state-owned industries, lifted price controls, and eliminated laws protecting local Chinese businesses from foreign competi-tion. In what journalist and best-selling author Beth Macy has called "the larg-est migration in human history," 160 million Chinese moved from rural areas to cities.[635] From 1978 to 2013, China grew at a rate of between 9.5 percent and 11.5 percent per year. Average wages rose six fold between 1978 and 2005, and poverty declined from 41 percent of the population to just 5 percent.

By the second decade of the 21st century, China, an industrial backwa-ter just 35 years earlier, boasted the second largest economy in the world. The changes in Wuhan since the first trip there by Parker's executives in 1980 exemplified the rise of China to an industrial power. By 2015, the city had become a sprawling industrial and financial megalopolis of more than 10 million people, more than four times its size in 1980. Wuhan had evolved into a key transportation hub, with seven bridges and a tunnel crossing the Yangtze, one of the busiest airports in central China, a large metro system, and an embarkation point for one of China's fastest trains. Six thousand for-eign-owned enterprises, with a total capital of over $22 billion, were operat-ing in the city, and the skyline was dotted with 130 skyscrapers, with 90 more under construction.

FROM 1981 TO late 1988, Vicic oversaw Parker's Asian sales from a ware-house at the Singapore airport, from which he planned to ship Parker prod-ucts all across Asia to meet the demands of its fast-growing economies. The Asian oil industry was booming, and it provided a ready market for Parker's seals, which prevented oil from leaking in off-shore oil platforms and drilling operations in remote islands in Southeast Asia. Vicic was committed, however, to diversifying sales into other areas, so that Parker would not become reliant upon any single Asian market. His vision, like that of Helen, Taylor and Cornell after World War II, was to make Parker a "one-stop-shop" for all a customer's fluid power needs.

In 1984, Vicic's wife, Eileen, suffered a stroke at their home in Singapore. His colleagues in Cleveland rallied around him, making it clear his first priority should be caring for his wife. Vicic later said it was like "my whole Parker family came to visit and help take care of me and my wife."[636] Pat Parker, Duane Collins, and George Stephens all came to Singapore, helping run Parker's Asian sales office while Vicic was spending most of his time at the hospital. After several weeks, his wife recovered enough to return home, and Vicic was able to return to his travels throughout Asia.

Collins told Vicic he needed to gain manufacturing experience if he hoped to continue to advance at Parker. He spent the next five years running a Parker plant in Canada and the marketing operations of Parker's Seal Group in Irvine. In 1994, Collins asked Vicic to return to Asia as the first president of Parker's Asia Pacific Group. Vicic moved the group staff from Cleveland to Hong Kong. The move symbolized the growing importance of China to Parker's ambitions in Asia. Vicic had approximately 60 employees in Asia, responsible for $23 million in sales. Most of those sales were to American companies that had started manufacturing operations in Asia, including Caterpillar, Ingersoll-Rand, and John Deere.

Collins empowered Vicic to make most of the decisions on how to grow Parker's business in Asia, just as he and Sullivan had empowered Washkewicz to design the new products for the Hose Products Division. Most of the products Parker sold in Asia in the mid-1990s were made in the company's U.S. plants. Parker had lagged behind many of its competitors in bringing its manufacturing plants to Asia. Without local manufacturing and service centers, Parker could only compete by lowering its prices. Determined to give Parker the leverage to increase its profitability in Asia, Vicic initiated an evolution of Parker's Asian operations, first to assembly plants, and ultimately, full-blown manufacturing facilities.

Many of Parker's new plants in Asia were the result of acquisitions. Just as in Europe and Latin America, Pat Parker played an important role in courting prospective acquisition candidates in Asia. Vicic watched with admiration as

Pat earned the respect of the owners of Asian companies Parker was interested in purchasing. They seemed, Vicic thought, to look upon Pat as a "father figure," the honored descendant of Parker's founder, who was carrying on his family traditions of customer service, regard for others, teamwork, empowerment, and persistence in hard times. These were values much like those held in high regard in the Asian culture. Confucianism teaches a similar approach to the meaning of life, revering stability, hard work, loyalty and respect for others. The companies Pat helped acquire included a cadre of talented local executives, dedicated to customer service and manufacturing excellence, and familiar with the Asian markets. Collins and Vicic spent a great deal of their time familiarizing those executives with Parker's culture. Nearly all the executives of the acquired companies decided to continue their careers with Parker, and several rose to high levels of responsibility within Parker's Asian organization.

Pat Parker with executive team in Asia, circa 1996. Joe Vicic is in the back row at the far left; George Stephens is in the front row at the far right.

Collins was patient in growing Parker's operations in Asia, telling Vicic they were investing for the long run. Collins understood it would take years to build the infrastructure necessary to compete with Asian companies for local business. In the meantime, Vicic concentrated on serving American and European companies that had moved their manufacturing operations to Asia. Parker built its first manufacturing plant in China in the late 1990s to serve General Motors, which was making Buicks in Shanghai. The local Chinese suppliers were not yet capable of meeting General Motors' quality standards. The company turned to Parker as a preferred source due to its reputation (earned over a period of years) for providing high quality products to General Motors' North American assembly plants.

By 2016, 41 percent of Parker's sales, a total of $4.6 billion, were being made to customers outside the U.S., achieving a growth rate of 10.6 percent per year since Parker's $225 million in non-U.S. sales in 1985. The company's products were helping build and operate hospitals, schools, highways, railroad lines, power plants, water purification facilities, oil refineries, chemical plants, and other critical infrastructure in every corner of the globe, raising living standards for billions of people.

Parker was part of an international industrial revolution that helped more people live better lives than ever before. The gains in Asia alone in the late 20th century were astounding. Parker's sales in Asia increased from just $23 million in 1994 to $1.5 billion in 2016, an annual growth rate of 21 percent.

The economist Michael Schuman has written that the "economic gains achieved in Asia are almost impossible to comprehend. Asia has produced the most sustained economic boom in modern history, a massive surge in income that has brought unprecedented gains in wealth and economic opportunity to 3 billion people."[637] In 1965, China's per capita GDP was $100; by 2007, it was 2,260 percent larger, at $2,360. Singapore's per capita GDP increased by 5,913 percent during that same period, from $540 to $32,470; Malaysia's increased by 1882 percent, from $330 to $6,540; and Japan's increased by 4133 percent, from $890 to $37,670.[638]

Dennis Sullivan, Duane Collins and Pat Parker, circa 1993.

Due to increases in prosperity in Asia, Latin America, and Eastern Europe, the average worldwide life span of humans is longer than it ever has been; child malnutrition is at its lowest level ever; and a smaller portion of women die in childbirth than at any time in history.[639] The proportion of the world's population living in extreme poverty fell by more than half, from 35 percent in 1993 to 14 percent in 2011, the most recent year for which figures are available from the World Bank. In 1990, more than 12 million children died before the age of five. That toll has dropped by more than half. In the 1980s only half of girls in developing countries completed elementary school; today 80 percent do.[640]

Nicholas Kristof has written in the New York Times that "Historians may conclude that the most important thing going on in the world in the early 21st century was a stunning decline in human suffering... [that constituted] the greatest gains in human well-being in the history of our species."[641] Such progress would not have been possible without the hundreds of thousands of Parker products around the world that were powering nearly every world-changing piece of machinery at the disposal of humankind.

PAUL SCHLOEMER retired as CEO in 1993. During his 11 years leading the company, he oversaw the largest increase in sales of any of his four predecessors. Parker's revenue grew from $1.1 billion in 1982 to $2.5 billion in 1993, despite the challenges of high interest rates, slow economic growth, stagflation, the arrival on American shores of high quality goods made abroad, and two serious recessions. Schloemer had the foresight to expand Parker's manufacturing footprint in Europe, Latin America, and Asia, and to begin to move Parker from a components manufacturer to a supplier of integrated fluid power systems. He oversaw the completion of 39 acquisitions that filled gaps in Parker's product lines. During Schloemer's tenure as CEO, shareholders saw Parker's market capitalization nearly quadruple, from $444 million to $1.609 billion.

Schloemer's notable acquisitions included the Uniroyal hose business, which helped make Parker a worldwide leader in the hose market; Schrader Bellows, which brought Parker into the pneumatic cylinder and valve business; Stratoflex, which extended Parker's hose business into aircraft applications; Compumotor, which gave Parker technology for electric motors and controls that could direct machines to cut metal to precise tolerances; Gull Corp., known throughout the world for its fluid measurement and electronic

Duane Collins and Paul Schloemer, circa 1993.

instrumentation products; and three companies that made Parker a significant player in the filtration business—Racor Industries, Finite Filter, and Commercial Filter.

During Schloemer's tenure, and that of his three successors, Parker would complete more than 200 acquisitions, forever altering the worldwide fluid power market. Many of the competitors that were not acquired simply fell by the wayside, unable to compete with a company like Parker that could serve its customers anywhere in the world. Where there had been hundreds of small fluid power companies competing in the fluid power market in the aftermath of World War II, by the end of the 20th century there were only a handful, each of them a multinational behemoth. The large multinationals, including Parker, Eaton, Bosch, Rexroth, SMC, and Freudenberg, had transformed the fluid power industry into a concentrated, high-technology industry with high barriers to entry.

PAT PARKER and Schloemer considered several candidates to propose to the board for election as the company's next CEO. Each was a talented executive with a long period of successful service at Parker. Duane Collins, however, stood out from all the rest. In his years leading Parker's international operations, he had acquired an understanding of the business cultures of Europe,

Latin America and Asia that only Pat could match. In Europe alone, Parker's sales had increased by 54 percent during Collins' tenure as head of international, from $308 million in 1987 to $474 million in 1993.

Collins was elected CEO in July 1993. He was the first leader of the company to serve while a member of the Parker family was no longer an active employee. Pat retired as Chairman of the Board and became Chairman Emeritus in 1999, spending his time traveling around the world promoting the company's products, explaining its history and culture, looking for acquisition candidates, and meeting with stock analysts.

Collins was faced with intense competition from three other large companies with a worldwide reach—Eaton, a multi-billion dollar public company headquartered in Cleveland, with a broad line of hydraulic and filtration products; Swagelok, a privately held manufacturer of sophisticated instrumentation valves and fittings headquartered in Solon, an eastern suburb of Cleveland; and Bosch Rexroth, a German industrial behemoth, which made a wide range of motion and control products.

Collins knew Parker's board was not satisfied with the company's growth rate, nor with its profitability. He hoped the directors would give him enough time to implement strategies that would help Parker perform better against competitors such as Eaton, Bosch Rexroth, and Swagelok. Collins knew that the greatest percentage, by far, of the world's markets were outside the borders of America, and that those markets presented untapped opportunities for Parker.

Collins was convinced Parker could not succeed as a multinational company unless it harnessed the collective power of all its divisions on a global basis. There was too much duplication of effort among divisions and not enough coordination across national boundaries. Divisions were designing products just to meet the standards of their home country, rather than making them for a global marketplace. Collins wanted his group presidents to start thinking of themselves as global managers, rather than just as American executives. The transformation in their thinking, he believed, would have to start with learning to understand, and to respect, the cultures of other countries. As he said, "Americans as global managers did not have a global mind set and needed to learn respect for colleagues abroad."

Within a week of being elected CEO, Collins gave Parker's group presidents worldwide responsibility for managing their product lines, and tasked them with the responsibility of devising ways of designing and marketing products on a global basis. This organizational change was the last step in the process begun by Barnd, Mockler, and Jarrad in Europe in the late 1970s to make Parker's executives think beyond the borders of their countries, cultures, and product lines.

Collins admired the decentralized operating approach adopted by Taylor and Cornell after World War II. He had experienced the power of empowerment at Parker, first as the general manager of the Hose Products Division, and later as president of the Fluid Connectors Group, when he had a large group of general managers reporting to him. He believed Parker's divisional structure fostered "close-to-the-customer accountability." He was convinced the divisional approach gave a large number of up-and-coming Parker leaders valuable executive experience early in their careers. As he explained, "We're structured to grow lots of leaders trying different ideas in an environment in which trial, error, and success help leaders emerge for the future."

Collins realized, however, the divisional approach had to be tempered by central-led initiatives that would knit all of Parker's operating units together. He made sure the divisions adopted common Information Technology systems that would give Parker's executives, at a glance, a picture of how each of the company's divisions and groups were performing. He oversaw procurement initiatives that would allow the divisions to use their collective market power to obtain more favorable pricing for raw materials.

Collins viewed Parker's network of independently owned distributors around the world as an important aspect of Parker's decentralized operating philosophy. He believed the distributors gave Parker a visibility to the needs of customers that the company could never achieve on its own. As he said, "Our distribution organization is the envy of the industry. Distributors add their own capital, entrepreneurial zeal, local contacts, and independent mindedness, among the attributes Parker could never duplicate."

Like Art Parker, Collins had a missionary zeal for premier customer service. He had spent most of his life serving customers, from the checkout aisles at his parents' grocery store, to Parker sales offices, the Hose Division, the presidency of the Fluid Connectors Group, and the presidency of the International Sector. He learned from those experiences that, if Parker could deliver quality products, more quickly than its competitors, its customers would be willing to pay the company a premium price. Everywhere he went as CEO, from the factory floor to the executive suite, Collins preached the need for delivering quality parts on time. One of his favorite Power Point slides, with which he closed nearly all his presentations, was a listing of what he called "Parker's Top

100 goals." The first 98 goals all said the same thing: "Serve the Customer." The last two were "Financial Performance" and "Profitable Growth."

Having come up through the sales ranks, Collins appreciated what it took to work in partnership with customers. He made sure his general managers spent enough time with them to anticipate their needs. He wanted Parker's executives to maintain enduring friendships with customers, just as Art Parker had with the pioneers of the aviation industry.

In July 1987, when Collins was promoted to Vice President of International, Don Zito replaced him as the president of the Fluid Connectors Group. Zito had overcome several challenges since joining Parker in 1962 after obtaining his engineering degree from the Case Institute of Technology. In 1972, he became the general manager of the Rosaen Filter Division in a Detroit suburb. Rosaen, acquired by Parker in 1968, was the company's entree to the filter business, selling $2 million of filtration products a year. It did not take long for Zito to realize the potential of the filter business. He discovered that Parker's competitors were enjoying year-to-year profit margins of 20 percent, and he yearned to do the same for Parker.

In the late 1970s, Zito produced a spreadsheet for Pat Parker and the board of directors that outlined the companies he believed Parker needed to acquire in order to become a significant player in the filter business. The list included Finite Filter, another Detroit company, and Racor, located in Northern California. Zito oversaw the acquisition of those companies in 1985 and 1986, creating a Filtration Group that could compete with the dominant companies in the filtration market.

Zito served as president of the Fluid Connectors Group from 1987 to 1997, a period that spanned the tenure of Schloemer and Collins as Parker's CEOs. Both men empowered Zito to make the major operating decisions for his group. For a period of three years, he spent $100 million each year on new equipment, at a time when the group's sales were just slightly more than $500 million a year. His new machines were equipped with software that enabled them to accept orders directly from buyers, bypassing the usual paperwork in the front office, and speeding products to customers.

Zito's financial gamble paid off handsomely. As a result of his investments, he was able to improve the quality of the group's products and reduce delivery times. The group's days outstanding for accounts receivable dropped from 45 days—considered a reasonable goal by most manufacturers—to just 29 days. Inventories also declined drastically, from a six-month supply to just three months' worth, with dramatically improved customer service levels. The combined effects of the receivables and inventory completely offset the cost of the additional capital investments made by the Fluid Connectors Group.

Zito's reputation for pleasing customers allowed him to capture additional market share in the competitive market for connectors products. When he became the Fluid Connectors Group president in 1987, the group and its largest competitor, Aeroquip, were both making slightly less than $400 million in sales per year. When Zito retired from Parker 10 years later, Aeroquip had annual sales of $400 million, while the yearly sales of Parker's Fluid Connectors Group had grown to more than $1.2 billion.

COLLINS POSSESSED A NATURAL business sense, acquired from his early days at his parents' farm and in their grocery store, and in working his way up through the ranks at Parker. His favorite response to a questionable proposal was to say, "It just doesn't pass the smell test." He rejected the latest fads in "financial engineering" that were being touted by Wall Street in the 1990s, and likely set the stage for the Great Recession a decade later. Collins resisted any suggestions to leverage the company with greater debt, or to acquire companies outside its charter of fluid power products. He rejected a proposal from Parker's finance department to re-incorporate in Bermuda in order to reduce taxes. As Jack Breen explained: "Typical of the company doing the right thing was the tempting Bermuda tax inversion plan idea. Some of Parker's peers and competitors were taking advantage of it. It is important for companies to pay their fair share of taxes where they live, and we declined the Bermuda tax inversion plan for all the right reasons."

Like the five Parker leaders who preceded him, Collins realized sales growth was the key to Parker's success. Never satisfied with the status quo, Collins continually encouraged his colleagues to grow the company, both through acquisitions and the development of new products. He realized that not only did increasing sales allow for economies of scale in Parker's manufacturing operations; it also gave Parker's employees the opportunity to take on new and increasing levels of responsibility, and to be better compensated for their efforts.

Collins was a man who kept his eyes on the future, and he wanted all his employees to do the same. He believed that continuous innovation in all aspects of the company's operations was the only way to survive in a competitive worldwide economy. One day, in the midst of a discussion on funding new product development, Collins warned a group of Parker executives they should never give up on trying new things, saying "We always need to have someone out there who's trying to do something crazy."

In a March 2005 interview, Collins was asked how he would characterize Parker's culture. He replied, "Mentorship, treating people well, expansionism, high performance expectations, mutual respect, are key drivers of the organization. We respect colleagues, seek mutuality of interest, and enjoy an easy collegiality. Leading by example is the Parker way."

Collins once explained that no Parker employee should ever be satisfied with things as they are, but should keep his or her eyes focused on future challenges. He compared a Parker career to the trip of a mountain climber

who scales a sheer cliff, finds a ledge on which to rest for a short time, just long enough to catch a breath, and then resumes his or her never-ending climb up the mountain. During his own journey up the mountain, Collins never lost faith in Parker's ability to continue to grow, and to prosper. Under his leadership, Parker acquired 53 companies around the world. The company's sales increased from $2.5 billion in 1993 to $6 billion in 2001, and its market capitalization tripled, from $1.6 billion to $4.9 billion, creating $3.3 billion in new wealth for Parker's shareholders.

Collins oversaw the completion of several sizable acquisitions, including Chomerics, which gave Parker an entree to the market for electromagnetic shielding of computers and cellular phones; VOAC Hydraulics, which brought Parker hydraulic cylinders, accumulators, valves, and pumps for construction and agricultural equipment; Abex NWL, which vaulted the company into the sale of aircraft thrust-reverse actuators and pumps for aircraft hydraulic systems; Commercial Intertech, which added gear pumps for construction and agricultural equipment to Parker's line of hydraulic products; Wynn's International, which broadened the company's line of sealing products; and Honeywell's solenoid valves, capable of controlling air in pneumatic powered systems.

Duane Collins during his tenure as CEO.

Don Washkewicz, Lee Banks and Tom Williams.

PART 6

# ENGAGING A NEW CENTURY

## 2000 AND BEYOND

---

*"I would hope that Parker's people would think of me as someone who sustained the best values of our past and helped implement new strategies that lifted Parker to even higher levels of success. Most of all, I want to be remembered as someone who trusted, valued, and respected all Parker's team members, gave them every opportunity to succeed, and kept them safe."*

Tom Williams, on how he would like to be remembered at the end of his own tenure as CEO

# CHAPTER 22

# Harnessing Parker's Collective Power

After Washkewicz designed the new products for the Hose Division in the 1970s, Collins and Sullivan recognized him as a rising star, and they promoted him in 1982 to be the general manager of the newly formed Parflex Division. In October 1994, he was named an operating vice president of the Fluid Connectors Group, and in November 1997 the president of the Hydraulics Group, which had annual sales of $700 million.

Collins never forgot how Washkewicz succeeded at one of the most difficult assignments he had ever given to one of his employees: leading the research teams that developed the products that took Parker from last place to first in the worldwide hose market. Collins was convinced Washkewicz possessed the qualities essential for a successful CEO of a large public company—persistence in the face of hard times, a passion for innovating to serve Parker's customers, and the ability to motivate and empower a team of employees to solve difficult problems.

In December 1998, Collins called Washkewicz to his office and asked if he would agree to be included on the list of potential CEO successors. Washkewicz told Collins he appreciated being considered, but he believed other more senior executives were better prepared to lead the company. He had been the president of the Hydraulics Group for just a year. He told Collins he loved his job and would be happy to continue in that position until he retired. Collins told Washkewicz he would not be retiring for two years, and Washkewicz would have plenty of time to consider the CEO job in the meantime.

A year went by, during which Washkewicz heard nothing further from Collins about CEO succession. He assumed Collins had forgotten all about making him a candidate. One morning in December 1999, Collins asked Washkewicz to come to his office. Once again, Collins tried to convince him to be included on the list of CEO candidates. Washkewicz thanked Collins for considering him, but said he still had a lot of unfinished business to attend to in the Hydraulics Group. After 30 minutes of back and forth, Washkewicz finally agreed to be included on the succession list, out of respect for Collins. As he walked out of Collins' office, he felt certain the other CEO candidates were far more qualified than him, and much more likely to be picked to succeed Collins.

In January 2000, Washkewicz attended Parker's winter planning meeting at the La Quinta resort, near Palm Springs, a green oasis in the Santa Rosa Mountains of the California desert. Since the 1920s, the resort had welcomed movie stars such as Greta Garbo, Clark Gable, Bette Davis, Katherine Hepburn, Shirley Temple, and Kevin Costner, and sports superstars such as Joe Montana and Michael Jordan. Like Parker's other executives, Washkewicz expected Collins to name his successor shortly. Speculation raged in corridors, bars and conference rooms during the LaQuinta meeting over who Collins was about to pick. Washkewicz's name was rarely, if ever, mentioned in those conversations.

Washkewicz was surprised when Collins came up to him on the last day of the La Quinta meeting and invited him to dinner, ostensibly to discuss the integration of a major product line into the Hydraulics Group. As they sat down at a quiet table in a corner of the expansive dining room at the La Quinta resort, Collins raised a glass and said, "Congratulations, Don, you're in!"

Washkewicz replied, "What do you mean, I'm in, Duane? Congratulations for what?"

Collins said, "The board decided this afternoon to vote you in as the next president and Chief Operating Officer of the company. If you perform as I expect you to over the next year and a half, I'm going to ask the directors to elect you Parker's CEO."

Washkewicz thought, "Oh my God, watch out for what you ask for!"

He was unable to sleep that evening, as he thought about the responsibility he was about to assume for the livelihoods of more than 44,000 employees and $5 billion in shareholders' wealth. From that day forward, Washkewicz always felt that if he did not have a heart attack that evening, he would never have one.

Washkewicz was elected Parker's president and Chief Operating Officer on February 1, 2000. Less than six years earlier, he had been the manager of a $100 million Parker division, and now he was expected to prepare himself to lead a multi-billion dollar company. Of the five candidates for the job, he had been the darkest of dark horses. His rise through the ranks had been so precipitous that many of the company's directors and executives hardly knew him.

The company Washkewicz was elected to lead had become the largest manufacturer of motion and control products in the world, with $6 billion in sales, more than 450,000 customers, and 44,000 employees working from over 250 locations in 46 countries. The company's catalogues included a nearly inexhaustible list of hundreds of thousands of products supporting almost every industrial and aerospace application involving motion or control.

Before he was elected president, Washkewicz had been looking forward to enjoying more time outside the office. He had worked day and night for the last 29 years, on projects that were emotionally and physically exhausting. He was 52 years old, with a son and two daughters who would soon be leaving for college, and he wanted to spend more time with them while they were still at home. Now, as he assumed the job of president and Chief Operating Officer, he realized he was going to have very little personal life during the decade of his fifties.

At each turning point in Parker's history, a leader suited to the challenges of the time had stepped up to guide the company to a higher level of performance. Art Parker sent the company on its first growth path, guiding it through the disaster on the Lincoln Highway, a bankruptcy, the Great Depression, and two world wars. Helen Parker, Ghost Taylor and Bob Cornell implemented strategies of diversification and decentralization that brought the company back from near-bankruptcy, and shielded it from future economic downturns. Pat Parker began Parker's evolution to a multinational company. Paul Schloemer completed Parker's transition from a family-run to a truly public company. Duane Collins found a way to make Parker's men and women think of their business in a global context, and to begin to harness the collective strength of a multi-billion dollar company. Now Don Washkewicz was about to devise a strategy that would build upon Collins' initiatives, giving Parker's disparate divisions a clear-cut road map for working together to achieve growth and operational excellence.

Shortly after Washkewicz was elected Parker's president, Collins met with a stock analyst from New York, who asked him why he had chosen Washkewicz over the other candidates for the job.

Collins replied, "There were several people I could choose to run the company. But I knew we needed someone who could really lead the company to future success, and that was Don."[642]

DURING HIS FIRST DAYS as president, Washkewicz missed walking through a plant, and talking with Parker's workers. As a general manager, he had been able to communicate with his employees by gathering them all in a single room. How, he wondered, would he be able to explain to more than 40,000 people around the world, scattered in 250 facilities in 46 different countries, his vision for how they could work together to make the company more successful?

Washkewicz decided to tour Parker's far-flung facilities around the world—not to give advice but to listen to his employees, and learn where the most creative and effective work in the company was being done. Washkewicz knew Parker had faced a host of rivals during its 85-year history, most of them larger and more powerful. Somehow Parker had prospered while most of its competitors failed.

During his worldwide tours, Washkewicz set out to learn why Parker had been so successful. He was looking to distill and pass on the accumulated wisdom that allowed Parker to help start passenger air travel, survive a bankruptcy and a Great Depression, and provide the products to win a war, begin the Jet Age, land Neil Armstrong on the Moon, and rescue the Apollo 13 astronauts.

Washkewicz decided to catalogue the best practices he observed in the three stages of the industrial distribution chain—procurement, manufacturing, and marketing—as he traveled to 220 of Parker's 250 locations around the world. During his first year as president, he spent 200 days away from the office. He was working long hours, often staying up well past midnight to gather his thoughts on the future of the company. He was gaining weight from too many high-calorie meals on the road, and when he looked in the mirror he noticed dark circles forming under his eyes. He began to experience stomach cramps from the constant stress of the job.

During his tour, Washkewicz discovered that many of Parker's divisions had adopted world-class approaches to procurement, manufacturing and marketing. Lee Banks, the president of Parker's Hydraulics Group, had run two Parker divisions. At one of them, he doubled sales, and more than doubled profits, in two years.

One of Banks' mentors at Parker had been Larry Hopcraft, who died in the crash of Swissair Flight 111 off the coast of Nova Scotia in September 1998, as he was flying to his home near Geneva, Switzerland. Hopcraft, a follower of Edward Deming and an advocate of Japanese methods of lean manufacturing, instilled in Banks an appreciation for the importance of continuous improvement on the factory floor. Banks used lean manufacturing techniques to improve delivery times to customers, and the quality of his division's products. He also adopted new methods of purchasing raw materials on a strategic basis, ensuring that his divisions were using their bargaining power to obtain the most favorable pricing and quality assurances from their suppliers.

Washkewicz discovered another center of excellence at the plants of the Control Systems Division of the Aerospace Group in Irvine, California and Ogden, Utah. The division, the successor to Bertea's flight control business, was making sophisticated controls for the rudders, ailerons, and flaps on the military and passenger planes made by Boeing, Airbus, and Lockheed Martin. The division could not countenance any shortcuts in quality. Its products were responsible every day for ensuring safe landings for millions of passengers around the world. The division, however, was faced with a dilemma—it had to continually reduce its manufacturing costs to meet the demands of the aircraft manufacturers for less expensive flight controls. As the division implemented more efficient manufacturing techniques, based largely upon suggestions from workers on the factory floor, its managers discovered they were able to reduce costs, and at the same time, enhance the quality of their manufacturing processes.

Washkewicz thought to himself, "Our products are powering machines that are making manufacturing processes more efficient all over the world. Why shouldn't all our plants become world leaders for the best manufacturing techniques?"

As Washkewicz learned the operating efficiencies that had been achieved by the divisions, he started to think of Parker as a company with multiple centers of excellence. He saw no reason why he could not spread the best practices from the most successful Parker divisions to every division in the company.

Adam Bryant, a New York Times business reporter, conducted hundreds of interviews with CEOs, trying to discover which elements of corporate culture had the greatest impact on performance. He concluded that "One of a leader's most important roles is to boil down an organization's many priorities and strategies into a simple plan, so that employees can remember it, and act on it. With clear goals and metrics, everyone can pull in the same direction, knowing how their work contributes to these goals."[643]

In the spring of 2001, Washkewicz began to draft a strategy on best practices he could communicate to every part of the company. He decided the strategy needed to have elements of inspiration and aspiration in order to appeal to the hearts and minds of Parker employees everywhere, and it had to be grounded in the culture that had made Parker successful for 85 years. Washkewicz called his new approach the Win Strategy, and on a single page, it set forth the best practices the company needed to execute to achieve operational excellence and growth.

Washkewicz's plan was designed so that any Parker division could follow it, regardless of the division's products, markets, or location. He made sure the strategy was straight-forward enough to be understood and followed by any employee in any Parker location around the world. He wanted his approach to resonate with Parker's employees as a method of doing business that was consistent with the values that had prevailed at Parker since Art Parker founded the company in 1917. Washkewicz explained why he kept his strategy simple:

> *"People can't relate to long, complicated books describing corporate strategies. Most end up in wastebaskets, where they belong. They have to see something that jumps out at them, that appeals to their common sense, and their highest values. I wanted to keep the Win Strategy simple and inspiring, a summary of the right things to do. I wanted everyone to concentrate on perfecting a few important things. I believed, if we could do that, there would be no limit to what we could accomplish."*

Written in bold letters across the top of the Win Strategy was Washkewicz's over-riding vision for Parker—to remain the No. 1 motion and control company in the world. He focused on three goals he wanted Parker's employees to rally around, and to master. Like every Parker chief executive who preceded him, he considered "premier customer service" the No. 1 goal for the company, and he placed it in a prominent spot on the Win Strategy. To Washkewicz, as to each of his predecessors, that meant delivering quality products on time.

Washkewicz realized his customer service goals could only be achieved if Parker maintained a strong balance sheet, and so he made "financial performance" the second goal of his strategy. It would require mastery of the three elements of the industrial distribution chain, through strategic procurement, lean manufacturing, and strategic pricing.

Washkewicz made "profitable growth" the third goal of his strategy. The elements required to achieve such growth had been responsible for Parker's past success—innovative products (a keystone of the company's strategy since Carl Klamm installed a Parker fuel system on the Spirit of St. Louis), systems solutions (first championed by Paul Schloemer when he was president of the Aerospace Group), and strong distribution (emphasized by Collins, the master salesman, as a general manager, group president, and CEO).

The opening of a Parker Store in Vietnam, circa 2005.

Like Collins, Washkewicz saw Parker's distribution system as a touchstone of the company's premier customer service. One of his first customer service initiatives was to enhance the breadth of Parker's "company stores"—retail outlets provided by distributors for customers who had an immediate need to replace a Parker product. These outlets were similar to hardware stores, except that they were stocked exclusively with replacements for Parker hoses, seals, connectors, valves and filtration products. Distributors loved the Parker stores, because they could charge full retail prices, giving them the profit margin necessary to locate the stores near their customers and staff them with knowledgeable sales people sensitive to their customers' needs.

The maintenance specialists from thousands of customers around the world would come to rely upon the assistance they received from the sales people at the company stores, thus giving Parker a "leg up" over its competitors in selling replacement products.

When Washkewicz was elected CEO, Parker had only 300 Parker stores, nearly all of which were in North America. By the end of Washkewicz's tenure as CEO, the company had more than 3,000 Parker stores, operating in nearly every developed or developing country in the world, including 1,000 in the Asia-Pacific region.

The Parker Store in Thailand was the 1,000th store to open
in the Asia-Pacific region.

Washkewicz remembered how Sullivan and Collins had supported and trusted him during the darkest hours of his research on new products for the Hose Products Division. He was able to persist in his efforts because he knew they would support him even if he failed. As a shorthand way to describe this feeling of support, Washkewicz wrote "Empowered Employees" across the base of his Win Strategy. He often pointed to lean manufacturing as an example of the power of empowerment at Parker:

> *"We need to ask the workers on the factory floor how to improve the manufacturing process. Who understands that better than the workers at their machines? They know better than anyone else how to make their work more efficient. While I was the general manager at Parflex, we didn't tell our workers how to improve; they told us."*

Washkewicz believed Parker's factory workers should receive more than a pat on the back when they improved their efficiency. Like his employees at the Parflex Division, they should share in the economic rewards of their efficiency efforts. In order to share increased profits broadly across Parker's divisions, he mandated that the RONA program be extended to as many plants and as many workers around the world as possible.

There was a tension at the heart of Washkewicz's Win Strategy. The best practices he was espousing had flourished at Parker divisions where general managers, and their employees, felt just as empowered as he had been at the Hose Products Division. He knew the most successful division general managers were, like Art Parker, entrepreneurial, adopting innovative approaches to motivating their employees and serving their customers. Washkewicz once told a reporter that he believed the decentralized divisional philosophy initiated by Taylor and Cornell and sustained by Pat was the "key to the company's success because it kept the entrepreneurial spirit alive in the company. It's what Pat believed in. We would have lost our entrepreneurial advantage if everything was centralized."[644]

How, Washkewicz wondered, could he retain the decentralized, entrepreneurial approach that had served Parker so well, while at the same time making certain all divisions followed what he considered to be a world-class approach to operations? As a former general manager, Washkewicz was convinced the divisions had to be free to respond quickly to the unique challenges of their businesses. He retained Parker's entrepreneurial culture by leaving the execution of the Win Strategy initiatives up to the general managers, who were empowered to adapt them to the unique characteristics of their work force, their suppliers and their customers.

At the same time, Washkewicz was determined to expand upon Collins' initiative to harness the collective power of all Parker's divisions. He realized the company could only achieve across-the-board, world-class operational excellence if every one of its 118 divisions was pulling in the same direction. He made it clear to his general managers that the three goals of the Win Strategy were not optional. He expected every one of them to work toward world-class customer service, financial performance, and profitable growth in a way appropriate for each of their divisions. Only then, he believed, would Parker reach its full potential.

On the backside of the Win Strategy, Washkewicz listed the metrics all divisions would be required to track to show their progress toward achieving the three goals of the Win Strategy. He defined what it meant to "win" in each strategic area. He defined "premier customer service" as more than 95 percent of quality parts delivered on time; "financial performance" as 15 percent operating income; and "profitable growth" as 10 percent compound growth, more than 20 percent market share, a strong distribution network, and a balance of 50 percent of sales to the original equipment market and 50 percent to the replacement market.

In July 2001, Washkewicz was elected the seventh CEO in Parker's history. Collins remained the Chairman of the Board. Like Taylor, Cornell, Pat Parker, and Schloemer before him, Collins made a conscious effort to step back and let Washkewicz run the company. Shortly after Collins became Chairman, a Parker executive asked him how it felt to suddenly become so much less important. Collins replied, "Well, it's an adjustment, but it's fun to watch the next guy start his race. I like to compare management succession to a relay race. Let's say you're the guy finishing his last turn, getting ready to hand off the baton to your teammate, the next guy in line. Wouldn't you want to do everything you could to make sure he runs the fastest race he can?"

Washkewicz had to contend with skepticism when he introduced the Win Strategy to Parker's executives and its board of directors. Many of them did not share his belief that such a seemingly simple approach could transform the company. A few took to calling the Win Strategy "tactical" rather than "strategic," a program more fit for a Chief Operating Officer than a CEO. Just as in Washkewicz's early years at the Hose Products and Parflex Divisions, the doubts among his colleagues made him even more determined to succeed.

Don Washkewicz and Duane Collins, circa 2002.

Some of Washkewicz's critics believed he should not publicize the Win Strategy outside the company. They feared Parker's competitors might copy it. Washkewicz answered his critics by telling a story:

> *"Vince Lombardi never tried to hide his playbook. A sports reporter once asked him, 'Aren't you afraid other teams will learn your game plan?' Lombardi replied, 'I never worry about whether other teams know our plans for a game. We execute the fundamentals of the game better than anyone else. We can beat the others even if they have a copy of our plans.'"*

THE 9/11 ATTACKS on New York City and Washington took place 103 days after Washkewicz became CEO. A few days after the Twin Towers collapsed in lower Manhattan sanitation workers began taking the debris to a landfill on Staten Island. They had to sort through millions of tons of rubble that contained the remains of the 2,600 people who died when the towers fell. Parker donated hoses, connectors, filters and pumps and staffed a full service and repair facility at the site, absorbing the entire cost of an operation that continued for months. Henry Paulette, a New York City worker at the site, wrote Washkewicz a letter, saying "After the tragedy of September 11, other companies came because it was fashionable. Parker came without fanfare and stayed the course. As a New Yorker, I thank you."

The recession that followed the 9/11 attacks put even more pressure on Washkewicz to make the Win Strategy succeed. One morning at 4:00 a.m., he woke up with a worrying thought. He had come to realize there was an inherent weakness at the heart of his Win Strategy, one that could destroy all he was trying to accomplish. Washkewicz remembered the divisions' pricing personnel had always marked up their prices by a predetermined percentage over their costs, usually aiming for a 35 percent margin. His sudden realization was this: If the pricing managers continued their cost-based approach, Parker would lose all the additional profits he expected to capture from the Win Strategy's operating initiatives. A mark-up based on costs, implemented at the time a division was reducing its costs, could not yield any higher margins for the division. As the Wall Street Journal explained in an article on the Win Strategy, "Washkewicz had an epiphany. Parker had to stop thinking like a widget maker and start thinking like a retailer, determining prices by what a customer is willing to pay rather than what a product costs to make."[645]

Washkewicz decided the divisions should no longer focus on cost-plus pricing. He instructed his general managers to extract the maximum prices possible for the value Parker was delivering to its customers with its innovative products, superior quality, and best-in-class service.[646]

ONE OF THE PRIMARY GOALS of the Win Strategy was to harness the collective power of all Parker's divisions to reduce procurement costs. Late one evening shortly after Washkewicz became CEO, Pat Parker walked into his office with a suggestion. He recommended that Washkewicz consider John Dedinsky, who held a mid-level job in Parker's accounting department, to head up all the company's procurement initiatives.

Most of Parker's executives doubted Parker's 80-year-old Euclid Avenue building was worth saving when Parker moved its headquarters to Mayfield Heights, a Cleveland suburb, in 1998. Pat told Washkewicz that Dedinsky had co-led a team that devised a way of donating the Euclid Avenue building to the Cleveland Clinic. The transaction allowed Parker to take a tax deduction for the donation and benefited the Collinwood neighborhood by putting over a thousand Clinic employees into a building that otherwise would have been destroyed.

Pat told Washkewicz, "Without Dedinsky, they would have imploded my father's building on Euclid Avenue. This guy is wasted in accounting. He has the energy, the passion, and the courage to do anything. I know you're looking for a Vice President of Global Procurement. It's an area we have struggled with for years. You should consider John for the job."

After interviewing Dedinsky and speaking to his Parker colleagues, Washkewicz was ready to take a chance on entrusting him with one of his most important initiatives. It was an unconventional choice at best, as Dedinsky had no experience in running a procurement operation. Now he would be responsible for overseeing all the company's worldwide purchasing initiatives.

It did not take long for Dedinsky to validate the trust Washkewicz had placed in him. During the next few years, he would implement initiatives that reduced Parker's purchasing costs by more than $1.5 billion.

BY THE SPRING OF 2002, the Win Strategy was hanging on the walls of Parker facilities around the world, translated into local languages. In every Parker plant and office, employees posted tracking boards that allowed them to follow their progress in achieving the Win Strategy goals. Sixty thousand Parker employees in 50 countries were all on the same page, working on identical initiatives to enhance the company's customer service, financial performance and profitable growth.

In October 2004, Collins retired as Chairman of the Board, and Washkewicz became the company's Chairman and CEO. In March 2007, The Wall Street Journal, in a front-page article, explained the Win Strategy had boosted Parker's operating income by $200 million in the five years since Washkewicz became CEO. Parker's net income soared to $673 million in 2006, compared to only $130 million in 2002. Parker's return on invested capital increased from 7 percent in 2002 to 21 percent in 2006. Since Washkewicz's election as CEO in 2001, Parker's stock had risen nearly 88 percent, at a time when the S&P 500 Average had risen only 25 percent.[647]

Jeffrey Immelt, the CEO of General Electric, read The Wall Street Journal article on the Win Strategy. Intrigued by Washkewicz's approach, Immelt asked him to address a meeting of GE's top executives in the summer of 2007. Washkewicz traveled to GE's headquarters in Fairfield, Connecticut, where he met Immelt and 100 of his executives in a large auditorium. He spoke for nearly an hour, explaining the elements of the Win Strategy. When he finished, Immelt stood up, turned to his executives, and said, "That was the best explanation of a corporate strategy I have ever heard. Why aren't we doing this?"

It was a satisfying moment for the CEO of a company that, in the dark days after World War II, had adopted a goal that seemed like a fantasy for an enterprise flirting with bankruptcy—to become the "GE of fluid power."

In January 2015, the board elected Tom Williams to succeed Washkewicz as the eighth CEO in the company's history, and Lee Banks as Chief Operating Officer. During Washkewicz's tenure, shareholder value had soared, as Washkewicz increased the dividend every year, and Parker's stock achieved a compound annual growth rate of 12 percent, more than twice the annual growth rate of the S&P 500. Washkewicz oversaw the completion of 102 acquisitions, including Denison International, which expanded Parker's hydraulic pump line; Sporlan, which added high technology valves for the company's refrigeration business; Domnick Hunter, which provided technology for medical filtration applications; and Taiyo, which gave Parker an entree to the Japanese cylinder market. The company's sales more than doubled, from $6.1 billion to $13.2 billion, and its market capitalization increased by 249 percent, to more than $17 billion.

# CHAPTER 23

# Enduring Values

The company that survived so many near-death experiences in its early years has gone on to benefit its shareholders handsomely. Parker has increased its dividends to shareholders for 60 consecutive fiscal years, a feat accomplished by only a few other companies.

Not a trace remains of the small factory above the Flats where Art, Klamm, and Helen Parker struggled to steer the Parker Appliance Co. through its early days. The site is now a parking lot behind St. Malachi's Church. The Irish shantytown that stretched down to the Cuyahoga River behind the factory has been replaced by bars and restaurants catering to young professionals working in downtown Cleveland.

The factory where Art, Klamm, and Helen began to change the world is gone, but their legacy remains visible from the site where they survived a World War, the accident on the Lincoln Highway, a bankruptcy, and the skepticism of their early investors.

Jet planes equipped with Parker flight controls fly overhead as they descend to the Cleveland airport; at steel mills in the Flats, Parker valves and motors drive machinery that has transformed dirty and dangerous work into cleaner, safer and easier jobs; heavy trucks rumble over the Detroit Superior Bridge, using Parker hose products, filtration devices, and other fluid connectors; locomotives with Parker seals on board pull mile-long freight trains across a Cuyahoga River bridge; excavators, bulldozers, and dump trucks powered by Parker cylinders move earth to shape the foundations of new apartment buildings on the shore of the river; ore freighters heading down the Cuyahoga to Lake Erie transport a ton of cargo on a single gallon of fuel, using efficient Parker fuel nozzles to power their engines; and the full moon that rises over the lake every month contains the footprints of men brought there by a Parker propulsion system.

UNTIL HE RETIRED IN 1963, at age 75, Carl Klamm spent nearly every evening after dinner, sitting in a winged chair in his living room. After a 30-minute nap, he would pick up a piece of drafting paper from a table next to his chair and sketch out a drawing of a new Parker valve or fitting. In 1968, as a consultant to Parker, Klamm designed fittings and valves for the U.S. Navy's nuclear submarines. A Navy crew challenged him to join them on a mission. One of the crew said, "If you're so sure your stuff is going to work, come on the cruise with us."[648] The 80-year-old Klamm worked out on a chinning bar in his basement to prepare for the trip. He later recalled, "We had quite a rough ride going out during which time the only two who didn't get sick were the captain of the submarine and me."[649]

Klamm's love of shaping wood, first developed when he made his wooden patterns in the Flats in the early 1900s, never deserted him. Whenever his grandson Carl came to visit, Klamm would sit down at the kitchen table and ask him, "What do you want to make today?"

Invariably, Carl would ask his grandfather to make him a toy. Klamm would sketch out a design for the toy at the table. Then the two of them would walk down to the basement, and Carl would watch as Klamm took pieces of wood and shaped them into a finished plaything.

In 1977, Klamm's grandson Carl received a call from a headhunter about a job opening at a Cleveland company. The headhunter would not disclose the name of the company until Carl filled out an application. Carl was astonished to discover the application was for a job in accounting at Parker's Euclid Avenue headquarters. One question on the form asked: "Do you know anyone who works here?"

Carl wrote in, "Carl Klamm, retired."

Bob Lawler, the supervisor of Parker's accounting department, interviewed Carl for the job. Lawler had known and admired Klamm during his last years at the company. In the middle of the interview, Lawler asked Carl how he had come to know Klamm. Carl answered, "He's my grandfather." Lawler was impressed that Carl had not used his relationship with Klamm to obtain an advantage over other applicants. Lawler paused for a moment, and then looked across the table at Carl and asked, "Can you start this afternoon?"

Carl worked in Parker's accounting department for several years. Not wanting to be shown any favoritism, he was careful not to mention to his Parker colleagues that Klamm was his grandfather.

In a 1979 interview,[650] a reporter asked Klamm what he considered to be his greatest accomplishment. He replied, "All the fittings I designed held up and we had absolutely no trouble with them." He added with a laugh, "I wish one of them had failed so I could have fixed it."[651] Klamm explained that helping design Parker's products had given meaning to his life: "Anybody can go to a store and buy something. All it takes is money. But, when you can figure out how to build something and make it yourself, that's a different story. When I've got something into which I've put my time and effort, that's what I call having a feeling of satisfaction that money can't buy."[652]

Klamm's favorite hobby during retirement was designing and making products that would improve the lives of those with disabilities—wooden crutches and braces for crippled children, equipment to hold handicapped children's feet on bicycle pedals, dishes and trays that could be used more easily by stroke victims, and wire frames to help the infirm pull up their

Carl Klamm.

socks. Dr. Myron Pardee, the head of orthopedics at a hospital in the Cleveland suburb of Lakewood, said, "You run out of adjectives when describing Klamm. Exceptional, talented, innovative—anything we would need to return people to a normal life, he would make. He devised types of equipment that had to be so individualized that they were not available anywhere else, and his concepts are still viable."[653]

Klamm died in 1980 at age 91. Until a few months before his death, he lived in the same house on Ramona Avenue in Lakewood that he and Alvina had moved to shortly after their marriage in 1916. After Klamm died, his grandson

Carl returned to the basement where he had spent so many happy hours with his grandfather, as together they built wooden toys. The walls of the basement were lined with shelves filled with fittings, tools and other products Klamm had designed for Parker. On one of the shelves, Carl found an old Parker air compressor. By consulting one of Klamm's first engineering drawings for Parker, Carl was able to confirm the compressor had been made for the pneumatic brake system Art patented in 1918. Carl took the compressor home as a memento of his grandfather. In the fall of 2015, Carl used the compressor to blow the water out of his backyard irrigation system. The compressor was still working perfectly, nearly 100 years after it had been made in the Parker Appliance Co.'s second-story loft.

PARKER'S LAST CONNECTION to its founder was severed on July 6, 2005, when Pat Parker died after a long fight with cancer. Pat came to Parker's offices for the last time just a few days before his death. He showed up in a wheelchair and went immediately to a tent set up in the parking lot to demonstrate Parker's newest products to employees and customers. Pat was too weak to stand up, but he flashed his usual smile as he said hello to several employees. Even as he faced death, Pat was looking toward the future of the company his father started and his mother saved, as he gave Parker's engineers advice on how to improve the company's energy-saving system for buses and trucks.

A few months before he died, Pat gave his last interview to a television reporter in his office at Parker's headquarters. He had designed the office to convey the look of a captain's quarters on a British Galleon. Wide oak planks, cut in the 1690s, lined the floor and walls. Pat discovered the planks during one of his European trips, stored in the backroom of a London shipyard. On the office wall, next to a framed copy of the 1927 letter from Art Parker to Carl Klamm announcing Art's marriage to Helen Fitzgerald, Pat had placed a picture of three 18th century galleons racing before the wind.

Pat told the reporter he chose the painting because he viewed both business and life as a voyage, filled with uncertainty, but also with excitement. Pointing to the picture, he used it as an analogy for the culture he and his parents had bequeathed to Parker, and that he believed would guide the company in the future. Pat, the consummate sailor, said he was confident he and his parents, together with those they chose to lead the company, had built a ship that could withstand any storms it might encounter. For nearly 100 years, Parker's culture of customer service, persistence in hard times, em-

powerment, and teamwork had brought the company through hurricanes, typhoons and maelstroms of change and misfortune. Pat had no doubt Parker would continue its voyage for another century.

With a light in his eyes, Pat gazed toward the picture of the British galleons and said, "We got GPS, we got DVDs, we got Internet, we got voice mail, we got smart phones. They all tell us either where we are, or where we've been. But they don't tell us what unexpected challenges we might meet along the way to the future. And so we're still like those guys out there on the ocean 300 years ago. We got a compass to tell us where we are now. But we still can't see over the horizon. So we better keep on plotting a course that can save us no matter what we might encounter."

After Pat died, his family scattered his ashes from a boat in the Mediterranean Sea, not far from the rocky Sicilian coastline where Archimedes had dreamed of new ways to control motion in the 3rd century B.C.

Six months after Pat's death, his son Streeter visited Parker's headquarters. As he walked into the lobby, he noticed an older man watching a video of Pat's last television interview. The man told Streeter he was a retired Parker employee. He had never met Streeter before, and thought he might have been a customer visiting Parker's headquarters. The retiree told Streeter he had known Pat for years and had admired him greatly. He went on to explain to Streeter how special Pat was, a man at the pinnacle of the company who enjoyed most of all chatting with workers on the factory floor. Then the retiree said, "I wish you could have met Pat. I'm sure you would have liked him too." Streeter, a man rarely at a loss for words, could not think of what to say. All he could do was smile at the retiree, thank him for telling him about the man in the video, and walk back toward the front door, blinking away the tears in his eyes.

IN JANUARY 2015, nearly 100 years after Art Parker and Carl Klamm began to market their single product—a pneumatic brake system—from their second-story loft above Cleveland's Flats, Tom Williams and Lee Banks took the reins of a company that was making, selling, and servicing hundreds of thousands of products, with a value of more than $11 billion a year, from Parker facilities in more than 50 countries. Fifty thousand Parker employees were focused on building a better world by serving more than 400,000 customers. Seventy years after Ghost Taylor, Bob Cornell, and Helen Parker dared dream their nearly bankrupt company could become the "GE of Fluid Power" by diversifying into new markets, the unrelenting focus by thousands of Parker's men and women on serving their customers had created a range of technologies capable of powering and controlling nearly every mechanical object that moved.

Williams and Banks are continuing an initiative first begun by Washkewicz shortly before he retired as CEO, through the development of new technologies designed to extend Parker's reach to a new frontier—the control of human motion itself.

One evening in late 2010, Washkewicz summoned Parker's Chief Technology Officer Craig Maxwell into his office. Washkewicz had a challenge for Maxwell. He said, "You know, we control everything that moves, except for the human body itself. I've seen story after story about our wounded veterans returning home confined to wheelchairs. With all the knowledge we have gained about mechanical motion and control over the last

100 years, isn't there anything we can do to help those unable to walk? We would be doing the world a great good, and at the same time stretching ourselves to conquer the last form of movement not yet touched by our products."

In early 2011, Maxwell took up Washkewicz's challenge and asked Dr. Gino Banco, a young research engineer at Parker, to look for a human motion application that intersected with Parker's motion and control technologies. Banco researched the work being done at various universities on devices that could assist paralyzed patients in regaining their ability to walk. He discovered that Dr. Michael Goldfarb, an engineering professor at Vanderbilt University, had recently built a prototype of an "exoskeleton" that might help paralyzed patients stand up and walk on their own.

For nearly a year, Banco tried unsuccessfully to reach Goldfarb. Like so many Parker men and women before him, he persevered. Finally he tracked Goldfarb down at a medical conference in Las Vegas late in 2011. Banco was impressed by what Goldfarb told him of the elegant simplicity of his device and its potential to be easily used by patients paralyzed by injuries to their spinal cords.

Goldfarb explained to Banco that paralyzed patients were already testing his exoskeleton at the Sheperd Center in Atlanta, one of the foremost rehabilitation centers for spinal cord injuries in the country. In 2010, the first paraplegic had walked with the assistance of Goldfarb's exoskeleton.

Michael Gore had fallen from scaffolding at a construction site and severed his spinal cord in 2005. He lost all feeling in his legs, and his doctors told him he would never walk again. In December, 2010 he spent three days at the Sheperd Center, working to master the use of Goldfarb's device. During the last day of his stay, Michael was being assisted by Clare Hartigan, a physical therapist intimately familiar with the operation of Vanderbilt's exoskeleton prototype. Ryan Farris, a doctoral candidate, whose Ph.D. project focused on the development of the device, was watching readouts on his computer, as Hartigan lifted Michael up between two parallel bars. Michael's exoskeleton was attached to Farris' computer by electrical lines that provided control commands to the device.

Farris pressed a key on his computer, and Michael took a step forward as motors attached to his hips and knees moved him along. It was the first time Michael had stood up and walked since his accident in 2005. Farris was concentrating so carefully upon the readouts on his computer screen that he had not seen Michael stand up. Hartigan began to cry and yelled over to Farris, "Don't you see what's happening? This is incredible! Michael is paralyzed, and he just stood up and walked."

For the first time in five years, Michael was able to look another person in the eye, as he glanced over at Hartigan. He later told a reporter, "Being able to speak with you eye-to-eye is just a big emotional boost. Being able to walk up to you and say hello is not a big thing until you cannot do it."[654]

After hearing about the promise of the Vanderbilt exoskeleton from Dr. Goldfarb, Maxwell decided to negotiate an exclusive license to Parker for the rights to the device. In June 2012, Maxwell approached Achilleas Dorotheou, an executive in Parker's Engineered Materials Group, and asked him to take the responsibility for negotiating the license.

Vanderbilt was willing to grant Parker an exclusive license, because Maxwell and Dorotheou convinced Goldfarb that Parker was committed to making a difference in paralyzed people's lives. As Goldfarb later explained, "We put our blood, sweat, and tears into this, and we just didn't want it to fail. The difference going from a research prototype to a commercial product is significant. Parker gave me their word they would do this right."

Michael Gore, standing tall in Indego.

Tom Williams became enthusiastic about the exoskeleton project in February 2013 (two years before he succeeded Washkewicz as Parker's CEO), when Maxwell and Dorotheou presented a business plan to him for the development of the exoskeleton by a new Parker division in the Cleveland suburb of Macedonia. Maxwell planned to call the division the "Human Motion and Control Business Unit," and to name Dorotheou Parker's Vice President for Human Motion and Control, tasked with assembling a team to develop a marketable version of Goldfarb's prototype. Dorotheou did not hesitate. He left his secure job to take a risk on leading a team that would be responsible for commercializing an unproven technology. He made the jump to his new assignment because it offered him a once-in-a-lifetime opportunity to make a difference in the world.

Williams continued to meet with Maxwell, Dorotheou and their researchers at least 3 or 4 times a year. He began to see the development of a Parker exoskeleton as a way to showcase Parker's technology and the "soul of the company"—the continuing search by Parker's men and women for ways to make the world a better place.

Dorotheou hired Ryan Farris (who had just graduated from Vanderbilt) as the Engineering Manager of the Human Motion and Control Business Unit. Together, Dorotheou and Farris assembled a talented group of engineers to begin the arduous process of producing a marketable human exoskeleton. Like Art Parker and Carl Klamm in their second-story loft, Dorotheou, Farris, and their team of researchers began as entrepreneurs, doing everything on the run—developing an entirely new technology, securing funding, finding the right clinics and patients to test the device, and obtaining regulatory approvals in the United States and Europe.

Just as Dennis Sullivan and Duane Collins had empowered Washkewicz, over several trying years of research, to develop two new-to-the-world hose products, Williams empowered Dorotheou, Farris and their team to complete the painstaking task of designing an exoskeleton that would meet the regulatory agencies' rigorous standards for human use.

Dorotheou, Farris and his engineering team embarked upon a complete redesign of the exoskeleton prototype developed at Vanderbilt. They reduced the weight of the device to just 26 pounds (50 percent lighter than competitors' exoskeletons) and made it easy to assemble, thus freeing paralyzed patients to take the device home and use it in their everyday lives.

Williams, Maxwell, Dorotheou, and Farris decided to call their exoskeleton "Indego" (a combination of "independent" and "go"). Like the Parker men and women who brought Lindbergh across the ocean, Neil Armstrong to the moon, the Apollo 13 astronauts safely home, and the Allies to victory in World War II, the Indego team was focused upon its customers' needs. Explaining why Parker took so much time, and spent so many resources, to make sure it could produce the right kind of product for patients, Farris said, "We won't release anything to a patient that we wouldn't choose to use for ourselves and our families."

After three years of effort, Parker's Human Motion researchers had built an exoskeleton that included motors at patients' hips and knees that could push their bodies forward at a natural and comfortable gait from place to place. They improved the software that controls the motors that respond to movements initiated by a patient. They added gyro chips (similar to those used to position images in cell phones) that steady patients and keep them from veering off course as they walk with the assistance of Indego.

Once Dorotheou saw the difference Indego could make in paralyzed patients' lives, he began to gain a sense of meaning from his job. He was particularly moved by David Carter, one of the early users of Indego, who the Sheperd therapists fondly called "Hollywood" because of his endearing smile. He had been confined to a wheelchair since a 2010 motorcycle accident had left him paralyzed from the waist down. He had lost 35 pounds and most of the muscle strength in his lower body by the time he began to test Indego in 2015. Walking regularly with Indego changed his life, strengthening his lower back and abdominal muscles and reducing the frequency of his muscle spasms.

In the summer of 2005, Rick Hart was a financial services executive in Tampa, one month shy of his 40th birthday. He was spending most of his weekdays traveling around the country to advise bankers on investment services. In his free time, he enjoyed golfing, water skiing and traveling the world with his wife of 20 years.

Rick was on a golfing trip that summer on a lake in northern Wisconsin with a group of his friends. He volunteered to be the first to try out a pair of jet skis on the lake. Next to a dock, he strapped himself into the jet skis, pointed them out toward the lake, and pushed a starter button. Suddenly the skis exploded and shot him up in the air. He landed on his back on the dock, severing his spinal cord. The doctors told Rick he would never again be able to enjoy the type of life he had lived before his accident.

Rick and his wife had a different plan. They listed their priorities for what they wanted to do with their lives—to continue to work, to travel in their free time, and most importantly, for Rick to learn to walk again. Their goal was to live their lives as closely as possible to how they had lived them before the accident.

Rick had undergone physical therapy at the Sheperd Center. Claire Hartigan told him about Indego during one of his therapy visits. Rick and his wife were thrilled when he was able to stand up and walk around the room after strapping Indego onto his legs and back. Rick's immediate thought was that "this is going to change my life." Rick believes that Indego is the only device that will allow him to live independently. Since his first experience with Indego, he has learned to attach the pieces of the exoskeleton together and strap the device on in less than five minutes. He has volunteered to demonstrate Indego to wounded veterans at VA hospitals. Many of the VA patients are men under 30 who have lost all hope of ever walking again. Rick met many wounded men with tears in their eyes, who with Indego, could hope for the first time that they would not be confined to a wheelchair forever.

Rick has said that, "Parker's people are really focused on Indego because it makes the world a better place." Indego, Rick is convinced, "is a life-changing device that, thanks to the passion and caring of Parker's men and women, will only get better, and will improve more and more people's lives."

In March 2016, Parker announced that the U.S. Food and Drug Administration had approved the use of Indego for both commercial and clinical use.[655]

Following in the footsteps of Art, Helen and Pat Parker, and Carl Klamm, the members of Parker's Indego team are helping their customers power yet another machine that can change the world. Parker's Indego team considers its mission to help Michael Gore, David Carter, Rick Hart and other paralyzed people walk again just as important as President Kennedy's mission to send American astronauts to walk on the moon. Maxwell, Dorotheou, and Farris envision a day in which devices like Indego will become commonplace and will improve the lives of millions—not only those afflicted with spinal cord injuries, but also those affected by strokes, multiple sclerosis, cerebral palsy, Parkinson's disease, and the wounds of war.

EACH LEADER OF PARKER over the last half-century had to work his way up through the ranks, earning each of his promotions on merit. Pat Parker started his career as a foundry worker on Euclid Avenue; Paul Schloemer as a salesman at his home in Dayton; Duane Collins as a salesman in a small office in Orlando, who had to go hat-in-hand just to earn a security badge to visit his most important customer; Don Washkewicz as a mechanic removing steaming hot hoses from truck engines; and Tom Williams as a machine operator in a factory. Each of these men never forgot how their colleagues at Parker helped them achieve their dreams, and they resolved to do the same for others during their own careers.

Shortly after Tom Williams became CEO, he was asked what a new employee should do to succeed at Parker. He replied:

*"First of all, do the best job you can in the position you're in. But don't be afraid to tell your boss you're eager to take on new challenges. Be on the lookout for better ways to serve your customers. There will always be people at Parker who will reach out and help you along the way. You'll find that we believe in finding new ways of doing things, and continually innovating to make the world a better place. It's what has allowed us to prosper for 100 years."*

Williams, Parker's eighth CEO, has a degree in mechanical engineering from Bucknell and an MBA from Xavier. He spent several years at General Electric, where he was promoted to increasing levels of responsibility in the company's aviation, lighting, transportation, and financial services operations. Early in his career, he operated a machine on the factory floor, and worked as a second shift supervisor. Like Pat Parker during his days working in the foundry at Euclid Avenue, Williams learned firsthand how difficult factory labor could be, and how important it was to empower the men and women on the floor to make their own decisions about how to do their work most efficiently.

During a General Electric training course, a teacher asked Williams how he would react to a series of problems confronting his team. For each situation, he answered that he would act as an understanding, helpful coach. Williams never forgot his teacher's response: truly effective leaders are able to change their approach to suit the unique challenges of their times. The teacher called such flexibility "situational leadership." Williams applied that lesson when he became Parker's CEO, and decided to build upon Washkewicz's Win Strategy, but at the same time, adapt it to the challenges Parker was facing in the second decade of the 20th century.

Williams has the quiet, determined demeanor of Art Parker, and his focus on providing meaningful work to Parker's men and women through service to each other, and to their customers. Williams and his Chief Operating Officer, Lee Banks, have developed a partnership similar to that enjoyed by Art and Klamm in the company's early years, and Ghost Taylor and Bob Cornell after World War II. They support and trust each other implicitly, and share the cultural values that have driven Parker's success for the last 100 years. Williams realizes how fortunate he is to have Banks as his Chief Operating Officer, and he treats him as a partner in running Parker's business.

One of Williams' first steps as CEO was to reaffirm the values that guided Parker through one of the most tumultuous centuries in history. He sent a letter to all Parker's employees, in which he said:

Tom Williams and Lee Banks.

*"I came to Parker 13 years ago because I believed in what this great organization represented and that our remarkable employees and culture provided us with a unique competitive advantage. My belief has grown stronger over the years. We have a caring, family-oriented culture, engaged employees, a wonderful suite of technologies and a relentless focus on meeting our customers' needs and engineering their success. These are the enduring qualities that have driven our past success and will propel us to success in the future."*

The first priority of Williams and Banks after they were elected to lead the company, was to travel to Parker's divisions, just as Washkewicz had at the beginning of his CEO tenure, to meet with employees from all levels of the company's operations, and solicit their opinions on how the Win Strategy should be refreshed. During their travels, they discovered that the values which sustained Parker in the past remained deeply ingrained in the company's culture. Everywhere they went, they found men and women focused on serving their customers and their fellow employees.

Williams and Banks benchmarked the long-term strategies of the most successful diversified industrial companies, met with Parker's largest shareholders, and discussed their new Win Strategy with each of Parker's directors. A consensus emerged from those discussions on the contours of an approach that could guide the company for the foreseeable future. When Williams and Banks introduced the new Win Strategy to Parker's employees in September 2015, they reaffirmed the "Parker Values Statement" that had guided the company for several years. It states in part:

*"We seek to raise the standard of living through responsible, global stewardship.... We are empowered—every idea counts and every role has a voice. We are dedicated and realize the value of our collective efforts. We believe our strength comes from the relationships we establish with each other, our customers and the world we serve."*

Williams emphasized to Parker's men and women that they were building upon the foundation that Washkewicz had established during his years as CEO. Williams wrote in his introduction to the new Win Strategy, "Without the original Win Strategy there would be no 'new Win Strategy.' It has served us well for 15 years." Williams' approach was consistent with the seamless transfer of power that has occurred between Parker's leaders over the last 100 years. Each leader of the company built upon the initiatives of his predecessors, adopting new strategies to meet the challenges of his own times, but retaining the core values that made the company successful.

The new Win Strategy's emphasis on improved distribution echoes the way in which Dennis Sullivan and Duane Collins leveraged Parker's aftermarket distribution system to transform the Hose Division from an "also-ran" to the most dominant hose maker in the world.

The new Win Strategy's "simplification initiative," designed to reduce the complexity of Parker's organization, is similar to the philosophy followed by Pat Parker during his years leading the company—to keep Parker's operations as simple, as lean, and as non-bureaucratic as possible. Writing in the 1976 Annual Report to Shareholders, Pat had explained a "timeless lesson" he had learned from studying Parker's then-55-year-history:

> *"The organization that maintains itself lean, flexible and responsive to problems tends to expand and prosper. The organization which burdens itself with fat, either physical, bureaucratic, or mental, inevitably leads to collapse from its own weight and its own inability to respond to shifting and changing problems which it surely will face."*[656]

Just as Art Parker freed his workers to determine the best way to make the 500 million aircraft fittings that helped the Allies win World War II, Banks and Williams are empowering their people to form high performance work teams that will make them think and act like entrepreneurs. The new Win Strategy puts "Engaged People" front and center as the company's foremost goal. As Williams said:

> *"At Parker, we believe those closest to the work know best how it should be done. We listen to them, and empower them to make decisions on how to improve our performance. We care about our people, and we trust them. We want them to think and act like entrepreneurs who control their own destiny. If our people feel like owners of their part of the business, they will be passionate about their work. With that kind of engagement by our people, we will be able to achieve our highest hopes and dreams for Parker's future."*

For 100 years, engagement with customers has provided Parker's men and women with meaning and purpose for their work. The new Win Strategy expands the notion of premier customer service to "Premier Customer Experience," which includes all Parker's interactions with customers, from initial order inquiry through the life cycle of a product. Plans are in place to build an eBusiness platform that provides inquiring customers, at a first glance, with visibility to the entire range of Parker products, systems, technology and engineering expertise, gained over an entire century. Like Taylor and Cornell, who dreamed of making Parker the "GE of fluid power" after World War II, the intent is to make the eBusiness portal a "one-stop-shop" for all a customer's motion and control needs. This initiative is a continuation of the long quest to harness the collective power of all Parker divisions, first initiated by Duane Collins and later embraced by Don Washkewicz.

Continuous innovation has been the hallmark of Parker's success for the last century. Just as Art and Klamm constantly improved their products to meet the needs of Glenn Martin, Charles Lindbergh, Bill Boeing, and Donald Douglas, Williams and Banks are asking Parker's men and women to spend more time with their customers, in order to understand and satisfy their unmet needs. They believe new technologies, such as sensors and the "Internet of Things" will provide a stream of data about the performance of Parker products, which will make their customers' experience more satisfying than ever before. Pat Parker first talked about adding wired sensors to Parker's products in the 1980s, and Paul Schloemer wrote of the "marriage of brain and brawn" between microprocessors and Parker's fluid power products. Now, with wireless technology, Parker will be able to provide "the voice of its machines" to its customers in real time, alerting them whenever a Parker product needs to be repaired or replaced, thus eliminating downtime and expense.

The new Win Strategy calls for Parker to achieve the highest quartile for profitable growth and financial performance, in comparison to the most successful diversified industrial companies. The challenge is to achieve organic growth at a rate of 150 basis points faster than the market, and at the same time, to raise Parker's levels of profitability to match or exceed that of the world's most successful diversified industrial companies.

Williams and Banks realize that, without the values passed down from generation to generation by Parker's men and women over the last 100 years, it would be impossible to achieve such ambitious goals. As Williams wrote in Parker's 2015 Annual Report: "It is the Parker culture and values, more than any strategy or measure that will determine our success in the future."

OVER THE LAST CENTURY, Parker's men and women changed the world, not just for money or fame, but for the satisfaction of helping their customers realize their dreams. It was a goal that gave meaning and purpose to their working lives. As Barry Schwartz, a professor of psychology at Swarthmore College, wrote in the New York Times, "Most of all, we want work that is meaningful—that makes a difference to other people and thus ennobles us in at least some small way."[657]

William Shakespeare wrote that "What's past is prologue."[658] There is every reason to believe the culture that sustained Parker in the past will continue to lead it to future success. The world has changed in many ways since Art walked into his second-story loft in 1917, but the values he taught his employees—customer service, teamwork, empowerment, a desire to build a better world, and the will to persist through hard times—have proved to be timeless. As Adam Bryant has written, "The companies that will thrive over the long haul will understand that culture is a key element of their strategy—for attracting and retaining the best talent, for encouraging employees to bring their best selves to work, and for fostering an environment in which everyone feels motivated to innovate. As the global economy presents more challenges to leaders, those who create a quick and nimble culture will emerge as winners."[659]

Like Art Parker, the members of the generation just entering Parker's workforce yearn to leave the world better than they found it. The first members of "Generation Z" (those born after 1995) are just turning 20. Their generation accounts for 25 percent of the American population. Having grown up in a time of global conflict and economic uncertainty, the members of Generation Z worry whether they will be able to enjoy lives as good as their parents.[660] Like the Parker men and women of the last century, they are searching for meaning in their work. A recent survey revealed that 66 percent of those in Generation Z want to make the world a better place; 76 percent are concerned about humanity's impact on the planet; and 58 percent worry about the future.[661]

A 2015 Sparks and Honey report on demographic trends concluded that "entrepreneurship is in the DNA" of the members of Generation Z, who are looking for careers where they can chart their own course. They should find such opportunities at Parker, where leaders have, for the last 100 years, empowered their people to determine how best to serve their customers.

The average tenure for the CEO of an American Fortune 500 company is 4.6 years.[662] The seven Parker CEOs who preceded Williams had an average tenure of 14 years, more than three times the average at other Fortune 500 companies. Contemplating how he would like to be remembered at the end of his own tenure as CEO, Williams said:

> *"I would hope that Parker's people would think of me as some-one who sustained the best values of our past and helped im-plement new strategies that lifted Parker to even higher levels of success. Most of all, I want to be remembered as someone who trusted, valued, and respected all Parker's team members, gave them every opportunity to succeed, and kept them safe."*

It is not hard to imagine Art, Helen or Pat Parker, or any of Williams' other predecessors, telling their employees exactly the same thing.

*Fig.1.*

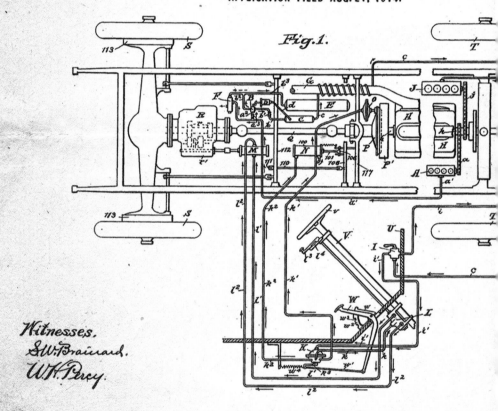

Witnesses.
S.W. Brainard.
W.H. Percy.

# APPENDICES

# Acknowledgments

I walked nervously through Parker's front door for the first time early on a September morning in 1981, on my way to an interview with Pat Parker at the Euclid Avenue plant. I was looking for a job in Parker's legal department. There was a lot riding on the interview; seven years after graduating from law school, I was still searching for a job with meaning. I had spent three years at a large Cleveland law firm writing memos for clients who I rarely met, and four years in the law department of a Dallas company whose executives were focused on continually shifting their portfolio of oil and gas companies. Neither job had given me any sense that I was helping make the world a better place.

My spirits fell as I arrived at Parker's plant. I was surprised the headquarters of a billion-dollar company were in a drab industrial building in a neighborhood filled with bars and boarded up storefronts. I became even more concerned as I walked down a large dark hallway lined with offices that looked like they had not been remodeled since the 1950s.

As I approached Pat's office, I was uncomfortably aware his name was on the building. I expected to meet the prototype CEO—aggressive, driven, impatient, and focused on himself, with a dash of the sense of entitlement of a second-generation leader of a large family company. The man who greeted me could not have been more different than the stereotype I had imagined.

Pat put me at ease, greeting me with a warm smile. He was tall and lanky and slouched comfortably in his chair behind a large desk. He told me his father had started using the desk when he bought the building in 1935. Pat chuckled at his father's optimism in buying a 250,000-square-foot plant at the height of the Depression, when he was running a company with only $500,000 in sales, and 50 employees. Pat said his father had often brought him to the building on Saturdays when he was a boy, and that the long hallways, remnants of the assembly lines on which the Hupmobile automobiles were built, were perfect for riding his red Schwinn bicycle on rainy days.

As Pat was talking, my eyes wandered to the wall next to his desk, where behind a picture frame, sat a handwritten letter on yellowed paper. I could see from my chair the letter was dated in December 1927. Assuming the letter was from a satisfied customer, I asked Pat why he had chosen to hang it in his office. He paused, smiled, and with a chuckle told me the letter had been written from the William Penn Hotel in downtown Pittsburgh. It was from Art Parker to Carl Klamm, telling him he had eloped with Helen Fitzgerald.

At the end of our interview, Pat told me that, if I really wanted to understand Parker, I would have to learn how its culture of customer service had evolved since his father started the company in 1917. He said the company's success had been due to the character of his parents and those they hired to help run the company. They confronted many crises over the years, but they survived by taking good care of their customers, and of each other. Their goal of premier customer service, Pat said, gave them a higher purpose for their work, and the persistence, the optimism and the will to overcome their challenges.

As I walked out of Pat's office, I began to think I, too, might find my vocation at his family's company; and for the next 33 years, I did, first as a member of Parker's legal department, and later, as the company's general counsel.

Beginning in 1981, when Pat hired me, until his death in 2005, he shared with me (and many others) stories about how he and his parents built the company. It was his way of passing on the company's culture to the next generation of Parker leaders, part of a tradition of oral history that has prevailed at the company since its earliest days. In his stories, Pat tried to convey a sense of what he and his parents were thinking and feeling at critical points in the company's history. The episodes in this book about how Art, Helen and Pat Parker responded to those events, including the descriptions of their interior thoughts and conversations at the time, are based on the stories Pat told me.

Carol Meermans, Carl Klamm's daughter, gave me valuable information of her father's career at Parker. Several members of the Parker family shared stories of the personal lives of Art, Helen and Pat Parker. They include Pat's wives, Peggy Parker Grauman and Madeline Parker, Pat's sisters, Cyndi Parker Matthews and Joyce Parker, and Pat's daughter, Nancy Parker. Sharon Hickey, Pat Parker's cousin on the Fitzgerald side of the family, provided me with several stories of the times she spent with Helen Fitzgerald Parker, which illustrated the strong will, independent character, and indomitable spirit that allowed her to help the company survive a bankruptcy in the 1920s and a near-liquidation after World War II. Keith King, Sharon's nephew, shared with me his research, assembled over a period of years, on the history of the Fitzgerald family in America, starting with Helen's grandfather, who in 1858 immigrated to Cleveland from Ireland.

Many of the stories in this book are based on Parker's people's memories of events that occurred years ago. I have told those stories as they were told to me, and whenever possible, have searched for support and back-up for those recollections from Parker's books and records, newsletters, and historical archives.

I was fortunate to work with the four men who succeeded Pat as CEO—Paul Schloemer, Duane Collins, Don Washkewicz, and Tom Williams. Together with Pat, that group comprised five of Parker's eight CEOs and altogether, they served for nearly half of Parker's 100 year history. Each shared with me their stories of how they continued the company's momentum during their years of service.

I am indebted to those who gave generously of their time to read early drafts of this book and give me their candid comments. They include David Ostro, Don Zito, Mark Jarrad, Joe Pophal, Dan Whitman, Ivan Marks, Joe Whiteman, Bob Kohlhepp, Candy Obourn, Maria Makowiecki, Charles Weller, Don Dailey, and Jim Woods.

Several staff members at Cleveland's Western Reserve Historical Society helped provide background on Cleveland's role in the Second Industrial Revolution and in the early history of aviation, as well as valuable papers relating to the early days of the Parker Appliance Co. They included Robert Soriano, the Society's archivist (who followed the trail of the testimony in Parker's 1924's bankruptcy filing all the way to a salt mine in Kansas); Ed Pershey, an expert in Cleveland history; John Grabowski, the Society's Director of Research and Planning, and a co-editor of The Encyclopedia of Cleveland History; and Kelly Falcone-Hall, the Society's Chief Executive Officer.

I am indebted to the skilled editors at Smart Business Books who helped me improve the manuscript through several drafts, and who aided in the design of the artwork. Dustin S. Klein, the publisher and Chief Operating Officer, and April Grasso, the senior editor, believed in this book from the time they read the first draft and spent many hours helping me improve its look and content.

Several years ago, Elaine Zettelmeyer, a communications specialist in Parker's Corporate Communications Department, began to take it upon herself to preserve in Parker's archives critical documents that illuminated the early years of the Parker Appliance Co. Elaine archived a large number of copies of Parker's *Fitting News* from the 1930s and '40s, which gave me access to firsthand descriptions of the travails of Parker's men and women during the Great Depression and World War II. Thanks to Elaine's efforts, Art Parker can still speak to us through the letters to his employees published in the copies of the *Fitting News*.

Four members of Parker's Corporate Communications Department—Chris Farage, the department's leader, Dave Grager, Global Branding and Advertising Manager, and Erica Isabella and Dan Mills, the department's senior communications specialists—took an enormous amount of time from their busy schedules to help shepherd the story of Parker's first 100 years to a successful conclusion. Their insights into how to preserve the Parker story for future generations of employees will help insure that the culture of this unique company survives for years to come.

My wife, Barbara McWilliams, encouraged me to write Parker's story after I retired as the company's general counsel. She never could have guessed the book would consume so much of my time and energy. I thank you, Barbara, for your understanding, for your wise counsel on the early drafts of the manuscript, and for your thoughts on how best to convey the essence of the men and women responsible for Parker's success over the last 100 years.

This book is dedicated to Barbara and the other three loves of my life: my daughters Meg, Ann and Molly. From my stories over the dinner table many evenings, they could tell there was something special about the place I worked, and I have done the best I could to capture that feeling in this book.

Thomas A. Piraino Jr.
Cleveland Heights, Ohio
June 1, 2017

# Sources

## INTERVIEWS

William Armbruster
Lee Banks
Jim Baker
Bob Barker
Dan Bora
Paul Carson
Duane Collins
Achilleas Dorotheou
Ryan Farris
Dick Ferrell
Evie Fitzgerald
Keith Fitzgerald
Robert Fitzgerald
Rosemarie Fitzgerald
Cheryl Flohr
Allen Ford
Margaret Parker Grauman
Rick Hart
Steve Hayes
Sharon Hickey
Suzy Highland
Mark Jarrad
Bob Jones
Keith King
Ivan Marks

Cynthia Parker Matthews
Craig Maxwell
Jack McClatchey
Joe Vicic
Joyce Parker
Madeline Parker
Nancy Parker
Patrick Parker
Rich Piechuk
Tim Pistell
Joe Pophal
John Rankin
Bob Rau
Paul Schloemer
Dennis Sullivan
Bill Swift
Jane Talcott
Steve Vaughn
Joe Vicic
Don Washkewicz
Tom Williams
Bill Wilkerson
Jim Woods
Don Zito

## BOOKS

Brian Albrecht and James Banks, *Cleveland in World War II* (History Press, Charleston, South Carolina, 2015).

Buzz Aldrin, *Magnificent Desolation*, excerpted in Joseph J. Corn (ed.), *Into the Blue: American Writing on Aviation and Spaceflight* (Literary Classics of the United States Inc., New York, 2011).

Daniel Alef, *William Edward Boeing: Sky King* (Titans of Fortune Publishing, Santa Barbara, California, 2009).

Rick Atkinson, *An Army at Dawn: The War in North Africa, 1942-1943* (Henry Holt and C., New York, 2002).

Rick Atkinson, *The Guns at Last Light: The War in Western Europe, 1944-1945* (Henry Holt and Co., New York, 2013).

A. J. Baime, *The Arsenal of Democracy: FDR, Detroit, and an Epic Quest to Arm an America at War* (Houghton Mifflin Harcourt, New York, 2014).

Kevin Baker, *America the Ingenious* (Artesan, New York, 2016).

Adam Begley, *Updike* (HarperCollins, New York, 2014).

A. Scott Berg, *Lindbergh* (Berkley Books, New York, 1998).

A. Scott Berg, *Wilson* (G.P. Putnam's Sons, New York, 2013).

Richard Bessel, *Germany 1945* (HarperCollins, New York, 2009).

Wayne Biddle, *Barons of the Sky* (Simon & Schuster, New York, 1991).

H. W. Brands, *Reagan: The Life* (Doubleday, New York, 2015).

Douglas Brinkley, *Wheels for the World: Henry Ford, His Company and a Century of Progress, 1903-2003* (Viking, New York, 2003).

Douglas Brinkley, *Cronkite* (HarperCollins, New York, 2012).

Courtney G. Brooks, James M Grimwood and Lloyd Swenson Jr., *Chariots for Apollo: A History of Manned Lunar Spacecraft, The NASA History Series* (Superintendent of Documents, U.S. Government Printing Office, Washington D.C., 1979).

Daniel James Brown, *The Boys in the Boat* (Penguin Books, New York, 2013).

Henry Bruno, *Wings Over America* (Halcyon House, New York, 1942).

Adam Bryant, *Quick and Nimble: Lessons from Leading CEOs on How to Create a Culture of Innovation* (Times Books, Henry Holt & Co., New York, 2014).

A. Bullock, *Hitler* (Odhams Press, London, 1952).

Brian Butko, *The Lincoln Highway: Pennsylvania Travelers' Guide* (Second Edition, Stackpole Books, Mechanicsburg, Pennsylvania, 2002).

Ron Chernow, *Titan: The Life of John D. Rockefeller* (Random House, New York, 1998).

Brian Clegg, *Inflight Science: A Guide to the World from Your Airplane Window* (Icon Books, London, 2011).

Michael Collins, *Carrying the Fire: An Astronaut's Journeys* (Copper Square Press, New York, 2001).

Jim Collins and Morten T. Hansen, *Great by Choice* (Harper Business, New York, 2011).

Joseph J. Corn (ed.), *Into the Blue: American Writing on Aviation and Spaceflight* (Literary Classics of the United States Inc., New York, 2011).

Tom D. Crouch, *Wings: A History of Aviation From Kites to the Space Age* (Smithsonian Institution, 2005).

Arthur C. Clarke, *Profiles of the Future* (Bantam Books, New York, 1953).

Virginia P. Dawson, *Engines and Innovation: Lewis Laboratory and American Propulsion Technology* (National Aeronautics and Space Administration, Washington D.C., 1991).

Paul Dickson, *Sputnik: The Shock of the Century* (Walker & Co., New York, 2001).

Harold Evans, *They Made America* (Little, Brown and Co., New York, 2004).

Thomas L. Friedman, *The World is Flat: A Brief History of the Twenty-First Century* (Farrar, Straus & Giroux, New York, 2005).

Lawrence Goldstone, *Birdmen: The Wright Brothers, Glenn Curtiss, and the Battle to Control the Skies* (Ballantine Books, New York, 2014).

Doris Kearns Goodwin, *Lyndon Johnson and the American Dream* (St. Martin's Griffin, New York, 1976).

Doris Kearns Goodwin, *No Ordinary Time* (Simon & Schuster, New York, 1994).

Grace Goulder, *John D. Rockefeller: The Cleveland Years* (Western Reserve Historical Society, Cleveland, 1972).

R.G. Grant, *Flight: The Complete History* (DK Publishing, New York, 2007).

Winston Groom, *The Aviators* (National Geographic, Washington, D.C., 2013).

David Halberstam, *The Fifties* (Villard Books, New York, 1993).

David Halberstam, *The Reckoning* (William Morrow and Co., New York, 1986).

Peter Hart, *The Great War: A Combat History of the First World War* (Oxford University Press, New York, 2013).

Mark Henry and Stephen Walsh, *The U.S. Army of World War I* (Osprey, United Kingdom, 2003).

Arthur Herman, *Freedom's Forge: How American Business Produced Victory in World War II* (Random House, New York, 2012).

Laura Hillenbrand, *Unbroken* (Random House, New York, 2010).

Joe Jackson, *Atlantic Fever: Lindbergh, His Competitors, and the Race to Cross the Atlantic* (Farrar, Strauss & Giroux, New York, 2012).

John D. Kasarda and Greg Lindsay, *Aerotropolis: The Way We'll Live Next* (Penguin, London, 2011).

John Keegan, *The First World War* (Alfred A. Knopf, New York, 1999).

L. Douglas Keeney, *The Pointblank Directive: Three Generals and the Untold Story of the Daring Plan that Saved D-Day* (Osprey Publishing, Oxford, England, 2012).

Thomas Kessner, *The Flight of the Century: Charles Lindbergh and the Rise of American Aviation* (Oxford University Press, New York, 2011).

Victor Klemperer, *I Will Bear Witness 1942-1945: A Diary of the Nazi Years* (Random House, New York, 1999).

Gene Kranz, *Failure Is Not an Option* (Simon & Schuster, New York, 2000).

Milton Lehman, *This High Man: The Life of Robert H. Goddard* (Farrar, Strauss & Co., New York, 1963).

Jonathan Norton Leonard, *Flight Into Space,* excerpted in Joseph J. Corn (ed.), *Into the Blue: American Writing on Aviation and Spaceflight* (Literary Classics of the United States Inc., New York, 2011).

Charles A. Lindbergh, *The Spirit of St. Louis* (Scribner, New York, 1953).

*Innovation with Purpose: Lockheed Martin's First 100 Years*, e-book, www.lockheedmartin.com/us/100years.html.

Mary S. Lovell, *The Sound of Wings: The Life of Amelia Earhart* (St. Martin's Griffin, New York, 1989).

Jim Lovell and Jeffrey Kluger, *Apollo 13* (Houghton Mifflin Co., New York, 2000).

Beth Macy, *Factory Man* (Little, Brown and Co., New York, 2014).

Norman Mailer, *Of a Fire on the Moon* (Little, Brown and Co., Boston, 1969).

David Maraniss, *Once in a Great City: A Detroit Story* (Simon & Schuster, New York, 2015).

Thomas G. Matowitz Jr., *Cleveland's National Air Races* (Arcadia Publishing, South Carolina, 2005).

David McCullough, *Brave Companions: Portraits in History* (Prentice Hill Press, New York, 1992).

David McCullough, *The Wright Brothers* (Simon & Schuster, New York, 2015).

T. Bentley Mott, *Myron Herrick: Friend of France: An Autobiographical Biography* (Doubleday, Doran & Co., Garden City New York, 1929).

Robert Muccigiosso and Celia Dame Robbins, *Manufacturing in America: A Legacy of Excellence* (Greenwich Publishing Group, Lyme, Connecticut, 1995).

NASA, *Saturn Flight Manual* (National Aeronautics and Space Administration, April 1969).

John Newhouse, *Boeing vs. Airbus: The Inside Story of the Greatest International Competition in Business* (Alfred A. Knopf, New York, 2007).

Michael J. Neufeld, *Von Braun: Dreamer of Space, Engineer of War* (Alfred A. Knopf, New York, 2007).

*New York Times Presents Smarter by Sunday: 52 Weekends of Essential Knowledge* (St. Martins' Press, New York, 2010).

John Julius Norwich, *Sicily: An Island at the Crossroads of History* (Random House, New York, 2015).

Steven Parissien, *The Life of the Automobile* (Thomas Dunne Books, St. Martin's Press, New York, 2013).

Douglas Perry, *Eliot Ness: The Rise and Fall of an American Hero* (Viking, New York, 2014).

Henry Petroski, *The Road Taken: The History and Future of America's Infrastructure* (Bloomsbury, New York, 2016).

Ernie Pyle, *Brave Men* (Henry Holt and Co., New York, 1944).

Brad Ricca, *Super Boys* (St. Martin's Griffin, New York, 2013).

Craig Ricketts and Angelina W. Capone, *From Sea to Shining Sea: The Lincoln Highway* (Summer, 2010, Spring, 2011), pabook.libraries.psu.edu.

Jeffrey Rodengen, *Parker Hannifin Corporation: A Winning Heritage* (Wright Stuff Enterprises, Fort Lauderdale, Florida, 2009).

William Ganson Rose, *Cleveland: The Making of a City* (19th Edition, Kent State University Press, 1990).

Dan Ruminski and Alan Dutka, *Cleveland in the Gilded Age: A Stroll Down Millionaires' Row* (History Press, Charleston, South Carolina, and London, 2012).

Michael Schuman, *The Miracle: The Epic Story of Asia's Quest for Wealth* (Harper Business, New York, 2009).

James M. Scott, *Target Tokyo: Jimmy Doolittle and the Raid that Avenged Pearl Harbor* (W.W. Norton & Co., New York, 2015).

George Seldes, *You Can't Print That* (Payson & Clarke Ltd., New York, 1929).

Neil Sheehan, *A Fiery Peace in a Cold War: Bernard Schreiver and the Ultimate Weapon* (Random House, New York, 2009).

Alan Shepard and Deke Slayton, *Moon Shot* (Turner Publishing, Atlanta, 1994).

William L. Shirer, *The Nightmare Years: 1930-1940* (Little, Brown and Co., Boston, 1984).

Richard Snow, *I Invented the Modern Age: The Rise of Henry Ford* (Scribner, New York, 2013).

Jay Spenser, *The Airplane: How Ideas Gave Us Wings* (Smithsonian Books, HarperCollins, New York, 2008).

William Stadiem, *Jet Set* (Ballantine Books, New York, 2014).

Nicholas Stargardt, *The German War: A Nation Under Arms, 1939-1945* (Basic Books, New York, 2015).

Sherman Stein, *Archimedes: What Did He Do Besides Cry Eureka?* (University of California, Davis, 1999).

Joshua Stoff, *Charles A. Lindbergh: The Life of the 'Lone Eagle' in Photographs* (Dover Publications, Mineola, New York, 1995).

Henk Tennekes, *The Simple History of Flight* (The MIT Press, Cambridge, Massachusetts, 1997).

Martin Van Creveld, *The Age of Air Power* (Public Affairs, New York, 2011).

David D. Van Tassel and John J. Graboski, *The Encyclopedia of Cleveland History* (Second Edition, Indiana University Press, 1996).

Mark Vanhoenacker, *Skyfaring: A Journey with a Pilot* (Alfred A. Knopf, New York, 2015).

Sam Howe Verhovek, *Jet Age: The Comet, the 707, and the Race to Shrink the World* (Penguin Group USA Inc., New York, 2010).

Richard Wager, *Golden Wheels* (Western Reserve Historical Society, Cleveland, 1986).

James A. Ward, *Three Men in a Hupp* (Stanford University Press, Stanford, California, 2003).

Jim Winchester, *Civil Aircraft* (The Aviation Factfile), "Ford Trimotor," (Grange Books, London, 2004).

Simon Winchester, *Atlantic: Great Sea Battles, Heroic Discoveries, Titanic Storms, and a Vast Ocean of a Million Stories* (HarperCollins, New York, 2010).

Richard Zogten, *Hope: Entertainer of the Century* (Simon and Schuster, New York, 2014).

## ARTICLES AND PAPERS

Giselle Abramovich, "Mind-Blowing Stats About Generation Z," The New York Times, September 18, 2015.

"A Correction," The New York Times, July 17, 1969, at 43.

"Alcock and Brown: The First Non-Stop Aerial Crossing of the Atlantic," www.aviation-history.com/airmen/alcock.htm.

Timothy Aeppel, "Changing the Formula: Seeking Perfect Prices, CEO Tears Up the Rules," The Wall Street Journal, March 27, 2007, at A1.

"Announcement of Bankrupt Sale," Cleveland Plain Dealer, December 21, 1924, at 42.

Mark Archer, "The Year of Globalization," The Wall Street Journal, June 15-16, 2013, at C5.

George Bilger, "1929 TriMotor over Cleveland," *Science and Technology*, July 23, 1929.

David Brooks, "The Roosevelt Approach," The New York Times, February 16, 2016.

Adam Bryant, "Management be Nimble," The New York Times, January 5, 2014, at BU1, BU4.

Adam Bryant, "If You Want to Win, Just Say Yes," interview with Bernard L. Schwartz, former chairman and CEO of the Loral Corp., The New York Times, June 15, 2014, at BU2.

Adam Bryant, "Corner Office: When Running the Meeting, Speak Last," The New York Times, August 31, 2014, at BU2.

David Calvin Burr, "The People's Express Pioneer," reprinted in Harold Evans, They Made America (Little Brown and Co., New York, 2004).

"Captain Alcock's Own Narrative of his Flight from Newfoundland to Ireland," The New York Times, June 16, 1919, at 1.

Alan Cate, "How World War I Lead to 'Wizard War' Innovation," The (Cleveland) Plain Dealer, April 19, 2015, at D8.

Don Chapek, "Carl Klamm's Creation Made 'Lucky Lindy' Leakproof," Lakewood Lore, September 26, 1991, at 42.

"China Clipper Off on First Mail Trip Across the Pacific," The New York Times, November 23, 1935, at 1.

"Clevelander has Truck Air Brake: New Device May Revolutionize Overland Haulage Methods," Cleveland Plain Dealer, January 12, 1919, at 14.

Doug Clifton, Raising Comeback "Flag Tales LeBron, and More," The (Cleveland) Plain Dealer, July 18, 2014.

Jim Collins and Morten T. Hansen, "What's Luck Got to Do With It?," The New York Times, October 30, 2011, at BU1.

Joanna Connors, "Author Sets Sights on Cleveland," The (Cleveland) Plain Dealer, October 19, 2014.

Patrick Cooke, "Interstate Highways Are a Long-Haul Project," The Wall Street Journal, June 5, 2011.

Patrick Cooke, "From Minnesota to the World," The Wall Street Journal, November 16-17, 2013.

Patrick Cooke, "Stars and Stinkers: The Life of the Automobile," The Wall Street Journal, May 24-25, 2014, at C14.

Adam Davidson, "Do Technological Advances Determine the Health of our Economy?," The New York Times Magazine, February 21, 2016, at 16.

Mark Dawidziak, "Bob Hope Enlisted a Cleveland Critic of be His Straight Man," The (Cleveland) Plain Dealer, November 27, 2014.

Charles Duhigg, "What Google Learned From its Quest to Build the Perfect Team," The New York Times, February 25, 2016.

Modris Eksteins, "Exultation, Hunger and Revenge," review, The Wall Street Journal, September 28-29, 2013, at C7.

Charles N. Edel, "Bombers' Early Light," The New York Times, July 3, 2014.

Ralph Waldo Emerson, "Self-Reliance," Essays: First Series.

Harold Evans, "On the Brink," The New York Times Book Review, May 12, 2013, at 1.

Harold Evans, "An Armistice, Not a Peace," The New York Times Book Review, November 29, 2015, at 10.

"FDA Clears Parker's Indego® Exoskeleton for Clinical, Personal Use," Global Newswire, March 10, 2016.

Niall Ferguson, "How America Lost its Way," The Wall Street Journal, June 8-9, 2013, at C1.

"Five Huge Industries Who Never Saw Disruption Coming," USA Today, August 20, 2015.

Porter Fox, "From Montreal to Minnesota by Inland Sea," The New York Times, August 19, 2016.

Deborah Friedell, "Kryptonomics: Why Superman's Creators Got a Raw Deal," The New Yorker, June 24, 2013.

Will Friedwald, "The F. Scott Fitzgerald Songbook," The Wall Street Journal, May 9, 2013, at SR9.

Joe Gall, "With an Assist from Klamm," Ohio's Heritage, Vol. 11, No. 3, May-June, 1979 (Ohio Commission on Aging), at 12.

David Gelles, "Business Dynasties Try to Pass Torch Without Dropping It," The New York Times, June 13, 2015.

Malcolm Gladwell, "The Gift of Doubt," The New Yorker, June 24, 2013, at 74.

Alison Grant, "Airport Flew Into History When it Opened in 1925," The (Cleveland) Plain Dealer, July 5, 2015, at C1.

Alison Grant, "Air Show History: Daredevils Kept Early Fans on Edge," The (Cleveland) Plain Dealer, September 2, 2015.

Guy Gratton, "The Conversation: Why the Sun is Setting on the Boeing 747," CNN, February 1, 2016.

Amy Haimerl, "Lifting the Second Generation Curse," The New York Times, July 13, 2016.

Max Hastings, "The American Iliad," The Wall Street Journal, May 11-12, 2013, at C5.

Nathan Heller, "Air Head: How Aviation Made the Modern Mind," *The New Yorker*, February 1, 2016, at 62.

David R. Henderson, "German Economic Miracle," The Concise Encyclopedia of Economics, www.conlib.org.

Adam Higginbotham, "Bombs Away," *Smithsonian Magazine*, January-February, 2016, at 56.

"History of the Cleveland National Air Races," www.clevelandairshow.com/about-us/national-air-racing-history.

Adam Hochschild, "A Brutal Peace," *The New York Times Book Review*, September 29, 2013, at 18.

Adam Hochschild, "The Long, Long Road Ahead," *The New York Times Book Review*, May 18, 2014, at 16.

Don Holloway, "Doolittle Tames the Gee Bee," *Aviation History*, November 1994.

"The Human Moon," editorial, The New York Times, November 16, 2009.

"Jay Winik on Voices of World War II," The Wall Street Journal, October 10-11, 2015, at C10.

Holman W. Jenkins, "Detroit was a Cluster," The Wall Street Journal, July 30, 2013, at A26.

George Johnson, "What Made Him Tick," *The New York Times Book Review*, June 30, 2013.

Stephen Joiner, "What Couldn't the F-4 Phantom Do?," *Air and Space Magazine*, March 2015.

Jonathan W. Jordan, "Maryland's Finest," review, The Wall Street Journal, March 5-6, 2016, at C6.

Michael Kelley, "Parker Hannifin Makes Unheard of Strides," The (Cleveland) Plain Dealer, October 6, 1974.

John Leo Kosher, "Cleveland Past, Chandler Motor Car Co.," The (Cleveland) Plain Dealer, April 1978.

Nicholas Kristof, "The Most Important Thing," The New York Times, October 1, 2015, at A27.

Nicholas Kristof, "The Best News You Don't Know," The New York Times, September 22, 2016.

John Lancaster, "Money Trap: Can Europe Survive the Euro?," *The New Yorker*, October 24, 2016, at 73.

John Lanchester, "On Money," *The New York Times Magazine*, December 18, 2016, at 20, 23.

Naomi R. Lamoreux, Margaret Levenstein and Kenneth L. Sokoloff, "Financing Invention During the Second Industrial Revolution, Cleveland, Ohio, 1870-1920," National Bureau of Economic Research Working Paper 10923, November 2004.

Jeanne Marie Laskas, "Helium Dreams: A New Generation of Airships is Born," *The New Yorker*, February 29, 2016, at 28.

"Leases Viaduct Building: Automobile Parts Concern Takes Two-Story Structure," Cleveland Plain Dealer, April 27, 1919, at 9.

"Lindbergh's Own Epochal Flight," The New York Times, May 23 and 24, 1927, at 1.

Jill Lipore, "The Tug of War," *The New Yorker*, September 9, 2013, at 81.

Wendy Lower, "Wilkommen: How Nazi Scientists Went to Work for the United States," *The New York Times Book Review*, March 2, 2014, at 16.

Margaret Lynch, "Life in the Angle," *The Cleveland Heritage*, Vol. 2, No. 3, March 1983.

Christopher Martin, "Green Startups: Trapped in the 'Valley of Death,'" *Bloomberg Business*, October 7, 2010.

Ben Macintyre, "The Price of Victory," *The New York Times Book Review*, May 26, 2013, at 9.

Robin McKie, "How Michael Collins Became the Forgotten Astronaut of Apollo 11," The Guardian (London), July 19, 2009.

Michael Meyer, "Gunter Schabowski: The Man Who Opened the Wall," The New York Times, November 6, 2015.

*The Motor Truck*, April 1920, at 163.

Barry Neild, "Old Pics Show Crazy, Boozy Way We Used to Fly," CNN, December 16, 2015.

Anna North, "Smarts vs. Personality in School," The New York Times, January 11, 2015, at SR2.

Daniel Okrent, "'The Wright Brothers,' by David McCullough," *The New York Times Book Review*, May 4, 2015.

Catherine Rampbell, "Bad Marks: Inflation was Only One of Weimar Germany's Economic Woes," *The New York Times Book Review*, January 5, 2014, at 16.

Richard Rothschild, "The Greatest 45 Minutes Ever in Sport," *Sports Illustrated*, May 24, 2010.

Dan Saltzstein, "Capturing the Magic of a Life in the Air," The New York Times, August 9, 2015, at TR4.

Grant Segall, "Saving the City's Super History," The (Cleveland) Plain Dealer, September 8, 2013, at C2.

Orville Schell, "The Man Who Remade Asia," The Wall Street Journal, March 28-29, 2015, at C1.

Paul Schloemer, "Technology Will be Growth Driver," *Iron Age*, January 2, 1984, at 88.

Barry Schwartz, "Rethinking Work," The New York Times, August 30, 2015, at SR1.

Arthur P. Schulze, "Researching in Cleveland," *The Clevelander*, July 1948, at 11, 21.

Amity Shales, "The Myth of Gatsby's Suffering Middle Class," The New York Times, June 2, 2013, at SR9.

David M. Shribman, "The Year of Hesitation," The Wall Street Journal, June 15-16, 2013, at C5

Jerry Shriver, "Green Day, Ringo Rock Hall of Fame Ceremony," USA Today, April 19, 2015.

Frederick W. Smith, "How Trade Made America Great," The Wall Street Journal, March 25, 2016.

Robert L. Smith, "The Innovators: Looking Back to Look Ahead," The (Cleveland) Plain Dealer, October 26, 2014.

Wesley L. Smith, "How I Fly at Night," The Journal of the Society of Automotive Engineers, September 1926.

Deborah Solomon, "American Enigma," *Smithsonian Magazine*, October 13, 2013.

Nick T. Spark, "Secrets of the Spirit: Charles Lindbergh, Donald Hall, and the Plane that Made History," American Aviation Historical Society Journal, www.aahs-online.org.

Shelby G. Spires, "Von Braun's Brother Dies: Aided Surrender," The Huntsville Times, June 27, 2003, at 1A.

James B. Stewart, "A Fearless Culture Fuels Tech," The New York Times, June 19, 2015, at B1.

Mimi Swartz, "Still Made in the USA," *The New York Times Book Review*, August 17, 2014, at 14.

Frederick Taylor, "The Follies of 1940," The Wall Street Journal, October 10-11, 2015.

S.B. Taylor, "A New Philosophy of Growth," *The Clevelander*, July 1955, at 20.

Evelyn Theiss, "A Century Sitting Proudly on Euclid," The (Cleveland) Plain Dealer, April 3, 2011, at E1.

Amy Shira Teitel, "The Recipe for Apollo 13 Disaster," *Popular Mechanics*, January 27, 2014.

Salamisha Tillet, "Jesse Owens, A Film Hero Once Again," The New York Times, February 12, 2016.

Jaclyn Trop, "In the Rearview Mirror: A History of the Automobile and the Boom-and-Bust Industry it Fostered," *The New York Times Book Review*, August 17, 2014, at 20.

Brian Truitt, "Why Superman is the Greatest American Hero," USA Today, June 17, 2013.

Russell J. Warren, "A Brief History of Enterprise and Entrepreneurs in Northeastern Ohio."

Julie E. Washington, "Office in the Sky Has an Iconic View," The (Cleveland) Plain Dealer, November 22, 2015, at C1.

"Wearable Robots, Now Lighter, More Versatile, Help People with Paralysis Become Iron Men and Women," Associated Press, May 9, 2013.

Austin Weber, "Timeline: 50 Years of Economic Change and Manufacturing Progress," *Assembly Magazine*, October 25, 2007, at 1.

Yaahov Weber, Christina Oberg and Shlomo Tarba, "The M&A Paradox: Factors of Success and Failure in Mergers and Acquisitions," *Financial Times*, January 16, 2014.

Leif Wenar, "Is Humanity Getting Better?," The New York Times, February 15, 2016.

Alison Widman, "The Goose Flying Over Skies of the North Coast," Sandusky (Ohio) Register, September 12, 2013.

John Noble Wilford, "Men Walk on Moon," The New York Times, July 21, 1969, at 1.

Alex Williams, "Move Over Millennials, Here Comes Generation Z," The New York Times, September 18, 2015.

John Williams, "Turning Points: Margaret MacMillan Talks About 'The War That Ended Peace,'" The New York Times, December 19, 2013.

Tom Vanderbilt, "Gotta Keep Rollin'," *The New York Times Book Review*, July 17, 2001, at 5.

Michael Zawacki, "Eyes Wide Open: Patrick S. Parker Led Parker Hannifin Corp by Seeking and Encouraging Innovation," 2004 Business Hall of Fame, October 2004, at 90.

Tom Zoellner, "Airborne: An Ode to the Wonder of Air Travel, From the Cockpit of a 747," *The New York Times Book Review*, July 5, 2015, at 11.

# Endnotes

i Verhovek, at viii.
ii Lindbergh, at 15.
iii Interview with Jack Breen, March 3, 2005.
iv Emerson.
v Davidson.
vi Kasarda and Lindsay, at 15.
vii Lindbergh, at 209.
viii Verhovek, at 97.

## PART 1: BUILDING THE FOUNDATION, 1885 TO 1927

### Chapter 1: Dreams
1 Fox.
2 Chernow, at 44; Dawson, at 10.
3 Zogten, at 35.
4 Jenkins.
5 Muccigiosso and Robbins, at 9.
6 R. Smith.
7 Clifton.
8 Warren; Lamoreaux, Levenstein and Sokoloff.
9 Goulder, at 84.
10 Ruminski and Dutka, at 13.
11 Ruminski and Dutka, at 14; Theiss.
12 Chernow, at 119-120.
13 Rose, at 607.
14 Wager, at 3.
15 Wager, at 9.
16 Wager, at 9.
17 Wager, at 20.
18 Koshar.
19 Evans, *They Made America*, at 184.
20 Evans, *They Made America*, at 197.
21 McCullough, *The Wright Brothers*, at 63.
22 Okrent; Verhovek, at 50.
23 Chernow, at 253.

24 Goulder, at 74.
25 Chernow, at 100.
26 Chernow, at 101.
27 Chernow, at 150.
28 Chernow, at 50.
29 Chernow, at 335, 430.
30 Rose, at 550, 707.
31 Device for Regulating the Speed of Generators to Secure Constant Potential, Application Filed November 9, 1908, No. 935,051. Patented September 28, 1909.
32 Parissien, at 96; Petroski, at 70.

## Chapter 2: Fluid Power

33 Goldstone, at 7.
34 Stein, at 5.
35 Petroski, at 44.
36 Sheehan, at 265.
37 Testimony of Arthur Parker In Re the Parker Appliance Co., Bankrupt, before the Honorable Carl D. Frieborn, Referee, January 16, 1925, at 18-19.
38 Testimony of Arthur Parker In Re the Parker Appliance Co., Bankrupt, before the Honorable Carl D. Frieborn, Referee, January 16, 1925, at 13.
39 Lynch.
40 Ferguson.
41 Rose, at 618.
42 Biddle, at 121-122.
43 Biddle, at 52.
44 *Innovation With Purpose: Lockheed Martin's First 100 Years*, at 16.
45 Biddle, at 58-59.
46 Biddle, at 65.
47 Biddle, at 55.
48 Biddle, at 12.
49 *Innovation With Purpose: Lockheed Martin's First 100 Years*, at 7.
50 Biddle, at 49.
51 Biddle, at 102, 121.
52 Biddle, at 82.
53 *Innovation With Purpose: Lockheed Martin's First 100 Years*, at 25.
54 Goldstone, at 261.
55 Biddle, at 117.

## Chapter 3: On the Western Front

56 Verhovek, at 129.
57 Archer, quoting Charles Emmerson, *1913: In Search of the World Before the Great War* (Public Affairs, New York, 2013).
58 J. Williams.
59 Archer, quoting Charles Emmerson, *1913: In Search of the World Before the Great War* (Public Affairs, New York, 2013); Hochschild, "The Long, Long Road Ahead."
60 Keegan, at 3.
61 Hart, at 11.
62 Evans, "On the Brink," at 13, quoting Christopher Clark, *The Sleepwalkers: How Europe Went to War in 1914* (Harper, New York, 2013).
63 Evans, "On the Brink," at 12.
64 Mott, at Chapter XVII.
65 Berg, *Wilson*, at 336.
66 Berg, *Wilson*, at 390.
67 Lipore.
68 Berg, *Wilson*, at 437, 441.
69 Berg, *Wilson*, at 441.
70 Keegan, at 398.
71 Keegan, at 398.
72 Van Creveld, at 29; R.G. Grant, at 84; Cate.
73 Hart, at 134-135.
74 Keegan, at 411.

75 Rose, at 750.
76 Mott, at Chapter XIX.
77 *Innovation with Purpose: Lockheed Martin's First 100 Years*, at 25.
78 Seldes, at 5; Henry and Walsh, at 4.
79 Keegan, at 423.
80 Rampbell.
81 Evans, "An Armistice, Not a Peace."
82 Bullock, at 79.

## Chapter 4: Hard Times

83 Testimony of Richard T. Carroll in bankruptcy case of Parker Appliance Co., Northern District of Ohio, 1924, Case 10050, at 273.
84 Vanderbilt.
85 Brinkley, *Wheels for the World*, at 119.
86 Brinkley, *Wheels for the World*, at 123.
87 Butko, at 1; Petroski, at 43-44.
88 Cooke, "Interstate Highways Are a Long-Haul Project."
89 Ricketts and Capone.
90 Butko, at 9.
91 *The Motor Truck.*
92 Testimony of Richard T. Carroll In Re Parker Appliance Co. in Bankruptcy, U.S. District Court, Northern District of Ohio, Taken Before Honorable Carl D. Frieborn, Referee, January 16, 1925, at 79-80, 82.
93 "Clevelander has Truck Air Brake: New Device May Revolutionize Overland Haulage Methods."
94 "Clevelander has Truck Air Brake: New Device May Revolutionize Overland Haulage Methods."
95 Testimony of Frank J. Wutrich, In Re Transcript of Testimony of the Parker Appliance Co. in Bankruptcy, U.S. District Court, Northern District of Ohio, at 35, 46.
96 Rose, at 758.
97 "Leases Viaduct Building."
98 Patrick S. Parker, Address to the Newcomen Society in North America, October 4, 1979, at 11-12.
99 *New York Times Presents Smarter by Sunday: 52 Weekends of Essential Knowledge*, at 497; Petroski, at 41-42.
100 Testimony of Frank J. Wutrich In Re the Parker Appliance Co. in Bankruptcy, at 25.
101 Testimony of Carl Klamm In Re the Parker Appliance Co. in Bankruptcy, at 92.
102 Testimony of Harry R. Allshouse In Re the Parker Appliance Co. in Bankruptcy, at 74-76.
103 Testimony of Richard T. Carroll In Re the Parker Appliance Co. in Bankruptcy, at 81.
104 Testimony of Carl Klamm In Re the Parker Appliance Co. in Bankruptcy, at 85.
105 Testimony of Carl Klamm In Re the Parker Appliance Co. in Bankruptcy, at 86, 104.
106 Testimony of Louis Dingleday In Re the Parker Appliance Co. in Bankruptcy, at 117.
107 Testimony of Frank J. Wutrich In Re the Parker Appliance Co. in Bankruptcy, at 67.
108 Testimony of Arthur Parker In Re the Parker Appliance Co. in Bankruptcy, at 34.
109 Testimony of Helen Fitzgerald In Re the Parker Appliance Co. in Bankruptcy, at 70-72.
110 Rose, at 848.
111 "Announcement of Bankrupt Sale."
112 Parker bankruptcy case file, at B.
113 Stewart.
114 Evans, *They Made America*, at 242.
115 Evans, *They Made America*, at 241.

## Chapter 5: Starting Over

116 Martin.
117 Jackson, at 103-104.
118 Friedwald; Brands, at 16.
119 Muccigrosso and Robbins, at 44.
120 Shales.
121 *Innovation with Purpose: Lockheed Martin's first 100 Years*, at 26.
122 Biddle, at 160.
123 Alef, at 7.
124 Verhovek, at 25.
125 Alef, at 4.
126 Alef, at 3-5.
127 Van Tassel and Grabowski, at 8.

128 Interview with Edward Pershey, Western Reserve Historical Society, December 15, 2015.
129 A. Grant, "Airport Flew Into History When it Opened in 1925."
130 Matowitz, at 7.
131 Biddle, at 136.
132 Collins and Hansen, *Great By Choice*, at 10; Gladwell; Bryant, "If You Want to Win, Just Say Yes."
133 Collins and Hansen, "What's Luck Got To Do With It?"
134 Brands, at 65.
135 Interview with James Donchess, Sherwin Williams Co., December 15, 2015.
136 Rose, at 848.
137 W. Smith.
138 Lindbergh, at 473.

## Chapter 6: The Spirit of St. Louis

139 Rose, at 781.
140 Groom, at 131.
141 Kessner, at 55.
142 Stoff, at 15-16.
143 Crouch, at 263.
144 Groom, at 127.
145 Stoff, at 11.
146 Lindbergh, at 14.
147 Lindbergh, at 244.
148 Lindbergh, at 16.
149 Lindbergh, at 79.
150 Lindbergh, at 79.
151 Lindbergh, at 83.
152 Groom, at 137.
153 Lindbergh, at 94.
154 Kessner, at 70.
155 Lindbergh, at 88.
156 Lindbergh, at 86.
157 Lindbergh, at 87.
158 Spark.
159 Lindbergh, at 532: The tanks were designed to hold 425 gallons in the main tank under the wing, 80 gallons in the forward tank and 145 gallons in each of the three wing tanks. Spark: The actual tanks installed on the plane had a slightly different capacity, with the ability to hold 450 gallons.
160 Lindbergh, at 532.
161 Lindbergh, at 533.
162 Biddle, at 152.
163 Memorandum from Patrick S. Parker dated October 2004.
164 Biddle, at 91.
165 Spark.
166 Lindbergh, at 119.
167 Stoff, at 17.
168 Lindbergh, at 145.
169 Berg, *Lindbergh*, at 100.
170 Kessner, at 79.
171 Lindbergh, at 165.
172 Lindbergh, at 178.
173 Evans, *They Made America*, at 284.
174 Berg, *Lindbergh*, at 114.
175 Berg, *Lindbergh*, at 113.
176 Letters from Theodore Roosevelt, Charles Lawrence and Sidney B. Veit (Western Reserve Historical Society, Cleveland, May 1927).
177 Lindbergh, at 182.
178 Berg, *Lindbergh*, at 116.
179 Berg, *Lindbergh*, at 296.
180 Berg, *Lindbergh*, at 120.
181 Lindbergh, at 297.
182 Lindbergh, at 191.
183 Lindbergh, at 198.
184 Lindbergh, at 228.

185 Lindbergh, at 457-462.
186 Lindbergh, at 462-464.
187 Kessner, at 93.
188 Lindbergh, at 470.
189 Lindbergh, at 480.
190 Lindbergh, at 485.
191 Lindbergh, at 485.
192 Lindbergh, at 488.
193 Lindbergh, at 490.
194 Lindbergh, at 539 (Section G).
195 Lindbergh, at 495.
196 Lindbergh, at 496.
197 Lindbergh, at 499.
198 Winchester, *Atlantic*, at 338.
199 Mott, at Chapter XLII.
200 Biddle, at 153.
201 Mott, at Chapter XLII.
202 Mott, at Chapter XLII.
203 Rose, at 848.
204 "Lindbergh's Own Story of Epochal Flight."
205 Baime, at 30.
206 McCullough, *The Wright Brothers*, at 260.
207 Stoff, at 100-101.

## PART 2: CREATING A SUSTAINABLE CULTURE, 1927 TO 1945

### Chapter 7: The Lindbergh Effect

208 Berg, *Lindbergh*, at 188.
209 Groom, at 140.
210 Biddle, at 151, 156-157.
211 Stoff, at vi.
212 Verhovek, at 133.
213 Verhovek, at 133.
214 Bruno, at 222.
215 Parissien, at 16; Evans, *They Made America*, at 236.
216 Evans, *They Made America*, at 241.
217 Evans, *They Made America*, at 236.
218 Swartz.
219 Winchester, *Civil Aircraft*, at 151.
220 Widman.
221 Cooke, "From Minnesota to the World."
222 Bilger.
223 Van Tassel and Graboski, at 70.
224 Berg, *Lindbergh*, at 190.
225 Berg, *Lindbergh*, at 189-190.
226 Kessner, at 176; Berg, *Lindbergh*, at 205-206.
227 Goldstone, at 322.
228 A. Grant, "Air Show History: Daredevils Kept Early Fans on Edge."
229 Lovell, at 147.
230 Matowitz, at 17.
231 Stoff, at 121.
232 Holloway.
233 "History of the Cleveland National Air Races."
234 Dawidziak.
235 Rodengen, at 16.
236 Interview with Patrick S. Parker, by Jim Wood, March 2005.
237 Interview with Sharon Hickey.
238 Biddle, at 161.
239 Biddle, at 164.
240 Biddle, at 161-165.
241 Chernow, at 664.

## Chapter 8: The Great Depression

242 McCullough, *Brave Companions*, at 211.
243 Perry, at 114-115.
244 Connors.
245 Prospectus for the Sale of 100,000 Common Shares of the Parker Appliance Co., October 11, 1940.
246 Berg, *Lindbergh*, at 206.
247 Cooke, "From Minnesota to the World."
248 R.G. Grant, at 123.
249 Verhovek, at 134-135.
250 Verhovek, at 134.
251 Verhovek, at 205.
252 Verhovek, at xxii.
253 Spenser, at 82.
254 Muccigrosso and Robbins, at 62.
255 Baker, at 31.
256 Verhovek, at 28.
257 Baker, at 31.
258 Gall.
259 Goodwin, *No Ordinary Time*, at 451.
260 Prospectus for the Sale of 100,000 Common Shares of the Parker Appliance Co., October 11, 1940, at 97.
261 Ward, at 1-2.
262 Zogten, at 44.
263 Goulder, at 187.
264 Washington.
265 Interview with Cynthia Parker Matthews, November 1, 2013.
266 Interview with Patrick S. Parker, March 2005.
267 Berg, *Lindbergh*, at 114
268 Berg, *Lindbergh*, at 191.
269 Evans, *They Made America*, at 290.
270 Evans, *They Made America*, at 291.
271 Evans, *They Made America*, at 292.
272 Evans, *They Made America*, at 293-294.
273 Spenser, at 229-230.
274 Evans, *They Made America*, at 294.
275 "China Clipper Off On First Mail Trip Across the Pacific."
276 Evans, *They Made America*, at 295; Verhovek, at 27, 29, 85.
277 Kasarda and Lindsay, at 464.
278 Verhovek, at 97.
279 Rodengen, at 26-27.
280 Prospectus for the Sale of 100,000 Common Shares of the Parker Appliance Co., October 11, 1940.
281 Prospectus for the Sale of 100,000 Common Shares of the Parker Appliance Co., October 11, 1940, at 14.
282 Prospectus for the Sale of 100,000 Common Shares of the Parker Appliance Co., October 11, 1940.

## Chapter 9: Storm Clouds

283 Rothschild.
284 Shirer, at 234.
285 Tillet.
286 Berg, *Lindbergh*, at 360.
287 Berg, *Lindbergh*, at 355-356.
288 Verhovek, at 132.
289 Berg, *Lindbergh*, at 357.
290 Berg, *Lindbergh*, at 357, 368.
291 Brown, at 359.
292 Prospectus for the Sale of 100,000 Common Shares of the Parker Appliance Co., October 11, 1940, at 7.
293 Herman, at 147.
294 Atkinson, *An Army at Dawn*, at 5.
295 Stargardt, at 30.
296 Shirer, at 523.
297 Atkinson, *An Army at Dawn*, at 6.
298 Herman, at 4.
299 Herman, at 13; Atkinson, *An Army at Dawn*, at 8.

300 Taylor.
301 Herman, at 10.
302 Scott, at 80.
303 Snow, at 151.
304 Herman, at 21.
305 Herman, at 146.
306 Shirer, at 464.
307 Goodwin, *No Ordinary Time*, at 177.
308 Edel.
309 Shribman.
310 Ricca, at 136-138.
311 Ricca, at 95.
312 Friedell.
313 Friedell.
314 Truitt.
315 Atkinson, *The Guns at Last Light*, at 18, 389.
316 Goodwin, *No Ordinary Time*, at 200.
317 Goodwin, *No Ordinary Time*, at 200.
318 Goodwin, *No Ordinary Time*, at 195.
319 Brooks.
320 Goodwin, *No Ordinary Time*, at 45.

## Chapter 10: Another World War

321 Atkinson, *An Army at Dawn*, at 8.
322 Herman, at 158; Goodwin, *No Ordinary Time*, at 314.
323 Herman, at 13.
324 Atkinson, *An Army at Dawn*, at 8.
325 Dawson, at 11.
326 Albrecht and Banks, at 54, 55, 57.
327 Hastings.
328 *Fitting News*, June 1944, at 4.
329 Scott, at 361.
330 Van Tassel and Graboski, at 8.
331 Friedell; Ricca, at 204-205.
332 Parker 1940 Stock Offering Prospectus, at 7.
333 Van Tassel and Graboski, at 306.
334 *Fitting News*, April 1943, at 6.
335 Baime, at 286; *Fitting News*, April 1943, at 7.
336 *Fitting News*, "Blueprints for Victory," April 1943, at 5.
337 *Fitting News*, April 1943, at 7.
338 *Fitting News*, May 1943, at 4.
339 *Fitting News*, April 1943, at 7.
340 Jordan, quoting Patrick K. O'Donnell, *Washington's Immortals* (Atlantic Monthly Press, New York, 2016).
341 Atkinson, *An Army at Dawn*, at 4.
342 Lanchester.
343 Solomon.
344 Address by Doris Kearns Goodwin to Cleveland Town Hall, Ohio Theater, Cleveland, Ohio, September 16, 2013.
345 Goodwin, *No Ordinary Time*, at 364.
346 Goodwin, *No Ordinary Time*, at 555.
347 Albrecht and Banks, at 110.
348 Goodwin, *No Ordinary Time*, at 555-556.
349 *Fitting News*, February 1943, at 17.
350 *Fitting News*, April 1943, at 15.
351 Goodwin, *No Ordinary Time*, at 391.
352 *Fitting News*, April 1943, at 1.
353 *Fitting News*, April 1943, at 19.
354 *Fitting News*, April 1943, at 21.
355 *Fitting News*, April 1943, at 32.
356 Keeney.
357 Goodwin, *No Ordinary Time*, at 367.
358 Boeing Historical Snapshot: B-17.
359 *Fitting News*, "We the People Americans All," June 1943.

360 Edel.
361 Rodendgen, at 33, 163.
362 "Jay Winik on Voices of World War II."
363 "Jay Winik on Voices of World War II."
364 Goodwin, *No Ordinary Time*, at 511.
365 Keeney.
366 Atkinson, *The Guns at Last Light*, at 567, 533.
367 Hillenbrand, at 292.
368 Hillenbrand, at 60.
369 Hillenbrand, at 84.
370 Interview with Jane Talcott, executive director, Washtenaw Camp Placement Association, October 7, 2015.
371 Hillenbrand, at 249.
372 Hillenbrand, at 249.
373 Herman, at 293.
374 Hillenbrand, at 250.
375 Hillenbrand, at 249-251.

## Chapter 11: Casualties

376 Pyle, at 318.
377 Macintyre.
378 Stargardt, at 323.
379 Atkinson, *The Guns at Last Light*, at 568.
380 Interview with Cynthia Parker Matthews, November 1, 2013.
381 Atkinson, *The Guns at Last Light*, at 487.
382 Goodwin, *No Ordinary Time*, at 604.
383 Higginbotham.
384 Van Creveld, at 169.
385 Atkinson, *The Guns at Last Light*, at 631.
386 Atkinson, *The Guns at Last Light*, at 604.
387 Klemperer, at 39.
388 Klemperer, at 205, 522.
389 Klemperer, at 245.
390 Klemperer, at 75.
391 Klemperer, at 462.
392 Macintyre.
393 Van Creveld, at 119.
394 McCullough, *The Wright Brothers*, at 260.
395 Eksteins.
396 Hochschild, "A Brutal Peace."

## PART 3: DIVERSIFYING, 1945 TO 1957

## Chapter 12: Survival

397 Interview with Jim Weeks.
398 Interview with Patrick S. Parker, March 2005.
399 Zawacki.
400 Zawacki.
401 Patrick S. Parker address to the Cleveland branch of the Newcomen Society in North America, Cleveland, Ohio, October 4, 1979.
402 Schulze.
403 Taylor.
404 Collins and Hansen, *Great By Choice*, at 57.

## Chapter 13: Boom Times

405 Bessel, at 278.
406 Henderson.
407 Lancaster.
408 Halberstam, *The Fifties*, at 496.

409 Halberstam, *The Reckoning*, at 321.
410 Baker, at 210.
411 Baker, at 210.
412 Interview with Patrick S. Parker, March 2005.
413 Halberstam, *The Reckoning*, at 462.
414 Halberstam, *The Reckoning*, at 322.
415 Halberstam, *The Fifties*, at 118.
416 Parissien, at 199-200.
417 Parissien, at 215.
418 Halberstam, *The Fifties*, at 127.
419 Petroski, at 48.
420 Brands, at 392.
421 Address by Patrick S. Parker to the Cleveland branch of the Newcomen Society in North America, Cleveland, Ohio, October 4, 1979.
422 Halberstam, *The Fifties*, at 29.
423 Johnson.
424 Zawacki.
425 Notes of Everett Hannifin.
426 Interview with Donald Zito, October 20, 2015.
427 Weber, Oberg and Tarba.

## PART 4: BREAKING BOUNDARIES, 1958 TO 1970

### Chapter 14: The Jet Age

428 Maraniss, at 351.
429 Verhovek, at 75-76.
430 Verhovek, at 70.
431 Verhovek, at 42.
432 Dawson, at 41-45, 69-72.
433 Verhovek, at 92.
434 Verhovek, at 29.
435 Verhovek, at 86.
436 Verhovek, at xxi.
437 Newhouse, at 202.
438 Verhovek, at 6.
439 Verhovek, at 174.
440 Verhovek, at 193.
441 Verhovek, at 7, 103.
442 R.G. Grant, at 386.
443 Stadiem, at xii.
444 Verhovek, at xvii-xviii.
445 Kasarda and Lindsay, at 118.
446 Verhovek, at 197.
447 Winchester, *Atlantic*, at 13-15.
448 Winchester, *Atlantic*, at 330.
449 Brands, at 39.
450 Begley, at 3.
451 Interview with William Armbruster.
452 Interview with Robert Rau, Laguna Beach, California, December 11, 2013.
453 Parker Presentation, "Gas Turbine Fuel Systems Division," December 5, 2012.
454 Parker Presentation, "A History of Leadership."
455 Joiner.
456 Tennekes, at 125.
457 Verhovek, at 104.
458 Evans, *They Made America*, at 299.
459 Newhouse, at 8.
460 Clegg, at 18.
461 Vanhoenacker, at 109.
462 Gratton.
463 Tennekes, at 118.
464 Interview with Paul Schloemer, August 15, 2015.

465 Vanhoenacker, at 117.
466 Neild.
467 Saltzstein.
468 F. Smith.
469 Interview with William Ponn, November 5, 2015.
470 Heller.

## Chapter 15: The Space Race

471 Dickson, at 40.
472 Lehman, at 188, 222 and 260.
473 Berg, *Lindbergh*, at 212.
474 Berg, *Lindbergh*, at 212.
475 Berg, *Lindbergh*, at 213.
476 Dickson, at 45.
477 Halberstam, *The Fifties*, at 613.
478 Halberstam, *The Fifties*, at 608; Lower.
479 Spires.
480 Halberstam, *The Fifties*, at 609.
481 Leonard, excerpted in *Into the Blue*, at 369, 376.
482 Neufeld, at 251.
483 Dickson, at 5.
484 Dickson, at 141.
485 Dickson, at 156.
486 Halberstam, *The Fifties*, at 627.
487 Dickson, at 158.
488 Dickson, at 159.
489 Dickson, at 173; Parker Hannifin's 1960 Annual Report, at 4, 7.
490 Neufeld, at 354.
491 Neufeld, at 355.
492 Interview with James Woods, January 24, 2016.
493 Shepard and Slayton, at 108.
494 Brinkley, *Cronkite*, at 228.
495 Rodengen, at 62.
496 Dawson, at 168.
497 Interview with Paul Schloemer.
498 "Project Apollo – The Lunar Module," Grumman Aircraft Engineering Corp., January 1968, at 22.
499 Brooks, Grimwood and Swenson, at 155.
500 "Project Apollo – The Lunar Module," Grumman Aircraft Engineering Corp., January 1968, at 22.
501 "Project Apollo – The Lunar Module," Grumman Aircraft Engineering Corp., January 1968, at 22.
502 Brooks, Grimwood and Swenson, at 155.
503 Memorandum from Patrick S. Parker, dated October 2004.
504 Halberstam, *The Reckoning*, at 229.
505 Interview with Nancy Parker, September 12, 2014.
506 Shepard and Slayton, at 214.
507 Shepard and Slayton, at 215.
508 Haimerl.
509 Interview with Timothy Pistell, May 26, 2015.
510 Zoellner.

## Chapter 16: Tranquility Base

511 Brinkley, *Cronkite*, at 412.
512 Mailer, at 57.
513 Mailer, at 33.
514 Mailer, at 38.
515 Lindbergh, at 83.
516 Baker, at 39.
517 Baker, at 39.
518 Berg, *Lindbergh*, at 537.
519 Berg, *Lindbergh*, at 537.
520 Rodengen, at 88.

521 Muccigiosso and Robbins, at 105.
522 Mailer, at 213.
523 Berg, *Lindbergh*, at 537.
524 McCullough, *The Wright Brothers*, at 262.
525 NASA, *Saturn Flight Manual*, at 5-14.
526 "A Correction."
527 Dickson, at 41.
528 Brooks, Grimwood and Swenson, at 341.
529 Wilford.
530 Aldrin, excerpted in *Into the Blue*, at 506, 507.
531 Mailer, at 364.
532 Mailer, at 365.
533 Kranz, at 281.
534 Kranz, at 283-284.
535 Kranz, at 283.
536 Baker, at 38.
537 Baker, at 38.
538 Aldrin, excerpted in *Into the Blue*, at 514.
539 Mailer, at 379.
540 Kranz, at 289.
541 Corn, *Into the Blue*, at 506.
542 Kranz, at 290.
543 Kranz, at 291.
544 Aldrin, excerpted in *Into the Blue*, at 515.
545 Brooks, Grimwood and Swenson, at 344.
546 Brooks, Grimwood and Swenson, at 344.
547 Aldrin, excerpted in *Into the Blue*, at 516.
548 Kranz, at 292.
549 Brooks, Grimwood and Swenson, at 345.
550 Mailer, at 402.
551 Mailer, at 424.
552 Berg, *Lindbergh*, at 537.
553 McKie.
554 Collins, at 446.
555 "The Human Moon."
556 Baker, at 39.

# Chapter 17: Apollo 13

557 Teitel; interview with John Rankin.
558 Lovell and Kluger, at 95.
559 Lovell and Kluger, at 102.
560 Kranz, at 314.
561 Kranz, at 103.
562 Kranz, at 316.
563 Lovell and Kluger, at 125.
564 Lovell and Kluger, at 126.
565 Lovell and Kluger, at 105.
566 Lovell and Kluger, at 128.
567 Brooks, Grimwood and Swenson, at 154.
568 Kranz, at 321.
569 Kranz, at 323.
570 Interview with Bill Swift, August 15, 2015.
571 Parker internal document, "Parker Highlights in History: Parker Played Key Role in Apollo 13 Crisis."
572 Lovell and Kluger, at 133.
573 Lovell and Kluger, at 147.
574 Lovell and Kluger, at 164-165.
575 Lovell and Kluger, at 166.
576 Lovell and Kluger, at 166.
577 Lovell and Kluger, at 311.
578 Lovell and Kluger, at 305.
579 Lovell and Kluger, at 322.
580 Lovell and Kluger, at 329.

581 Kranz, at 336.
582 Lovell and Kluger, at 334.
583 Lovell and Kluger, at 334.

## PART 5: COMPETING IN A GLOBAL MARKETPLACE, 1970 TO 1990

### Chapter 18: Another Parker at the Helm

584 Bryant, "Corner Office."
585 Interview with James Wood, September 2, 2011.
586 Interview with James Wood, January 20, 2016.
587 Interview with Paul Schloemer.
588 Parker internal document, "A Tale of Strawberries, Beans and Real Estate," by Ivan Marks.
589 Interview with Paul Schloemer.
590 Halberstam, *The Reckoning*, at 22.
591 Maraniss, at 19.
592 Halberstam, *The Reckoning*, at 328.
593 Weber.
594 Maraniss, at 30.
595 Schuman, at 1.
596 Halberstam, *The Reckoning*, at 311.
597 Halberstam, *The Reckoning*, at 314.
598 Cooke, "Stars and Stinkers."
599 Cooke, "Stars and Stinkers."
600 Halberstam, *The Reckoning*, at 385.
601 Kelley.
602 Kelley.
603 Swartz; Weber.
604 Trop.
605 Rodengen, at 79.
606 Zawacki.
607 Halberstam, *The Reckoning*, at 207.
608 Halberstam, *The Reckoning*, at 313.
609 Interview with Paul Schloemer.
610 Zawacki.

### Chapter 19: Passing the Torch

611 Laskas.
612 Aeppel.
613 Collins and Hansen, *Great By Choice*, at 21-22.
614 North.
615 Interview with Duane Collins.

### Chapter 20: First Steps to the World

616 Program from meeting of Newcomen Society, Cleveland, Ohio, October 4, 1979, at 6.
617 Program from meeting of Newcomen Society, Cleveland, Ohio, October 4, 1979, at 22-23.
618 Kelley.
619 Interview with James Wood, January 20, 2016.
620 Rodengen, at 67.
621 Schloemer.
622 Interview with Mark Jarrad, June 22, 2015.
623 Rodengen, at 59.
624 Interview with Mark Jarrad, June 22, 2015.
625 Rodengen, at 112.

### Chapter 21: Becoming a Multinational

626 Brands, at 333.
627 Meyer.

628 Meyer.
629 Friedman, at 115.
630 Schell.
631 Schuman, at 63.
632 Schell.
633 Schell.
634 Macy, at 145.
635 Macy, at 4.
636 Interview with Joe Vicic, July 25, 2015.
637 Schuman, at xxiv.
638 Schuman, at xxiv.
639 Wenar.
640 Kristof, "The Most Important Thing."
641 Kristof, "The Best News You Don't Know."

## PART 6: ENGAGING A NEW CENTURY, 1990 AND BEYOND

### Chapter 22: Harnessing Parker's Collective Power
642 Interview with Timothy Pistell, May 26, 2015.
643 Bryant, "Management be Nimble."
644 Zawacki.
645 Aeppel.
646 Aeppel.
647 Aeppel.

### Chapter 23: Enduring Values
648 Gall.
649 Gall.
650 Gall.
651 Gall.
652 Gall.
653 Chabek.
654 "Wearable Robots, Now Lighter and More Versatile, Help People With Paralysis Become Iron Men and Women."
655 "FDA Clears Parker's Indego® Exoskeleton for Clinical, Personal Use."
656 Patrick S. Parker, Some Personal Notes of the Approximately 55-Year History of Parker Hannifin Corp., 1976 Annual Report to Parker Shareholders, at 9.
657 Schwartz.
658 William Shakespeare, *The Tempest*, Act 2, Scene 1.
659 Bryant, *Quick and Nimble,* at 247.
660 A. Williams.
661 Abramovich.
662 "Five Huge Industries Who Never Saw Disruption Coming."

# INDEX

## A NOTE ABOUT THE AUTHOR

Thomas A. Piraino Jr. retired from the legal department of Parker Hannifin Corp. in 2014 after 33 years of service, 16 of those as the company's General Counsel. The Judiciary Committee of the U.S. House of Representatives has referred to him as "a noted legal commentator." Mr. Piraino is an adjunct professor at the Case Western Reserve University School of Law in Cleveland, Ohio, and a trustee at the Cleveland Museum of Natural History. His articles have been published in several law reviews and cited in three decisions by the U.S. Supreme Court, several cases in the U.S. Courts of Appeals, and in federal district courts. Tom and his wife Barbara McWilliams live in Cleveland Heights, Ohio. He can be reached at tpiraino49@gmail.com.